The PARTICLE ATLAS

Edition Two

An encyclopedia of techniques for small particle identification

Volume VI
Electron Optical Atlas and Techniques

Walter C. McCrone, Editor

John A. Brown
Ian M. Stewart

ann arbor science PUBLISHERS INC.

P.O. BOX 1425 • ANN ARBOR, MICHIGAN 48106

Type set by SSPA Typesetting, Inc., Carmel, Indiana
Printed by Thomson-Shore, Dexter, Michigan
Bound by John H. Dekker & Sons, Inc., Grand Rapids, Michigan

Editorial Assistance by Gail L. Bohnhoff, Jan Carter, Christina Bych and Andrée Fé Coers

Library of Congress Catalog Card Number: 72-90881
International Standard Book Number: 0-250-40196-7

Manufactured in the United States of America

Contents

VOLUME VI: ELECTRON OPTICAL ATLAS AND TECHNIQUES

FOREWORD 1459

I. ADVANCES IN ELECTRON OPTICAL
METHODS OF PARTICLE ANALYSIS .. 1461
Ian M. Stewart

   A. Introduction 1461

   B. The EMMA Series 1461

   C. Other Analytical TEMs 1463

   D. Electron Energy
      Loss Spectroscopy (EELS) 1463

   E. Scanning Transmission Electron
      Microscopy (STEM) 1464

   F. The Ultimate in Analytical TEMs 1464

II. IDENTIFICATION OF SUBMICRO-
METER PARTICLES 1466
John Gavrilovic

   A. Introduction 1466

   B. Special Methods of Sample Preparation
      for Analysis of Submicrometer Particles 1466
      1. Electron Microbeam Instruments ... 1466
      2. Electron Microprobe Analyzers 1467
      3. Electron Microscope-Microprobe
         Analyzer 1468
      4. Scanning Electron Microscope 1469

      5. High-Resolution Scanning Electron
         Microscopy 1469
      6. Scanning Auger Microprobe 1470
      7. Ion Microprobe Mass Analyzer 1470

   C. Organic Particles 1471

III. SOME TECHNIQUES FOR HANDLING
PARTICLES IN SEM STUDIES 1472
John A. Brown and Anna Teetsov

   A. Introduction 1472

   B. Particle Collection 1472

   C. Particle Mounting Techniques 1472
      1. Tape Mounting 1472
      2. Single Particle Considerations 1474
      3. Filter Substrates for Particle
         Mounting 1476
      4. Mounting on Smooth Substrates 1476
      5. Miscellaneous Methods 1477

   D. Conclusions 1478

IV. DESCRIPTIONS AND ELECTRON
MICROGRAPHS 1479
John A. Brown, Ian M. Stewart and
Gene R. Grieger

V. ASBESTOS IDENTIFICATION BY
ELECTRON MICROSCOPY 1644
Ian M. Stewart

A. Introduction 1644

B. Bulk and Powder Samples 1646

C. Fluid Samples 1646
    1. Condensation Washing Method 1646
    2. Wicking Method 1647

D. Tissue Samples 1648
    1. Direct Methods 1648
    2. Indirect Methods 1649

E. Beverages and Foodstuffs 1650

F. Conclusion 1651

VI. USE OF AUTOMATION IN LABORA-
    TORY INSTRUMENTATION 1652
    Charles H. Bowen and Donald A. Brooks

A. Introduction 1652

B. McCrone Associates' Automation
    Advances 1653

C. Dedicated Versus Time-Sharing
    Computer Systems 1653

D. Automation of the Electron Microprobe
    Analyzer 1654

E. Use of the CPS System for Mass Scan-
    ning Analyses 1655

F. Automation of the Ion Microprobe 1657

G. Gas Chromatography/Mass Spectrom-
    etry Automation 1658

H. Future Automation Possibilities 1660

I. Conclusion 1660

VII. LITERATURE SURVEY 1661
    Gail L. Bohnhoff

INDEX FOR VOLUMES I–VI 1675

Foreword

In Volume VI we have attempted to detail the advances in particle identification by electron optical methods since Volume III which was written in 1972. The advances since 1972 include instrumentation (see Sections I and VI), particle manipulation techniques (Sections II and III), the identification of smaller and smaller particles (Section III) and specialized applications, *e.g.*, asbestos (Section V).

In addition, the electron optical characterization of 412 new substances brings the total coverage for *The Particle Atlas* to 1,022 substances. In this volume many of the newly added 412 particles are described by TEM and SAED as well as SEM and EDXRA. Because pollens, fibers and some other substances do not require TEM and SAED, there are two formats for the descriptions (Section IV). Fibers, pollens, etc., have only SEM data in the form of 100X, 1,000X and 10,000X micrographs with an EDXRA, when appropriate, replacing one of the micrographs. This is the same format used in Volume III. However, nearly one-half of the new additions are very finely divided and/or crystalline, hence benefit from TEM and SAED characterization. The format for these includes both an SEM and a TEM micrograph. Beneath each is the respective EDXRA and SAED pattern. In either format the written description describes the particles in terms of SEM and TEM characteristics and includes a reference to the diffraction data in the ASTM card file of the Joint Committee on Powder Diffraction Standards. Unfortunately, the SAED photos were taken with two different electron microscopes having widely differently camera constants, hence no measurement can be made from the patterns as printed.

We should also note that a thinner window on our EDXRA has changed the peak heights of low atomic number elements relative to those higher. The intensities for the lighter elements are now more intense. This shows up, for example, in comparing *lizardite* (*710*) with *chrysotile* (*122*) or *antigorite* (*117*); in Volume VI the Mg:Si ratio is higher.

What can we expect in the future? Certainly more quantitative TEM instrumentation. This will take place in two directions: the easiest is the addition of E- or WDXRA capability; the more sophisticated second choice is electron energy loss spectroscopy (EELS). Some electrons striking a specimen are inelastically scattered and lose an amount of energy dictated by the specimen atom. Measurement of the energy losses then identifies the atoms in the specimen. It is particularly useful for the lighter elements. STEM instruments will become more apparent as they improve in resolution, now about 2 nm. Ian Stewart discusses these possibilities in more detail in Section I of this volume.

Since 1973 and Volumes I through IV, McCrone Associates has expanded in equipment, personnel and experience. Two major equipment acquisitions, MOLE (see Volume V) and EMMA, have kept us abreast of the analytical capabilities for smaller and smaller small-particle analysis. Automation of this instrumentation has continued with small dedicated computers for most of the instruments and further software to permit operation of and data reduction for all of the microprobes by the larger PDP-15 computer. Improved EDXRA systems and improved data read-out systems have also been added.

Most important, however, is the increased experience of the staff and the addition of new staff: Hazel Bales and Olga Kist in the clean room-particle handling area; Betty Majewski, Debbie Piper and Rick Ellis in the electron optics group; Skip and Mark Palenik in light microscopy and Mark Andersen with responsibilities in both light and electron optical areas.

Anna Teetsov and her group continue to develop new and better ways to isolate, fractionate, manipulate and mount particles as small as John Gavrilovic, John Brown, Rick Ellis, Gene Grieger, Debbie Piper and Betty Majewski can analyze.

John Delly continues to develop his own databank for the instantaneous recognition of diverse particles, and Chuck Bowen, with Bill Grew's assistance, manages to automate the instruments as fast as they appear. The broad view is continually updated by Ian Stewart for electron optics and by Bob Muggli for light optics. Jim Hertrich continues to improve his shop facilities for instrument design and construction. Lucy McCrone continues to handle the nasty problems no one else likes, such as asbestos in toy balloons, pigments on totem poles or talc analyses, besides handling course arrangements and finances for the rapidly expanding McCrone Research Institute. Ralph Hinch maintains the reputation of the micro XRD lab, and Howard Humecki attends nonparticle functions involving GC/MS, IR and UV. All of these highly professional chemists and physicists are aided more than they realize by an unusually dedicated office staff and by Anita Douthat in charge of visual aids, darkroom, drafting, art work and interior decoration.

Jim Martin, President of McCrone Associates, Inc., from 1962 to 1978, has retired, and Don Brooks is now President and Chief Executive Officer. Fortunately, like Jim, Don is a technical man with nuclear engineering and computer background. Thus, he is able to guide the company technically as well as administratively. Walt McCrone has now "retired" to the McCrone Research Institute where he teaches 2 to 3 intensive 1-week courses each month in various parts of the USA and Europe.

I. Advances in Electron Optical Methods of Particle Analysis

IAN M. STEWART

A. Introduction

Since publication of the first four volumes of this edition, there have been significant advances in the application of transmission electron microscopy (TEM) to the identification of particulate material. These advances have come in the area of chemical characterization of the particle species present by the addition of energy- or wavelength-dispersive x-ray systems (EDXRA and WDXRA) and electron energy loss spectrometers (EELS).

Historically, attempts at chemical analysis in the TEM date back to the early 1950s. Original attempts consisted either of attaching a flow proportional counter or a simple, nonfocusing, wavelength-dispersive spectrometer to measure the emitted x-rays. The flow proportional counter was an energy-dispersive system, but it suffered from very poor energy resolution, typically of the order of 1,000 to 1,500 electron volts. Deconvolution of the resulting spectra by computer processing was then necessary. In the 1950s, computer technology was not sufficiently advanced or economical for this to be a routine procedure, hence this interpretational technique was rarely used. The WDXRA did, of course, have much higher resolution and therefore was potentially of more value.

A major limitation of both systems, however, was inability to focus on a small particle. Both systems analyzed the entire area irradiated by the electron beam under normal operating conditions of the microscope. Thus, if there were numerous small particles present, all would be analyzed to give an integrated analysis. In practice, this meant that an area approximately 1 to 5 μm in diameter was normally analyzed.

In the early 1960s, the development of a mini-lens by LePoole resulted in a potential for smaller area analyses; this was soon realized in the EMMA series of instruments developed by Melford and Duncumb of Tube Investments Laboratories in Britain. It was from this point onward that effective analytical capabilities in the TEM began to be useful. Shortly after the development of EMMA, both WDXRA and EDXRA systems were developed with energy resolution an order of magnitude better than proportional counters. Further improvement of the spatial resolution with the conventional TEM, by means of special probe-forming condensers and improved high-intensity electron sources, has led to the widespread application of EDXRA to conventional TEMs.

A further technique for chemical characterization, EELS, has now become a practical commercial possibility on the TEM. In this technique the energy losses sustained by the electron beam as it passes through an electron transparent specimen are measured. These losses again are characteristic of the chemical composition of the target material.

B. The EMMA Series

The EMMA series of instruments was developed by Tube Investments research laboratories in Cambridge, England, to assist in characterization of materials of interest to that company. The first instrument was an inverted microscope, but it provided the main features which characterized the later series of instruments, namely, a combination of a high resolution TEM capable of SAED with the addition of chemical characterization. Only wavelength spectrometers were

Figure 1.   AEI EMMA-4 equipped with two wavelength spectrometers and EDXRA.

fitted to this instrument. Later modifications of the
instrument were all based on existing commercial AEI
TEMs, and the latest of the line, EMMA-4, was based
on the AEI type 802 metallurgical electron microscope.
Figure 1 shows an AEI EMMA-4 equipped with two
wavelength spectrometers and EDXRA. Figure 2
shows a cross-sectional schematic of the x-ray detection systems and the electron optical column around
the specimen objective lens area. The mini-lens, which
is the heart of the probe-forming system in the EMMA,
is a nonferrous lens, conically wound and capable of
carrying a high current so that the requirement of
high ampere turns for high field strength is met by
the number of amps rather than by the number of
turns in the lens. With this lens in use, the minimum beam diameter at the specimen is less than
0.2 μm. Additionally, electromagnetic stigmator coils
are placed around the lens which enable shaping of
the beam to conform to the particle or the structure

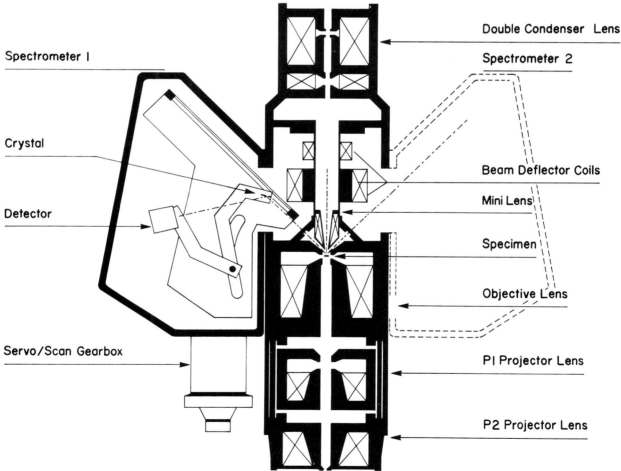

Figure 2.   Cross-sectional schematic of the x-ray detection systems and the electron optical column around the specimen objective lens
area of AEI EMMA-4.

being probed, thus enabling a higher signal-to-background ratio to be obtained. For example, for the analysis of a fiber, astigmatism is induced in the beam to give it an elliptical shape with the major axis of the ellipse lying along the fiber's long dimension.

The mini-lens fits in a barrier plate above the objective lens. This barrier plate carries the x-ray windows, each inclined at 45° to the electron optical axis. The specimen is inserted, via a side entry, into the objective lens iron circuit. Reference faces on the specimen rod determine the specimen height, which must be maintained in a preset position to maintain focus on the spectrometers. The standard specimen holder has six specimen locations to enable several samples to be examined in rapid sequence or, alternatively, for readily selected standards to be included. To minimize scatter from the specimen rod, beryllium inserts can be fitted to the rod. This metal is not detected by either the WDXRA or EDXRA; in addition, white radiation from the beryllium is minimal. Alternative specimen holders are available, including a tilting stage and a linear translation stage which allows for easy examination of serial sections.

The two spectrometers fitted to EMMA are of the Johanssen type. These spectrometers are linear and fully focusing with a constant take-off angle of 45°. Each spectrometer contains four crystals: lithium fluoride, mica, ammonium dihydrogen phosphate (ADP) and potassium acid phthalate (KAP). The x-ray detectors are gas-flow proportional counters, the Rowland circle radius for each spectrometer is 15.24 cm, and the range of elements covered is from atomic number 11 (sodium) upwards. Each spectrometer is controlled manually by servo motors. The system allows up to six preset angular positions for each spectrometer. For each position, the crystal used in analysis may be independently selected. A scanning drive with six different speeds controlled by stepping motors makes it possible to step-scan in either direction through a peak of interest. A fast motor drive and a fine manual drive are also included. Spectrometer sensitivity allows the detection of an element at the 100-ppm range or, on a small analysis area, a detection limit approaching 10^{-18} grams.

The EDXRA detectors have the same 45° take-off angle as the two WDXRA spectrometers. Several manufacturers produce EDXRA interfaces suitable for mating to the EMMA system, and the wide diversity of the signal processing facilities available will not be discussed here. EDXRA, with the same 45° take-off angle as the WDXRA, forms an extremely important part of EMMA and in most cases gives, by itself, all

the elemental data necessary for problem solving in minimum time. It is thus possible to obtain in a matter of seconds the chemical information to be used in conjunction with the electron diffraction pattern to assist in the identification of an unknown material.

C. Other Analytical TEMs

Almost every major manufacturer of TEMs now manufactures an analytical version. In most instances, this is a combination of EDXRA interfaced with their conventional TEM. In some systems the detector, as in EMMA, views the specimen at an angle, so there is no requirement to move the specimen from its normal viewing and diffraction position to a different position for analysis. In other systems the EDXRA is introduced horizontally, and it is then necessary to tilt the specimen in a eucentric goniometer stage before analysis.

Almost all modern systems now incorporate facilities to scan a very fine focused beam at the specimen surface. These high-resolution scanning attachments can be combined with secondary and back-scattered electron detectors to provide a normal SEM facility, and with a transmitted electron detector to convert the instrument to a scanning transmission electron microscope (STEM). The combination of a high-intensity electron gun, such as a field-emission gun, with suitable excitation of the condenser and objective lenses, enables high probe current densities to be obtained even at an electron probe diameter of less than 10 nm. Spatial resolution of the x-ray analysis is, to a first approximation, equivalent to the thickness of the sample being studied. Thus, it is possible to obtain spatial resolutions of the order of 20 nm with present-day systems. At the same time, the microprobe used for such an analysis can be used as a microcollimated electron beam, permitting diffraction analysis of extremely small particles.

D. Electron Energy Loss Spectroscopy (EELS)

When a high-energy electron beam strikes a target material, some of the high-energy electrons are elastically scattered with no decrease in energy. Others, however, undergo an inelastic scattering resulting in excitation of the atoms of the target material. Electrons in the target atoms are excited to high energy levels with a resultant decrease in the energy of the primary exciting beam. This energy loss, which characterizes the target atom, can be measured with an electron energy analyzer, and such energy analyzers are now being added to SEMs and TEMs. In a conventional TEM, the energy analyzer may be placed beneath the camera chamber. A portion of the electrons contributing to the image pass through an aperture in the fluorescent screen and into the analyzer. A retarding potential is applied so that the primary electrons are slowed before they enter the magnetic velocity analyzer. The technique is particularly sensitive for the light elements, thus extending the range of analyses possible in the TEM.

E. Scanning Transmission Electron Microscopy (STEM)

STEM is a technique analogous to conventional SEM, but it differs in that the primary beam transmitted through the specimen is used for image formation. If no lenses are used following transmission of the beam through the specimen, chromatic aberration effects, which cause a deterioration of resolution with thick samples, are avoided. Consequently, STEM allows the observation of thicker specimens than does conventional TEM for a comparable deterioration in resolution. In STEM the resolution deteriorates as the incident electron beam scatters or diffuses within the specimen bulk, but this effect is of a lower order of magnitude than the chromatic aberration effect.

Although attenuation of the beam current systems exists in both SEM and STEM, it is possible, by electrical processing, to enhance image contrast in the scanning mode and hence derive structural information from low-intensity signals which would not yield useful information by conventional TEM. A corollary to this is that lower intensity beams may be used to examine delicate materials which might otherwise degrade in the electron beam.

Many conventional TEMs are now provided with a scanning facility associated with the fine probe-forming systems which are used for x-ray analysis. These instruments may be used either conventionally or with STEM. Also available are several commercial STEMs lacking the capability to perform as conventional TEMs. Such instruments are generally of higher STEM resolution than the TEM when the latter is used in its STEM mode. Again, full capabilities exist for x-ray analysis, energy loss analysis and micro-area diffraction. A schematic diagram of one such instrument is shown in Figure 3. Such instruments claim resolution of the order of 2 nm at 100 kV, almost an order of magnitude better than that for a conventional TEM operating in a STEM mode and close to that obtained

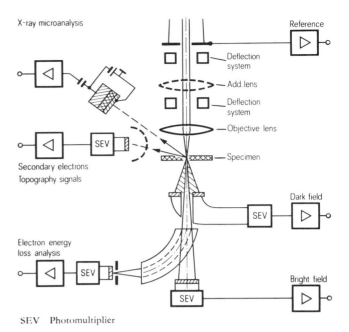

Figure 3. Beam path of the ELMISKOP ST 100F and detector channels. *Courtesy of Siemens Aktiengesellschaft.*

from a conventional TEM operating in its normal mode.

F. The Ultimate in Analytical TEMs

Bearing in mind the various options that have been mentioned above for analytical capabilities in electron microscopy, what is the most likely configuration of the ideal analytical TEM in the foreseeable future?

Future TEMs will almost certainly have STEM capabilities. They may or may not, in addition, have conventional TEM capability.

The accelerating voltage is likely to be in the 100 to 200 kV range. At a minimum, EDXRA will be incorporated; WDXRA may also be present. In the scanning mode, both scanning transmission and secondary electron detection will be employed. It will be possible to map elemental distribution in the plane of the specimen as is done now in the conventional electron microprobe.

EELS will also be provided, particularly for light element analysis, and it will also be possible to produce scanning images (elemental mapping) using the EELS signal. This will be done by zeroing in on any particular energy loss value to display those areas within the specimen which have imparted an identical energy loss to the beam.

A further degree of sophistication which may be incorporated is some form of quantitative image analy-

sis. In its simplest form this will make provision for the counting and measurement of individual features. It will be possible to make such measurements using any of the scanning display systems, back-scattered electrons, transmitted electrons, x-rays or energy loss electrons. It will be possible to interface this quantitative image analyzer with a computer and, depending on the computer and the sophistication of the software developed, to perform some pattern recognition operations.

In the ultimate instrument, all of these data, chemical as well as morphological, will be integrated by the computer. By utilizing scanning diffraction techniques to digitize the electron diffraction pattern, it will be possible to compare crystallographic informa-tion with similar information on standards incorporated in the computer memory bank. With such an instrument, it should be possible for the operator merely to align the area of interest in the field of view in the microscope, punch into his computer terminal the relevant instructions and receive from the computer, within a matter of minutes or seconds, a detailed characterization of his sample, indicating the size and shape of the phases present, their individual chemistry and, indeed, their phase identification.

Development of analytical SEMs and TEMs has proceeded at a rapidly accelerating pace since their introduction in the 1940s (TEM) and 1950s (SEM). There seems no reason to expect the pace to slow in the foreseeable future.

II. Identification of Submicrometer Particles

A. Introduction

The science of small particle identification is continually advancing and creating an ever-increasing demand for analysis and positive identification of smaller and smaller particles. Previously, it was not possible to discern two "particles" too close to each other, or to examine particles smaller than 2–3 μm in length because these were regarded as the ultimate limits for positive particle identification. But today, the development of microelectronic components, inertial guidance systems, miniaturized computer reading, recording heads and other components has reached tolerances of less than 1 μm. This presents challenging opportunities for small particle analysts.

B. Special Methods of Sample Preparation for Analysis of Submicrometer Particles

Since most single-particle analyzing instruments use a light microscope (as well as other imaging systems) for locating small particles, the proper mounting of submicrometer particles is extremely critical. Particle size is, in most cases, beyond the resolution capability of the light microscope incorporated in the instrument, and it is necessary to rely on a "star in the sky" effect. For this reason, the substrate must be particle-free, especially of all submicrometer size contaminants. The mounting adhesive, e.g., collodion film, must be extremely thin, preferably less than 20 nm. The position of the particle has to be unambiguously marked and well described in the attached paperwork or, simply, easy to find. The analysis of small particles is then carried out in one of the microbeam analytical instruments.

1. Electron Microbeam Instruments

Electron microbeam instruments include the electron microprobe analyzer (EMA), the scanning electron microscope (SEM), the electron microscope-microprobe analyzer (EMMA), the scanning transmission electron microprobe (STEM), the electron microscope with an electron loss spectrometer and the scanning Auger microprobe. Particles are analyzed in the last two instruments by electron emission rather than by characteristic x-rays.

Small particles in sizes down to 1 μm can be quantitatively analyzed in electron beam instruments using the standard ZAF correction procedure for solid (bulk) and infinitely large samples. The precision of such quantitative analyses is limited primarily by the particle size and subsequent loss of x-ray intensities which, in turn, increase experimental errors. Such errors cannot be effectively compensated for by small particle corrections since they are mostly random and are caused by instrument instability and counting errors. Ratios of x-ray intensities for particles below 1 μm and particularly below 0.3 μm are severely affected by particle size (Figure 4). The relative change measured in x-ray intensities on very small particles, as compared to bulk samples, is caused primarily by the decrease in x-ray absorption due to the shorter absorption path within the sample, and it is significantly higher than the experimental errors incurred during the analysis of such particles.

The optimum method for analysis of small particles appears to be the collection of x-rays from the small particle while it is being rastered by the electron beam. Such a raster normally also covers a certain portion of the substrate in order to incorporate the whole projected area of the small particle. To compensate for loss of x-ray intensity during the rastering of the substrate, the following correction factor can be used:

$$I_o = I_1 \times \frac{S_r}{S_p}$$

where I_o is the corrected intensity from the element, I_1 the measured intensity, S_r the total rastered area,

1466

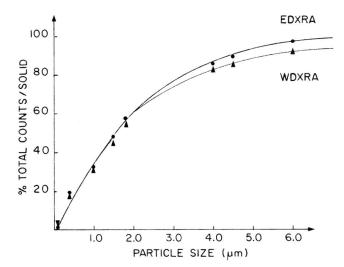

Figure 4. Size distribution vs total intensity in small particle of glass.

and S_p the projected area of the small particle. With this method the stability of the measurement is significantly increased and analysis of particles down to approximately 1 μm becomes routine. Even smaller particles, from 1 μm down to 0.1 μm, can be analyzed semiquantitatively with a relative accuracy of 20–40% without further correction except for the ratio of rastered to projected area as is shown on the diagrams in Figures 5 and 6.

An exceptionally clean vacuum system is a must for submicrometer particle x-ray analysis. Carbon buildup in a regular diffusion-pumped system may prevent meaningful analysis within minutes. Either a liquid nitrogen baffle on the diffusion pump or a different vacuum system is mandatory. Particularly suitable is the clean vacuum system provided by a turbomolecular pump. This pump is essentially a rotary compressor which produces blank-off pressures down to 10^{-10} torrs. However, the vibration from such a pump must be well damped; otherwise the high resolution imaging on the oscilloscope screen (which is a must for small particle analysis) is seriously impeded.

2. Electron Microprobe Analyzers

An extremely versatile instrument, the electron microprobe x-ray analyzer (EMA) is suitable for submicrometer particle analysis, combining efficiently both the energy-dispersive system (EDXRA) and the wavelength-dispersive system (WDXRA). For submicrometer particle analysis, the EDXRA has a distinct advantage in extremely high, solid angle of acceptance of the x-rays because the sensitive head can be positioned very close to the small particle sample. The EDXRA is, therefore, suitable for rapid, semiquantitative analysis of very small particles. However, the lower resolution of the detector and the higher background noise preclude detection of trace elements in

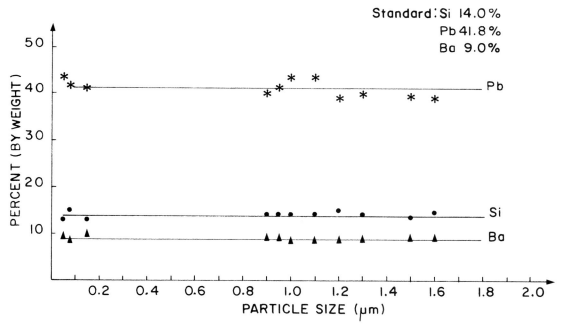

Figure 5. Percent by weight of major elements vs size as determined by WDXRA for K-230 glass particles.

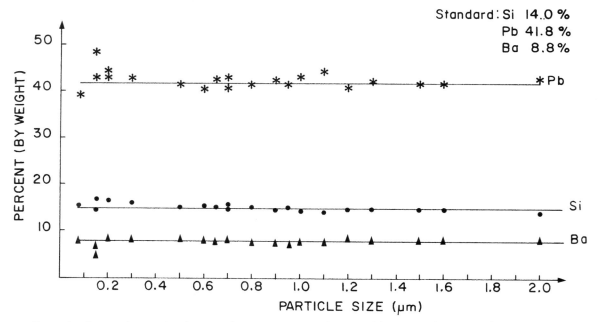

Standard: Si 14.0 %
Pb 41.8 %
Ba 8.8%

Figure 6.   Percent by weight of major elements vs size as determined by EDXRA for K-230 glass particles.

small particles. The WDXRA with its inherently lower x-ray noise may detect lower concentrations of trace elements on small particles than the EDXRA.

The new generation of EMA with its multiple ports,

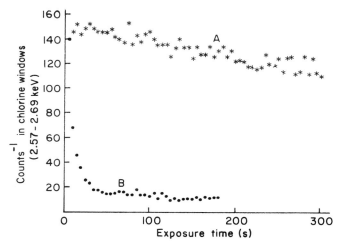

Figure 7.   The data shown here demonstrate the effect of temperature reduction from 22°C to −145°C on chlorine loss from a PVC thin film during electron beam irradiation at a beam current of roughly 5 × 10⁻¹¹ Å. A usable spectrum is obtained in 100 s at this current. A—PVC film mounted on 400-mesh copper grid at −145°C with exposed area 2.58 × 10⁻⁹ cm² and irradiated with a beam current of 6.8 × 10⁻¹¹ Å. B—Unsupported PVC film at 22°C with exposed area of 2.58 × 10⁻⁹ cm² irradiated with a beam current of 7.2 × 10⁻¹¹ Å. Illustration from T. E. Hutchinson, 1977.

and up to six x-ray spectrometers (ARL, SEM-Q) and a 10-nm electron beam diameter, is particularly suitable for submicrometer particle analysis. Fixed spectrometers can be optimized for several specific elements and can provide trace analysis even for elements such as carbon and oxygen.

3. Electron Microscope-Microprobe Analyzer

The electron microscope-microprobe analyzer (EMMA) is an extremely useful tool for submicrometer particle analysis. Its beam diameter of 0.1 μm, or spot size for analysis, is sufficient for most analytical problems. In the electron microscope mode, of course, the resolution is far better, equal to most other TEM instruments (1–2 nm). In EMMA, a standard TEM grid is used as a mounting substrate and, to minimize scattered x-ray radiation from the grid bars, a nylon or beryllium grid is used instead of copper. With such a low x-ray background and an extremely fine adjustable electron beam, small particles and fibers well below 1 μm will give sufficient x-ray intensities for chemical analysis and positive identification. Light element analysis in EMMA requires, as in other instruments, a clean, oil-free vacuum system. Additional problems may be encountered on thermally sensitive samples, since the substrate does not provide much thermal conductivity compared to solid beryllium or carbon blocks used for microanalysis of EMA or SEM. Severe loss of volatile elements is observed as an effect of increased temperature of small samples on

TEM grids. These losses can be minimized by a reduction in temperature (Figure 7).[1]

4. Scanning Electron Microscope

The scanning electron microscope (SEM) is primarily an imaging tool, but, with the addition of EDXRA and even the WDXRA, it has become an excellent microanalytical tool. Since the detector can be positioned extremely close to the sample, especially when equipped with the new telescopic heads, the rapid semiquantitative analysis of submicrometer-size particles is carried out with great speed. Problems can occur when the SEM is used for obtaining quantitative analysis from small particles, because SEM is normally optimized for imaging, and the sample chamber has many metallic parts where backscattered electrons may excite stray x-rays which will preclude accurate analysis of many common elements such as aluminum, iron, possibly copper, etc., *i.e.*, any element which may be used in or around the sample chamber. A second disadvantage is the extreme sensitivity of the WDXRA to the positioning of a small particle within the Rowland circle. Any deviation in the position of the small particle relative to the crystal and x-ray detector may drastically change the x-ray intensity. The extremely versatile specimen stage of an SEM is excellent for obtaining morphological information, but it is a drawback for routine quantitative x-ray analysis.

The new windowless EDXRA extends the capability of low atomic number elements to carbon and oxygen, but their application is extremely limited for two reasons. They require extremely clean vacuum systems to prevent contamination of the lithium-drifted detector sensing head, since even volatiles from samples or sample mounting media will eventually degrade the detector. Also, both carbon and oxygen x-ray lines have very low energy, and interference from low energy lines of some heavy elements is very common. Therefore, routine application of a light element detector for EDXRA analysis is seldom justified.

5. High-Resolution Scanning Electron Microscopy

An increase in brightness of the electron source, as well as improvement in the quality of the electron optics, is necessary in order to increase the resolution of the SEM image. The common hot filament electron source was first replaced by the LaB_6 filament (Figure 8) which gave almost an order of magnitude higher

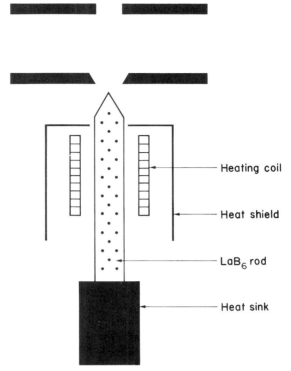

Figure 8. Schematic diagram of lanthanum hexaboride electron gun. *Illustration from Broers, 1967, 1969.*

brightness (Broers).[2] Subsequent development of an efficient field emission electron gun by Dr. Crewe *et al.*[2] at the University of Chicago offered a source with 10^3 times higher brightness than the conventional hot filament gun (Figure 9).

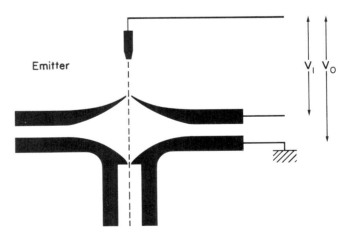

Figure 9. Schematic diagram of field emission electron gun. *Illustration from Crewe et al., 1968.*

[1] Meek, G. A., and H. Y. Eder, *Analytical and Quantitative Methods in Microscopy*, Cambridge University Press, Cambridge 1977, p. 222.

[2] Reed, S. J., *Electron Microprobe Analysis*, Cambridge University Press, Cambridge, 1975, p. 33.

Both of these guns give higher intensity electron beams and enable observation and analysis of smaller particles (<0.1 μm) with the EDXRA, provided the detector can be placed sufficiently close to the sample. Unfortunately, the WDXRA cannot be used with such instruments because of its lower collection efficiency and low total intensities of submicrometer size electron beams. This automatically precludes detection of trace elements in small particles due to the poor peak/background ratios of the EDXRA.

6. Scanning Auger Microprobe

While earlier scanning Auger microprobe (SAM) instruments suffered from rather poor spatial resolution (5 μm or worse), the new generation (so-called super-SAM) has an 0.2–0.5 μm electron beam with a superb 1.0-nm depth resolution (Figure 10).[3] Unfortunately, these two parameters work in opposition for submicrometer particle analysis; even so, the spatial resolution is probably sufficient for the majority of small particle analytical problems. The low escape depth of Auger electrons, however, means that any surface films and coatings on a small particle will effectively mask the true composition of the particle.

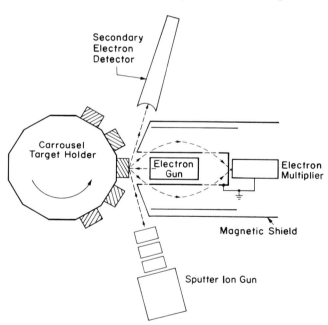

Figure 10. Schematic representation of the SAM analyzer with ion etching capability.

[3] McDonald, N. C., C. T. Hovland and R. L. Gerlach, "Scanning Auger microscopy for microelectronic device characterization and quality control," *Scanning Electron Microscopy* (March 1977).

This can be overcome only partially by ion-etching devices which may also remove mounting adhesives and thus cause a loss of particles due to charging effects.

In spite of these disadvantages, SAM can be extremely useful in submicron particle analysis *in situ*, since both x-ray analysis and ion microbeam techniques have poor resolution for such analysis for different reasons. In electron-excited x-ray analysis the primary x-ray will generate secondary x-rays from both the substrate and the surrounding particles. In ion microbeam analysis the large size of a primary beam will similarly sputter ions of the substrate and of the surrounding particles. Only the scanning Auger microprobe has sufficient resolution to accept the signal from a 0.5-μm particle without undue interference from substrate or from the surrounding particles.

7. Ion Microprobe Mass Analyzer

In micrometer and submicrometer particle analysis and identification, the ion microprobe mass analyzer (IMA) plays an important role. It does not supplement other microanalytical tools such as EMA, SEM, and SAM, but rather complements them.

The primary advantages of the ion microprobe are: (1) analysis of all elements including hydrogen, (2) analysis of isotopes, and (3) detection of trace quantities of various elements in particles (in ppm and ppb). For example, in Figure 11 the computer-generated mass spectrum of a 0.5-μm small particle shows the mass peaks of all the elements, isotopes and functional groups present in that particle. Those are $H_1{}^+$, $C_{12}{}^+$, CH^+, $CH_2{}^+$ (from the mounting material), O, OH (from the primary oxygen beam and the oxy-

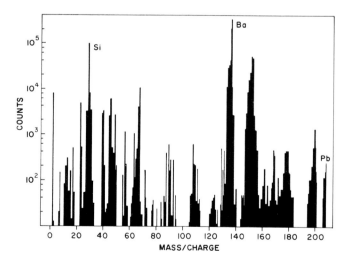

Figure 11. Ion microprobe mass spectrum of a 0.5-μm particle.

gen in the glass), Na_{23}^+, Mg_{24}^+, Al_{27}^+ and others from the particle.

It is important to realize that, in order to produce useful information from a <1-μm particle, at least 100–200 monolayers have to be sputtered away. If the analysis proceeds, the particle will be completely eroded away; therefore, great sensitivity cannot be utilized in every case because of the opposing requirements—detection of trace elements requiring a long counting time and small particle size demanding a low etching rate. Figure 12 illustrates this change in intensity of the Ba_{138}^+ signal during sputtering of a large sample as opposed to a small (1-μm) particle.

Fortunately, recondensation of the secondary par-

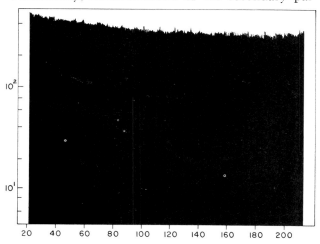

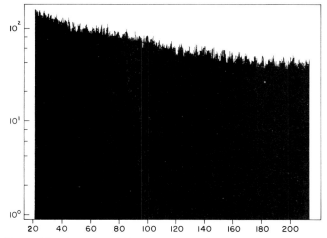

Figure 12. Intensity of Ba_{138}^+ ion signal in the ion microprobe with time in seconds. Top: large sample >100 μm. Bottom: small particle <2 μm.

ticles helps solve some of the problems. In many cases, ions sputtered away from the small particle and not collected by the secondary ion collector (approximately 90% of the total) will condense to form a layer around the area of impact of the ion beam. This condensed layer can then be looked at with the primary ion beam as if it were the original material present in the sample. In some cases, however, material will preferentially condense and not have precisely the same composition as the particle. In spite of possible segregation of condensed material, it is useful to analyze such layers during small particle analysis in order to postpone total destruction of a particle.

The ion microscope is less suitable for submicrometer particle analysis because of its large size ion beam (25–100 μm or more). It erodes relatively large areas and virtually eliminates condensation of material from a selected small spot.

C. Organic Particles

Organic particles have a unique place in small particle analysis, and light microscopy can offer relatively little toward positive identification of 1-μm particles. X-ray analysis with EMA or SEM results usually in an x-ray spectrum consisting of a heavy background and possibly several minute peaks of the characteristic x-ray lines of trace impurities in the small particle. The only abundant detectable elements are carbon and oxygen, which are present in most organic compounds. Auger spectrometry provides similar data with additional information about nitrogen content.

The ion microprobe analysis of an organic particle is another method which provides much more comprehensive information on trace elements and, at the same time, may produce a "fingerprint" of the organic compound. This fingerprint consists of one or more unusual molecular fragments which can be used to "fingerprint" the unknown particle.

By far the best technique for organic particles would be infrared spectroscopy, but the wavelength versus particle size ratio precludes such analysis on small particles. And last, the laser Raman microprobe, only recently developed, provides useful information for organic compounds (Volume V, pp. 1147–1154). However, wavelength versus particle size again imposes a limit on the analysis of submicrometer size particles.

III. Some Techniques for Handling Particles in SEM Studies

John A. Brown and Anna Teetsov

A. Introduction

Techniques for the collection, preparation and observation of particles for scanning electron microscopy (SEM) must provide a means for holding the particles well dispersed, mechanically stable and electrically conductive. The substrate must not contribute any confusing background structure to the observation of the particles. Well-dispersed particles will make it easy to differentiate individual particles from agglomerates, to measure particle size and shape and, when desirable, to obtain good EDXRA data. In addition, the sampling and mounting procedures should reveal whether the individual particles are fused, glued together or partially dissolved. Because the SEM can look only at surfaces, interior structures of some particles must be revealed by mild grinding, crushing, impaction, cutting and chemical etching or ion etching.

Particles with high vapor pressure may have to be replicated at atmospheric conditions and the replicas examined, or the particles may have to be examined on a cold stage. Biological particles have to be fixed and dried by freeze drying, or critical point drying, unless they are examined on a cold stage in the SEM. It is necessary that biological particles be thoroughly cleaned so that they are not covered by contaminating material such as the growth medium.

Energy-dispersive x-ray analysis (EDXRA) is becoming a very important aspect of particle evaluation. In order to avoid extraneous x-ray signals, mounting procedures require substrates such as beryllium or carbon. If organic materials are to be examined by wavelength-dispersive techniques (WDXRA), beryllium is used.

B. Particle Collection

Sampling must yield representative samples. Methods such as filtration from gas or liquid streams, sedi-mentation, grinding, spray drying, centrifugation, precipitation, impaction, collection on adhesive films, air elutriation and sieving can provide satisfactory samples. Only with some methods, such as filtration or collection on adhesive surfaces, are the samples satisfactory for SEM examination as collected.

C. Particle Mounting Techniques

Particle handling techniques for SEM were discussed by Johari and De Nee,[4] and Brown and Teetsov.[5] Their techniques can be applied with variations depending on the specific problem.

1. Tape Mounting

a. Particle mounting

The method of particle mounting most used for SEM examination today is to mount dry particles on double-sided adhesive tape, which is already mounted on specimen stubs. When mounting the tape on the specimen stub, it is good practice to curve the tape onto the stub from one side to the other in order not to trap air which will cause mechanical instability of the specimen during examination (Figure 13). The advantage of tape is that the tacky material has a sufficiently high viscosity so that it does not engulf the particles, yet is sticky enough to hold particles firmly. In using the double-sided tapes, it is advisable to use fresh sections or sections which are protected by paper to avoid contamination from airborne particles. Small portions of the particles are either transferred to the tacky surface, usually by spatula, or poured on from a bottle, in order to deposit a mound of par-

[4] Johari, O., and P. D. DeNee, *Scanning Electron Microscopy/1972*, IIT Research Institute, Chicago, pp. 249–255.

[5] Brown, J. A., and A. Teetsov, *Scanning Electron Microscopy/1976*, Vol. III, IIT Research Institute, Chicago, pp. 385–391.

ticles. In some cases, special sampling procedures may have to be used. An additional method is to dust the particulate powder onto the tape through a screen of appropriate size.

After the particles are on the tape, the stub is held with tweezers and is firmly tapped vertically several times on a solid surface with the tape and particles up, in order to set the particles into the tacky surface. After this is done, the stub is turned sideways and is again firmly tapped on a solid surface to dislodge loose particles. This is repeated several times until no more particles come off. The purpose of this is to remove rather loosely held particles which do not have enough contact with either the tacky tape surface or other particles to form a continuous conductive layer when metal-coated. Loose particles produce serious charging effects in the SEM even when metal-coated. Also loose particles may separate from the specimen mount and deposit in the SEM column, giving serious contamination problems.

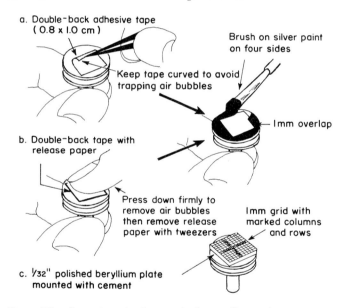

Figure 13.   Preparing aluminum stubs for small particle mounting. a—Double-back adhesive tape method. b—Tape method with release paper. c—Directly on a polished beryllium surface.

When tapping the stub sideways to remove excess particles, it is advisable to do so in such a way that the deposit of particles left on the tape does not completely cover the tape surface. Best is a deposit that tapers from a heavy layer in some areas to a thinner deposit in other areas (Figure 14). With this arrangement heavy deposits can be observed, as well as single particles at the edge of the deposit. This also provides some areas on the specimen stub where particles

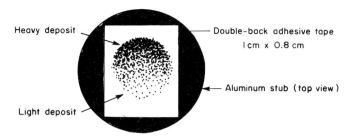

Figure 14.   Desired distribution of particles on adhesive tape.

are widely dispersed, so that the underside of some particles can be observed at high tilt angles.

After the particles have been deposited on the tape, the edges of the tape are covered with silver paint before coating overall with metal. The reason for the silver paint is that since the metal-coating is very thin, it is better to rely on a heavy silver paint coating for conductivity from the specimen surface to the stub than it is to rely on the thin metal film, which can easily separate at the edge of the tape when transferred in and out of the metal-coating vacuum system and the SEM. All areas of the sample which are not to be examined are masked with silver paint, care being taken that the solvent from the paint does not engulf the specimen. Some nonconducting areas of the preparation in the specimen chamber will give mild charging effects, such as poor resolution, even though they are not under the beam at the time. When EDXRA information is required on a sample, the silver paint may be replaced with carbon paint. However, carbon paints with high chlorine content should be avoided.

b. Description of tape

Any clear nonpigmented tape can be used. We prefer Scotch® brand tape #665.° It has a smooth surface with almost no pits or surface irregularities.

c. Metal-coating

Metal-coating of particulate specimens mounted on adhesive tape is essential to avoid developing a charge on nonconductive particles as the electron beam impinges on the surface. Most particles mounted on tape can be coated in a thermal evaporator by an initial coating of carbon, followed by a metal such as gold. Carbon has a tendency to coat the underside of the particles in contact with the tape, while metals give better emission characteristics. The coating is necessary even for smooth particles, even though they show

° 3M Company, 3M Center—Product Information Center, 220-6E, St. Paul, MN 55101.

less evidence of charging than particles with extremely rough or porous surfaces. Of course, charging effects themselves can be intentionally observed, and then the metal-coating step is eliminated. The sputter-coating technique for metal-coating can also be employed for particle coating.

An added caution in proper metal-coating should be noted. Particle distribution on the tape determines the quality of the coating. Large or agglomerated particles may hide other smaller particles, as well as lower parts of the large ones from the coating source, even though proper rotation of specimens is used during coating.

In some cases where the thermal properties of the particles are unknown and it is suspected that they may have very low melting or fusion points, it is better to eliminate the carbon shadowing and coat with aluminum, since it has a lower evaporation temperature than any of the other commonly used metals. Unfortunately, aluminum shadowing in some peculiar cases gives some problems. The areas on the stub and tape around an insulating particle are sometimes black instead of aluminum color. A second metal-coating of aluminum is then necessary to properly coat the sample.

When particles are mounted on tape and metal-coated, it is advisable to do the SEM examination within not more than a day or two after coating. The coating has a tendency to migrate and crack on the tape surface as well as to separate from the particles, causing charging effects. Reexamination of aged preparations usually requires recoating again with metal. Aged aluminum coating may have oxidized, yielding less conduction, even if not altered morphology.

If metal particles are mounted on tape, it is necessary to metal coat these as well in order to eliminate charging effects. Even conducting materials if they are "floating" electrically will give serious charging effects.

2. Single Particle Considerations

a. Substrate preparation

An important aspect of particle examination in the SEM in recent years has been the observation of single particles, especially in pollution and contamination studies.

Preparation techniques for single particles are more demanding than for multiple particle samples and require special handling techniques (Volume I, pp. 223–246). Since some of the particles examined are extremely small, down to the submicrometer level, it is necessary to do the preparation in a clean environment, preferably in a clean room, clean box or clean bench, and the mounting methods must provide a means of positive identification of the particle on the specimen mount. In addition to obtaining micrographs on the SEM, the characterization of particles usually demands at least elemental analysis normally supplied by x-ray analysis either in the SEM or electron microprobe. These requirements dictate that the specimen mount be a smooth, structureless surface with positive identification marks, and preferably one which does not contribute a detectable x-ray signal of its own. One of the most satisfactory mounts for this work is a polished beryllium plate.

The beryllium plates used for this purpose are 12 mm diameter disks, 3 mm thick, cemented to a specimen stub with conductive epoxy adhesive. We have had success with beryllium disks obtained from Brush Wellman Company.° The disks are polished by the usual metallographic techniques of abrading through at least seven or eight different polishing steps, from 240 grit paper down to $\frac{1}{4}$ μm diamond paste, using an automatic metallographic polishing unit. Since beryllium dust is toxic, all operations are carried out in a glove dry box, preferably with a nitrogen atmosphere and dedicated solely to beryllium operations. Also, to prevent the beryllium from oxidizing, the polishing medium carrying the various grits is oil rather than water. At each step of the process, going from one grit to another, complete cleaning of the apparatus and mounts with a solvent is required. The finished disk is then ultrasonically cleaned in xylene.

The polished disks are first marked by scratching on the surface, with a fine tungsten needle, a rectangular array of 1-mm squares. Each column and each row is indexed by a number engraved with the needle (Figure 13).

For further positive identification of particle position, an additional figure of some sort is inscribed inside a numbered square with a needle. Marking of the surface is done under an optical stereomicroscope. Such figures as houses with windows and doors or animals or plants with distinctive features are used. Then, a particle to be observed is mounted within a characteristic feature of these drawings, and the drawings are identified as being inside a specific numbered square on the beryllium plate. This arrangement provides positive identification of the particle to be observed. The position of the particle on the beryllium

---

° Brush Wellman Company, 17876 St. Clair Avenue, Cleveland, OH 44110.

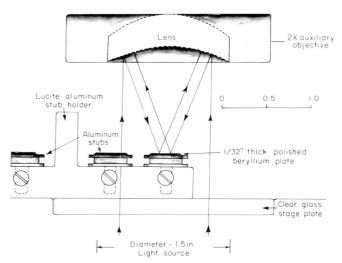

Figure 15. Arrangement for brightfield top lighting of aluminum stubs using the front lens of a stereobinocular microscope as a mirror.

plate is indicated on the analytical form by a sketch made at the time of mounting.

Mounting single particles on a beryllium substrate is carried out by observing the particle and beryllium surface using an optical stereomicroscope furnished with an additional convex-concave objective lens which has its concave surface facing the beryllium stub surface. When the system is illuminated by light from beneath the stage, some of the light reflects from this front concave surface back onto the surface of the beryllium stub, providing just the right kind of bright-field top light needed for observing small particles on the opaque plate (Figure 15).

b. Mounting tools

For all mounting techniques the two tools used are a fine tungsten needle and a micropipette. The tungsten needles are prepared by using 20-mil (0.5-mm) tungsten wire and either electro-etching one end of the wire in 15% KOH solution using an AC voltage of about 20 volts, or drawing a red hot tip of the wire across solid sodium nitrite. This gives needles with a tip radius of about 1 μm (Volume I, p. 225).

The micropipettes are made from $\frac{3}{16}$–$\frac{1}{4}$″ diameter polyethylene tubing drawn to a fine tip over a small flame (Volume I, p. 228). Glass pipettes are not used because of the danger of fracturing the glass and/or damaging the beryllium plate surface.

c. Mounting of particles

Particles greater than 10 μm are picked up with a dry needle and deposited into a microdrop of solvent

such as amyl acetate which has just previously been placed on the beryllium stub with a micropipette (Figure 16). Particles in this size range could move in the electron beam and should be tacked down as follows. A drop of softened collodion is placed next to the particle and an additional drop of solvent is placed next to the collodion and carried across the particle, with the needle at an angle, so only the meniscus of the liquid passes over the particle. This leaves a sufficient amount of collodion, 20–50 nm thick, to tack down the particle without leaving so much as to obscure detail. By optical microscopy, this thin film shows a gray interference color by reflected light (Figure 15).

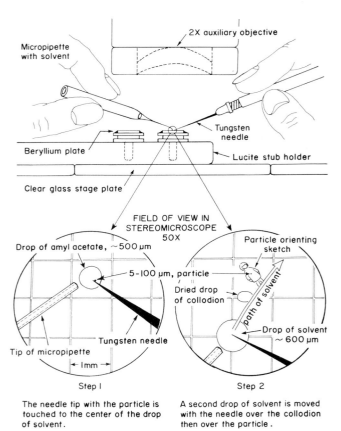

Figure 16. Securing a 5–100 μm particle under a stereomicroscope on a beryllium plate.

Particles in the 3–10 μm range are also picked up with a needle and deposited within a small drop (~200–300 μm diameter) of solvent which has previously been placed on the beryllium plate. Here, electrostatic attraction and perhaps nonvolatile impurities in the solvent are enough to cause adhesion of these small particles to the beryllium surface. If more ad-

III.C.2.c

hesion is required, collodion can again be used as previously described.

Dry particles smaller than 3 μm cannot be picked up with a needle. They are instead transferred from the surface on which they are provided by covering them with a film of collodion as previously described but thicker (~2–4 μm). A portion of this film, containing the particle, is removed from a surface by cutting a small square of collodion around the particle with a needle and floating it on a microdrop of water, and transferring the film and particle to the beryllium plate. Most of the collodion is then washed away by placing a drop of amyl acetate next to it on the beryllium plate and passing this drop across the particle with a needle. This is repeated five to six times or until the collodion film around the particle is in the 20–40 nm range and can no longer be discernible in the SEM. The thickness is determined by the interference colors, using the brightfield top light system with the binocular microscope (Figure 15).

Some particles may be soluble in the solvent used. In this case, water or other low vapor pressure solvents can be used instead. In many cases, the solvent upon evaporation will cause the particle to adhere to the beryllium plate without additional adhesive.

If EDXRA is required on these particles, it is done either in the SEM or in an electron microprobe analyzer, either with no metal-coating or with a mild carbon coating. Ion microprobe (IMP) examination can also be made at this stage if desired. For SEM micrographs, it is usually necessary to metal coat the particles, after first making the elemental analysis.

Cleaning of the beryllium stubs after use is done as follows. Stubs that have not been coated with metal are gently cleaned with acetone and rinsed with particle-free ethanol. The metal-coated beryllium stubs are cleaned by hand, first with a 1-μm diamond polishing compound, then washed with soap, then rinsed with acetone and finally rinsed with particle-free ethanol. Here again, polishing debris must be safely discarded.

3. Filter Substrates for Particle Mounting

Various types of filters have been used over the years for particle mounting. The better filters for this purpose are the membrane filters in which the surface is relatively flat. A discussion of these filters is given in detail by Kaiser.[6]

Many particulate dispersions from both liquids and

gases are collected on cellulose ester filters of 0.45 μm and larger pore size. For direct examination in the SEM, these filters have confusing backgrounds since the filter structure is highly porous. Quite often, small particles collected on these filters cannot be differentiated from the filter structure.

If particles are collected on cellulose ester filters, however, they can be examined if the filter is first dissolved away. This can be done by cutting a ⅛″ disk of the filter with particles on it and placing this disk of filter on a TEM screen substrate which has a carbon film covering the surface. This is placed in the vapor condensation apparatus used for TEM specimen preparation with acetone as the liquid, and refluxing until the filter material has dissolved away and has deposited the particle on the carbon film. It can then be viewed in the SEM by depositing it on a specimen stub with a small drop of silver paint (or carbon paint if EDXRA is to be performed). This preparation may or may not have to be metal-coated. The particles, of course, must be resistant to acetone.

Membrane filters can either be used in a normal filtering apparatus and cut into sections for examination, or 13-mm filters can be used in a syringe type filter. The filter is mounted on a specimen stub with double-sided tape. Again, the filter is curved onto the adhesive tape surface from one side to the other so that it lies flat on the tape. The edge of the filter is then covered with silver paint as for the adhesive tape method and for the same reason. Cleanliness of the filter apparatus and filter surface are, of course, necessary and should be checked by running a control if necessary.

Another method of depositing particles on a membrane filter is to take up dry particles in a liquid or, if they are already in a liquid, to place a drop or two from a micropipette in the marked center of a piece of filter which rests on an absorbent surface. The particles stay on the membrane filter where they were deposited and can be subsequently washed with a few drops of the proper liquid if necessary. This section of the filter is then mounted on a specimen stub with double-sided tape as before. The deposit is small enough so that the whole sample from the drop can be examined in the SEM, giving satisfactory representative data. In addition, this technique provides nicely separated particles for observation and is usable when extremely small samples are to be prepared.

4. Mounting on Smooth Substrates

Particle mounting on unpolished metal stubs or other comparable surfaces is to be avoided, if pos-

---

[6] Kaiser, R., *Particle Dispersion Studies*, Short Title VT 1415, ARPA No. 1702, National Technical Information Service, Springfield, VA, 1973, pp. 2–23 to 2–35.

sible, except for larger particles. The microstructure of machined surfaces is very disturbing at higher magnifications and tends to hide small particles. If EDXRA is to be done on the samples, then a beryllium mount should be used.

Glass coverslips are a good surface for mounting particles. Coverslips 12 mm in diameter can be obtained from some laboratory supply companies. These can be mounted on specimen stubs with double-sided tape. The disks should be firmly pressed onto the tape to eliminate entrapped air bubbles. After the particles are mounted on the glass, it is important to coat the edge of the glass with silver paint. The whole mount is then shadowed with carbon or gold.

Small particles can adhere to the glass by electrostatic attraction when mounted dry. Very often, depositing particles from a liquid suspension causes enough adherence of the particles to the glass. When placing liquid suspensions on a glass surface, it is advisable to use a small drop, the edges of which can be viewed when dry. This has the following advantages:

1. If there is any soluble material in the liquid, the mechanism of drying it on the glass tends to move the soluble portions to the edge of the drop leaving the particles in the center of the drop relatively free of this material. Too much soluble material when dried down obscures all detail of the particles and even, in more serious cases, hides particles completely. If information as to the soluble material in a system is not of any interest, then the suspension should be centrifuged and washed at least two or three times before deposition on the glass.
2. If a small drop of liquid carrying the particles is used, then enough data and micrographs can be taken to represent the whole drop, giving a more statistical picture of particles and their distribution even if there is some particle segregation in the drying process.

Deposition of small droplets of particle suspensions can also be made on a coverslip or other smooth substrate by spraying from an atomizer. This is discussed by Horne[7] for biological and other particulate suspensions, and a commercial spray mounter is available from Fullam.°

The shiny side of aluminum foil can be used as a smooth mounting surface, but it is second best because it has micropits and mechanical striations which disturb the mounting and observation of smaller particles.

Highly agglomerated dry particles can be mounted on the glass coverslip surfaces by mulling in a proper liquid to give dispersion; the mull is then drawn down with a microscope slide to give a more uniform thin dispersion of particles.

Biological organisms are often mounted on glass surfaces, but it is very necessary to clean the specimens of culture media and dissolved materials, as even small amounts of amorphous material often hide the small organisms and obscure their surface detail.

In all the methods using a glass coverslip for mounting, the usual cements such as Duco®, collodion, conductive paint or albumen may be used at the time when they are just tacky.[4]

5. Miscellaneous Methods

a. Recovery of particles

Occasionally, it is desirable to examine the actual particles observed on the SEM by additional techniques. Such particles can be removed from a surface by a heavy deposit of collodion which, when dry, can be removed along with the particles. These can then be observed by optical microscopy directly, or by the TEM after depositing them on a TEM carbon-covered grid and washing them in the condensation washing apparatus, or mounting them on a beryllium stub for electron microprobe or ion microprobe examination, as was discussed under the single particle preparation. Particles can also be recovered from sample preparations by micromanipulators in the SEM.

b. Fracturing of particles

The internal structure of many particles can be observed by fracturing. A thin layer of particles is placed on a microscope slide. Another slide is gently pressed on top of this layer to fracture the particles. The first slide is gently shaken to give various orientations of the fractured surfaces, and the whole layer of fractured particles is picked up by gently pressing a stub with double-sided tape onto the microscope slide. Treatment as with normal tape preparations is then continued. Cutting, mild grinding, milling and impaction can also be used to reveal internal structure.

c. Particles which sublime

Particles with a high vapor pressure which sublime in the vacuum of both the coating unit and the SEM

---

[7] Horne, R. W., *Techniques for Electron Microscopy*, D. H. Kay, Ed., F. A. Davis Company, Philadelphia, 1967, pp. 311–327.

° Ernest F. Fullam, Inc., P.O. Box 444, Schenectady, NY 12301.

can be observed by first replicating at atmospheric pressure. Either the normal acetate replicating tape or the silicone dental replicating material can be used if the particles are not affected. A thin layer of particles is placed on a microscope slide, and the replicating material is placed on top of the particles and allowed to set. Alternately, the particles can be dropped onto the surface of the replicating material if they do not sink into it. The replicas are then mounted on stubs, metal-coated and viewed in the SEM.

D. Conclusions

The necessity for evaluating each particulate sample and the condition in which it exists in terms of the information really sought should again be emphasized. Formulate the necessary questions, then do the sample preparation and observation to give the answers required to solve the problem.

IV. Descriptions and Electron Micrographs

JOHN A. BROWN, IAN M. STEWART AND GENE R. GRIEGER

10 mm = 100 μm   10 mm = 10 μm   10 mm = 1 μm

610   Acacia Pollen (*Acacia longifolia*)—The typical polyad nature of these pollen grains is well illustrated in the 1000X micrograph. The grooving in the external cell wall is shown in more detail at 10,000X. This appears as a true groove with no major structural discontinuities visible.

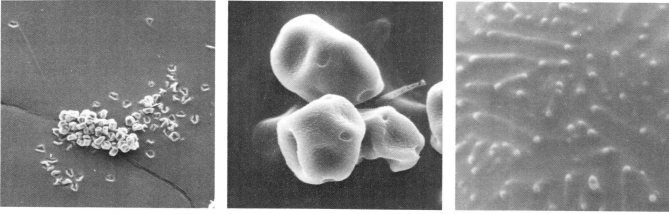

611   Alder (Red) Pollen (*Alnus rubra*)—These single, somewhat polygonal grains exhibit both surface "dimpling" and pores. The speckled, pebbly nature of the surface observed with the light microscope is seen, at 10,000X, to be due to numerous rod-shaped protuberances approximately 0.2 μm in diameter and 1–2 μm long.

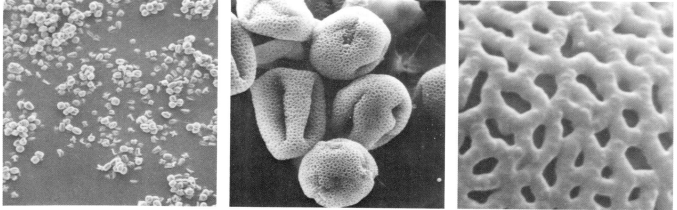

612   Ash Pollen (*Fraxinus toumeyi*)—These grooved, or furrowed, grains vary in shape from almost spherical to oval. Superficially, the oval particles resemble those of *sugar maple pollen* (16). However, the porous structure, readily observed at 10,000X, clearly differentiates the two.

10 mm = 100 μm   10 mm = 10 μm   10 mm = 1 μm

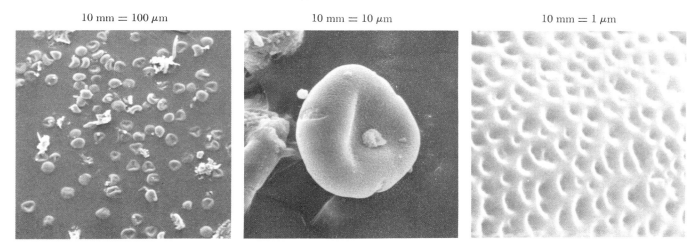

613 Basswood (Linden) Pollen (*Tilia* sp.)—Two of the three pores characterizing basswood pollen are clearly visible in the micrograph at 1000X. These pores appear almost as a slash through the exine. The fine reticulation, observed by light microscopy and alluded to in Volume V, is seen at 10,000X to consist of numerous fine pores, approximately 0.25 μm in diameter.

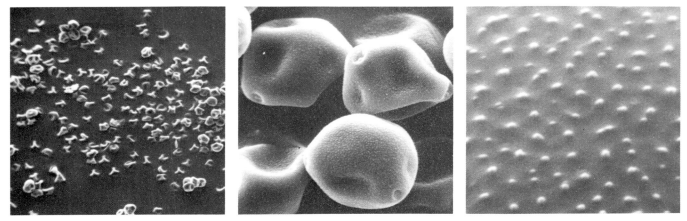

614 Bayberry Pollen (*Myrica cerifera*)—Many of these grains collapse into a tricorn morphology (100X). At higher magnification the aspidate surface pores are clearly visible. The speckled appearance of the surface, seen at 10,000X, is due to numerous surface protuberances 0.1–0.2 μm in diameter.

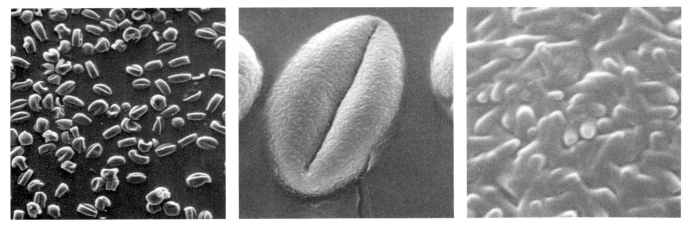

615 Beech (American) Pollen (*Fagus americana*)—These elongated, furrowed grains appear to have collapsed under vacuum, obscuring the large pore in the middle of the furrow. The surface structure, shown at 10,000X, apparently consists of interdigitating stellate structures.

10 mm = 100 μm   10 mm = 10 μm   10 mm = 1 μm

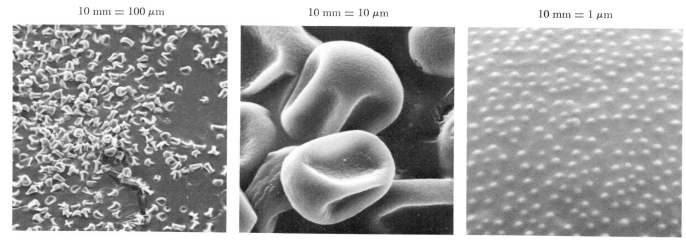

616 Bermuda Grass Pollen (*Cynodon dactylon*)—These 20–30 μm diameter grains each exhibit 3–4 dimples and are monoporate. Morphologically almost identical to *Timothy grass pollen* (23), the two are barely differentiated by the slight size difference.

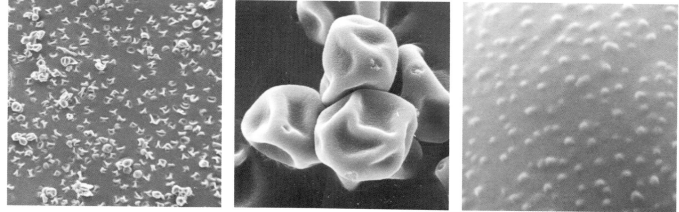

617 Birch (Sweet) Pollen (*Betula lenta*)—These triporate grains have the morphology of collapsed spheres. The pores, normally protuberant (aspidate), tend to be at the intersection of noncollapsed ridges. Surface mottling is due to small (0.2 μm) hemispherical bumps.

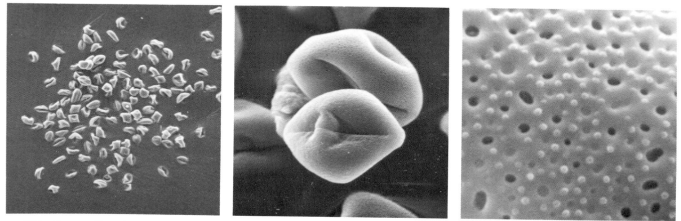

618 Castor (Bean) Pollen (*Ricinus communis*)—The trilobate furrowed grains, collapsed along the furrows, are characteristic in SEM preparations. The granular surface observed by light microscopy and at 1000X is seen at 10,000X to be due to a combination of fine pores (0.2–0.4 μm) and spherical or hemispherical nodules (∼0.2 μm).

10 mm = 100 μm   10 mm = 10 μm   10 mm = 1 μm

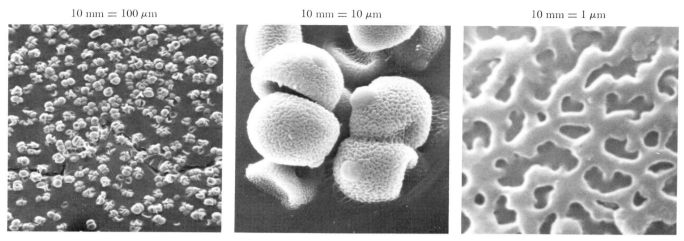

619 Cattail Grass Pollen (*Typha latifolia*)—These aggregated grains, generally equiaxed tetrads but also showing linear arrays (100X), show a reticulated structure with irregular lacunae (10,000X). The single pores appear, at 1000X, to be exuding a membrane, probably as a result of the vacuum to which they have been subjected.

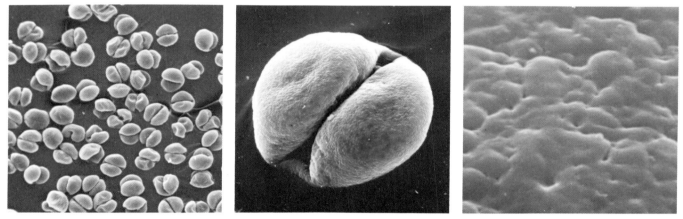

620 Cedar (Deodora) Pollen (*Cedrus deodora*)—The 50–60 μm diameter bilobate grains are characteristic of the cedar pollen. These lobes have folded in on themselves to give the appearance of a split sphere. Surface granularity is due to reticulation, but with ill-developed muri and lacunae (10,000X).

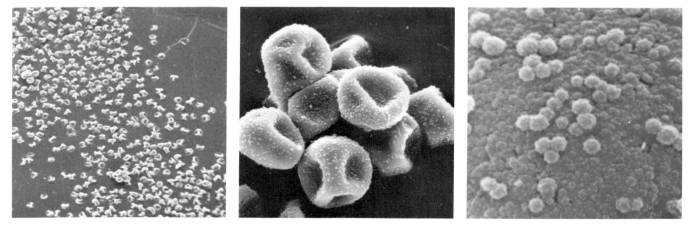

621 Cedar (Red) Pollen (*Juniperus virginiana*)—These collapsed spheres are approximately 20 μm in diameter and show no well-defined pores. The surface structure is granular and is covered with near spherical protrusions approximately 0.4 μm in diameter which themselves are echinate.

10 mm = 100 μm   10 mm = 10 μm   10 mm = 1 μm

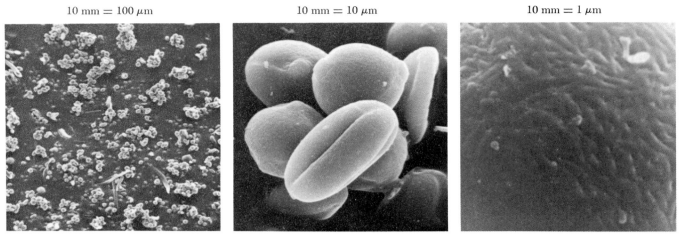

622   Chestnut Pollen (*Castanea dentata*)—Longitudinal furrows give these grains a trilobate appearance. Faint traces of transverse grooves are visible in the 1000X view as are pores (normally three to a grain) approximately 5 μm in diameter with bulging membranes. The surface texture is reticulate, tending toward rugulate.

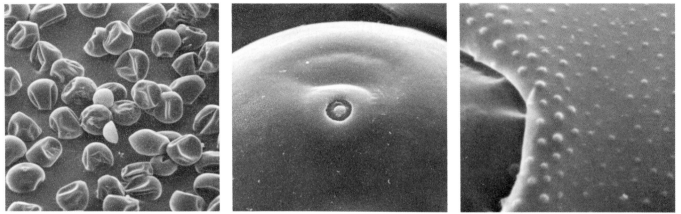

623   Corn Pollen (*Zea mays*)—These dimpled and collapsed spheres exhibit one prominent pore approximately 7–10 μm in diameter (100X and 1000X). The faint surface granularity is seen at 10,000X to be due to the presence of small protuberances 0.1–0.5 μm in diameter and more pronounced in the vicinity of the pore.

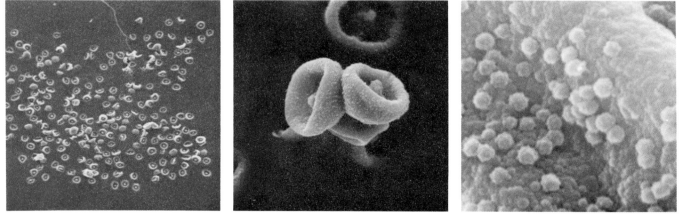

624   Cypress (Bald) Pollen (*Taxodium distichum*)—Collapse of these spherical grains has resulted in a morphology akin to small cap mushrooms, with the pore-bearing papilla as the mushroom stalk. The surface is granular and covered with small (0.5 μm) echinate balls (10,000X).

10 mm = 100 μm   10 mm = 10 μm   10 mm = 1 μm

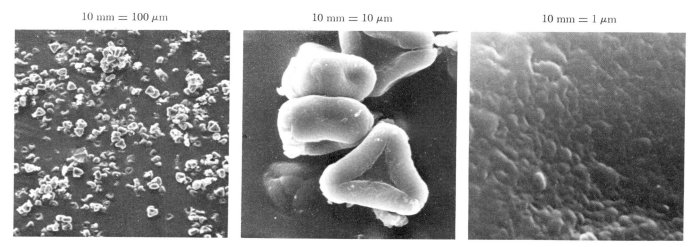

625 Eucalyptus Pollen (*Eucalyptus globulus*)—These tricornate grains show a central dimple with furrows emanating from this dimple to the corners of the triangle. At these corners are located prominent elongated apertures with some exudation. The surface texture is reticulate.

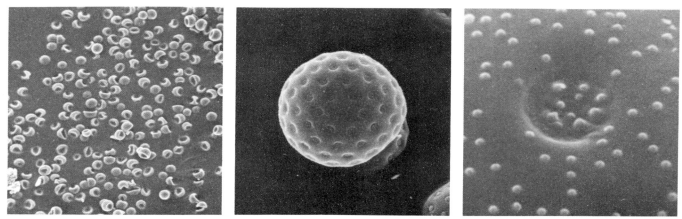

626 Firebush Pollen (*Kochia scoparia*)—The multiporate nature of these pollen grains and the regular distribution of these pores give them the appearance of 30–35 μm diameter golf balls (1000X). Many collapsed spheres are present in the preparation (100X). The surface consists of a smooth substrate bearing many hemispherical bumps 0.25 μm in diameter.

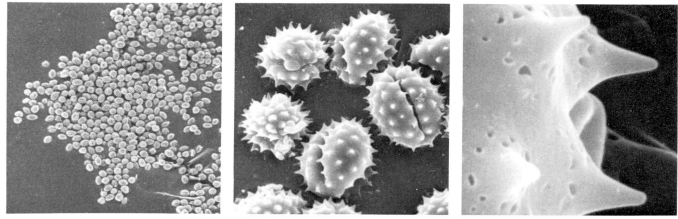

627 Goldenrod Pollen (*Solidago* sp.)—These echinate grains vary in shape from spherical to ovoidal. Furrows, three to a grain, are prominent. The bases of the spines tend to be ringed by small surface pores (10,000X).

10 mm = 100 μm　　　　　　10 mm = 10 μm　　　　　　10 mm = 1 μm

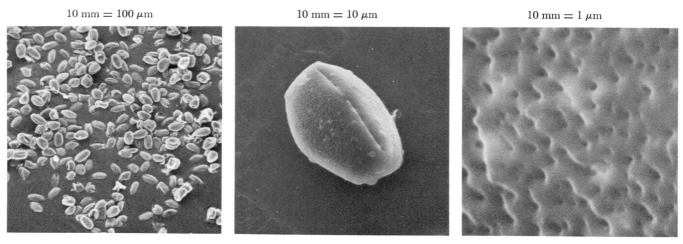

628　Gum (Black) Pollen (*Nyssa sylvatica*)—Three longitudinal furrows give these ovoidal grains a near triangular transverse section. The grainy, orange peel appearance of the surface texture is due to the presence of a reticulate structure with small, circular lacunae and broad muri.

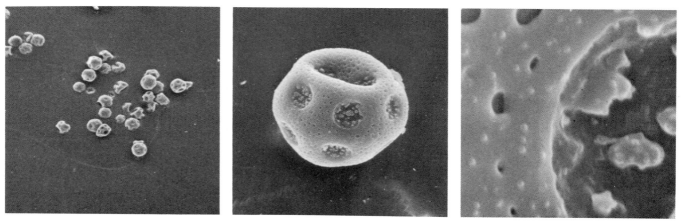

629　Gum (Sweet) Pollen (*Liquidambar styraciflua*)—The many (12–20) large pores in these grains give them a dimpled sphere morphology. The 7 μm diameter pores show much internal structure. The surface between the large pores is pitted with many small holes (0.1–0.5 μm diameter) and covered with numerous 0.1–0.2 μm protuberances.

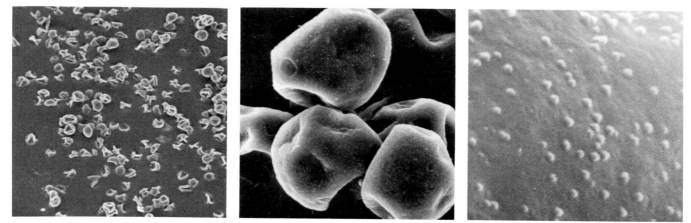

630　Hackberry Pollen (*Celtis occidentalis*)—These collapsed spherical grains show only weak evidence of their triporate nature. The uppermost grain of the 1000X micrograph shows one of these 3–4 μm pores clearly. The surface consists of a slightly rough substrate with many 0.2–0.3 μm protuberances.

10 mm = 100 μm   10 mm = 10 μm   10 mm = 1 μm

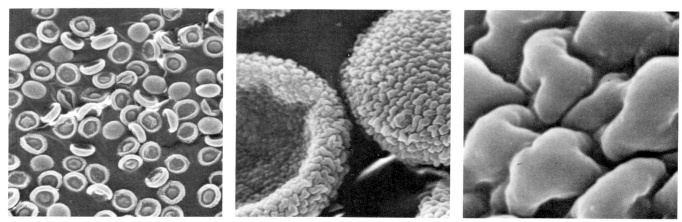

631 Hazelnut Pollen (*Corylus americana*)—Morphologically somewhat similar to *hackberry pollen* (*630*), these grains may be distinguished by somewhat more prominent, although smaller (1–2 μm), pores. The grains are again triporate. The surface at 10,000X is also somewhat smoother and the protuberances less prominent.

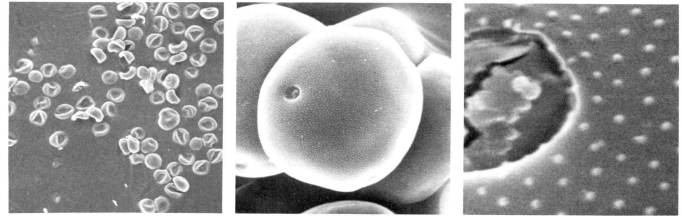

632 Hemlock (Eastern) Pollen (*Tsuga canadensis*)—These disclike grains exhibit a prominent depression giving them a near hemispheroidal appearance. The rough surface appearance is due to a dense packing of clavate elements.

633 Hickory (White) Pollen (*Hicoria alba*)—Spheroidal and collapsed spheroidal grains show three 4–5 μm pores asymmetrically located on the surface (see large grain to right center of 100X micrograph). Surface texture is due to numerous 0.2–0.3 μm hemispherical protuberances.

10 mm = 100 μm   10 mm = 10 μm   10 mm = 1 μm

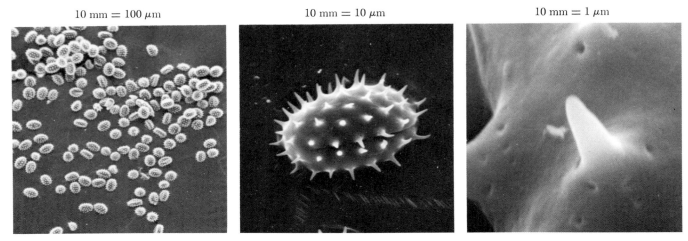

634 Marigold Pollen (*Tagetes* sp.)—These spherical to ovoidal, echinate grains can be differentiated from *goldenrod* (627) and *ragweed* (22) by their less prominent furrows and their longer, higher aspect ratio spines. Surface relief between the spines is low except for small pores close to the bases of the spines.

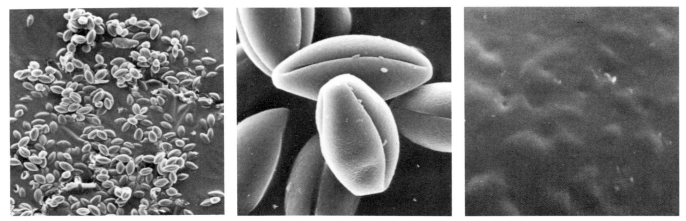

635 Mesquite Pollen (*Prosopis juliflora*)—Longitudinal furrows are the most prominent feature on these elongated ovoids. Although the surface appears grainy at low magnifications (100X and 1000X), the surface relief is low with ill-defined scabrae and verrucae.

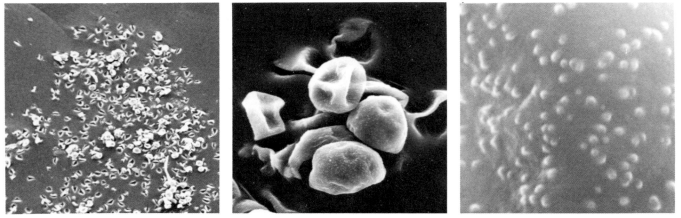

636 Mulberry (Paper) Pollen (*Broussonetia papyrifera*)—Highly irregular, collapsed spheres predominate. Some evidence of the two poorly defined pores may be observed, but is generally obscure. Surface texture is due to numerous 0.2–0.4 μm protuberances.

10 mm = 100 μm   10 mm = 10 μm   10 mm = 1 μm

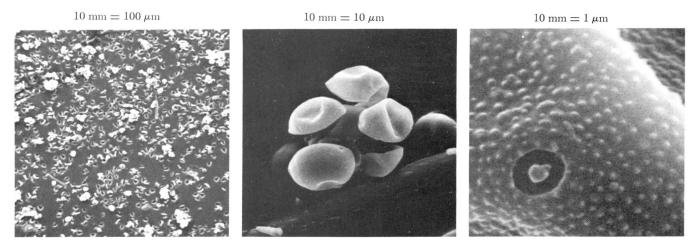

637   Nettle Pollen (*Urtica gracilis*)—These flattened and collapsed spheres show three prominent 1–1.5 μm diameter pores. The fine grainy structure is due to a multitude of 0.1–0.5 μm protuberances.

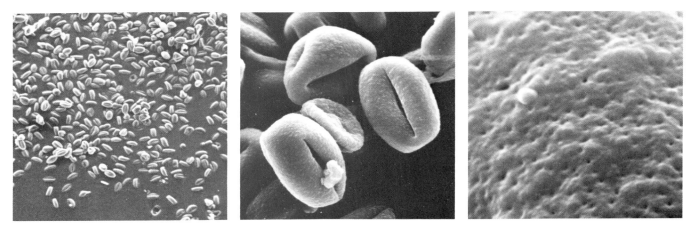

638   Oak (Live) Pollen (*Quercus virginiana*)—These deeply furrowed and apertured grains have a trilobate transverse section. Their surface texture is due to numerous small pores in an undulatory matrix. This texture assists in the differentiation of oak pollen from similar furrowed and trilobate grains such as *sugar maple pollen (16)* and *ash pollen (612)*.

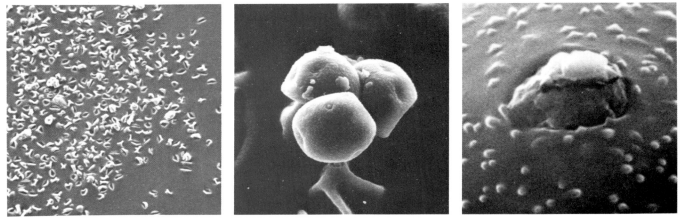

639   Osage Orange Pollen (*Maclura pomifera*)—These collapsed spheroidal grains are typically 20–25 μm in diameter. The 2–3 μm diameter pores (usually three in number) are circular to irregular, elliptical and generally show protruding membranes. The surface texture is due to numerous hemispherical to cone-shaped protuberances.

10 mm = 100 μm   10 mm = 10 μm   10 mm = 1 μm

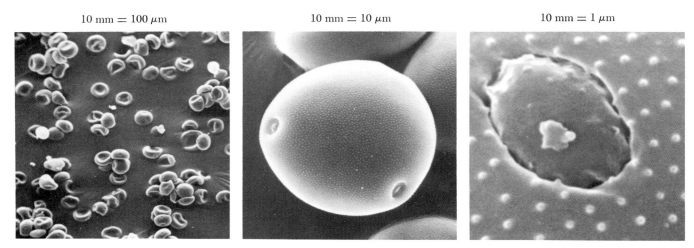

640   Pecan Pollen (*Hicoria pecan*)—The 40–50 μm spherical grains are frequently collapsed to give almost a discoid appearance. Three pores, 3–4 μm in diameter, are prominent. Surface texture is due to an even distribution of 0.2–0.3 μm hemispherical scabrae.

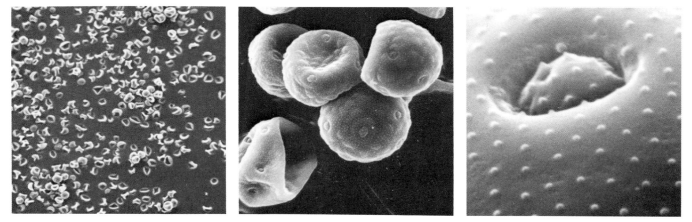

641   Plantain (English) Pollen (*Plantago lanceolata*)—These spherical and collapsed spherical grains are multiporate with from 6 to 12 prominent 3–4 μm diameter pores. The surface shows large-scale "bumpiness" on which is superimposed a regular distribution of 0.2–0.3 μm hemispherical scabrae.

642   Privet Pollen (*Ligustrum lucidium*)—These oval to spherical grains have a trilobate appearance due to deep grooving. The surface is distinctly reticulate with very high or prominent muri. The side walls of the muri contain many pores (10,000X).

10 mm = 100 μm   10 mm = 10 μm   10 mm = 1 μm

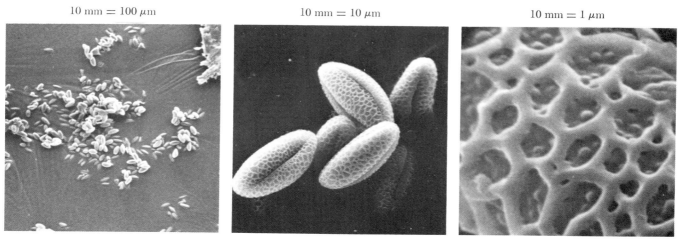

643   Pussy Willow Pollen (*Salix* sp.)—The majority of grains are ellipsoidal and trilobed due to three longitudinal furrows. Their major axes are in the range 25 to 30 μm and 10 to 15 μm. The surface is distinctly reticulate with 0.1–0.4 μm hemispherical protuberances present in the lacunae (10,000X).

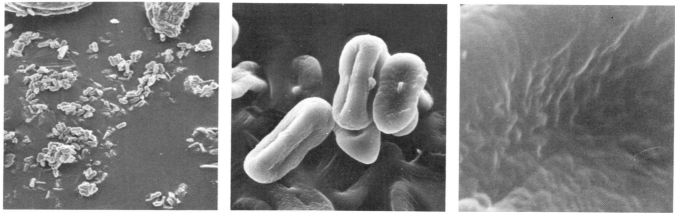

644   Queen Anne's Lace Pollen (*Daucus carota*)—These elongate grains show furrowing on their longitudinal axes which leads to a triangular or trilobate transverse section. The shape is reminiscent of a peanut, as is the rough surface texture. High magnification (10,000X) shows the texture to be rugulate, tending to striate.

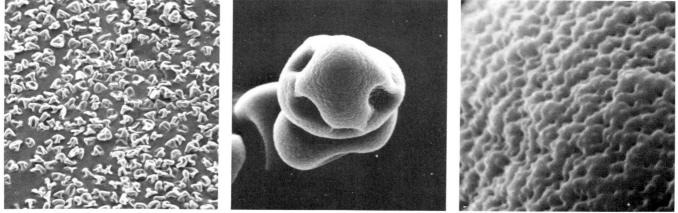

645   Sedge Pollen (*Carex* sp.)—These grains range in shape from irregular to polyhedral. Deep surface dimpling is characteristic, frequently giving the appearance of a deflated and pinched ball. The surface texture is rough with numerous fine (0.1–0.2 μm) pores.

10 mm = 100 μm   10 mm = 10 μm   10 mm = 1 μm

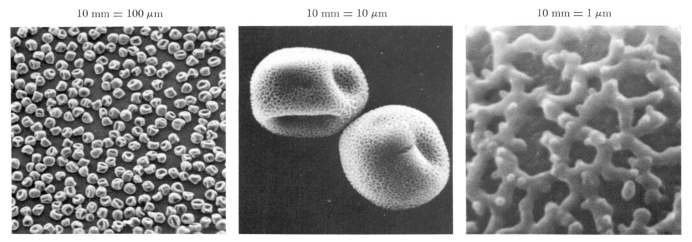

646 Silk Tassel Bush Pollen (*Garrya elliptica*)—The tetra-hedral to dimpled spheroidal appearance of these grains is principally due to collapse on three moderate furrows. The networklike appearance of the surface is due to a reticulate structure, many of whose muri are not totally interconnected. Hemispherical protuberances approximately 0.2–0.3 μm diameter frequently decorate the muri.

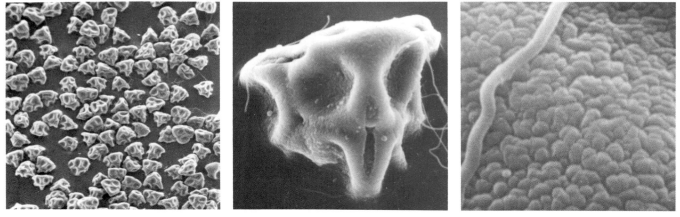

647 Rhododendron Pollen (*Rhododendron* sp.)—These heavily dimpled grains approximate to tetrahedra. Three deep furrows each contain a prominent pore (1000X). The rough surface texture (10,000X) is due to a dense packing of spherical to irregular structural units from 0.1 to 0.5 μm in size.

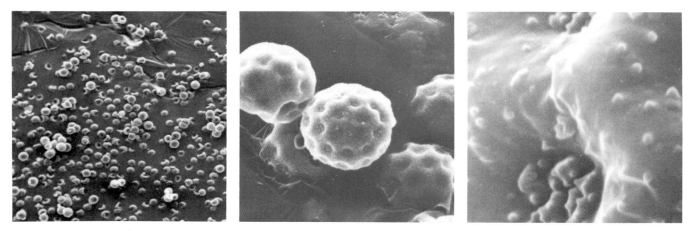

648 Russian Thistle Pollen (*Salsola pestifer*)—These spherical, 25–30 μm, grains are heavily decorated with pores, giving a rough golf ball appearance. Surface structure is evident both between the pores and within the pores (10,000X). Pore diameters are between 3 and 4 μm.

10 mm = 100 μm   10 mm = 10 μm   10 mm = 1 μm

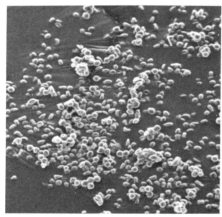
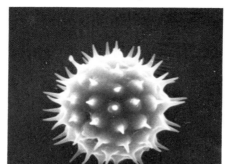

649 Sunflower Pollen (*Helianthus* sp.)—These 25–30 μm spheres are completely covered with long, thin, sharply pointed spines. These spines are approximately 5 μm long and are frequently curved or bent. Some surface grooving or furrowing is evident.

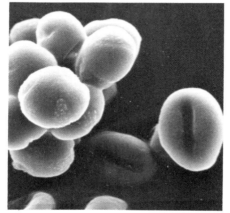

650 Sycamore Pollen (*Platanus occidentalis*)—These spherical grains, 15–20 μm in diameter, have three distinct scars (1000X), giving them the appearance of partially peeled oranges. Collapse along these scar lines frequently occurs to give a furrowed, trilobate appearance (see right-hand side of 1000X micrograph). Surface structure is more prominent within the scar—compare the left and right sides of the 10,000X micrographs.

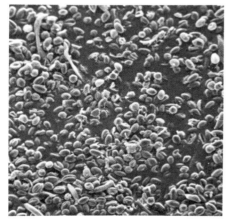
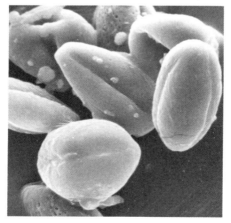
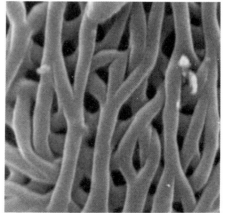

651 Tree of Heaven Pollen (*Ailanthus altissima*)—The spheroidal to ellipsoidal grains have three longitudinal furrows giving a trilobate transverse section. The surface structure (10,000X) is unusual and distinctive, consisting of a felted mass of branching and intertwining fibers.

10 mm = 100 μm   10 mm = 10 μm   10 mm = 1 μm

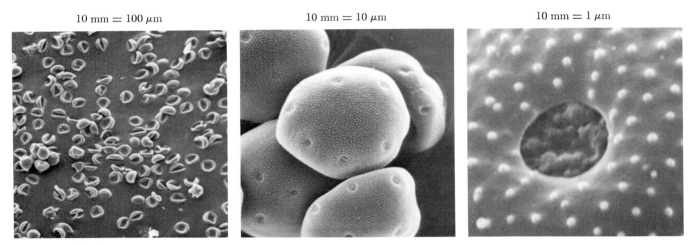

652 Walnut (California Black) Pollen (*Juglans californica*) Although these grains are spherical, most have collapsed to give a discoid appearance (100X). Numerous 2–3 μm pores are present, with a rough textured membrane clearly visible (1000X and 10,000X). Surface texture of the grain is due to numerous, evenly spaced scabrae approximately 0.25 μm in diameter.

653 Willow (Red) Pollen (*Salix laevigata*)—These ovoidal grains are characterized by three deep, longitudinal furrows and a prominent reticulate structure (1000X). The lacunae of this structure are decorated with numerous hemispherical protuberances, decreasing in size with proximity to the furrows.

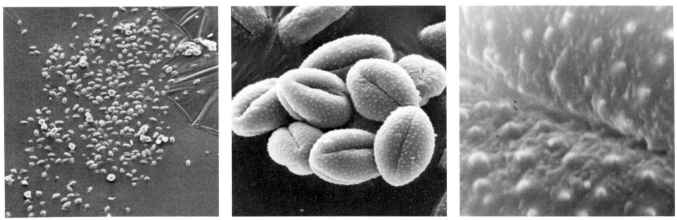

654 Wormwood Pollen (*Artemisia absinthium*)—These ovoidal grains have a trilobate appearance due to the development of deep longitudinal furrows. Some nearly spherical grains are present. The rough surface texture is due to 0.3–0.5 μm bumps superimposed on a substrate covered with many finer (0.1–0.2 μm) protuberances.

10 mm = 100 μm   10 mm = 10 μm   10 mm = 1 μm

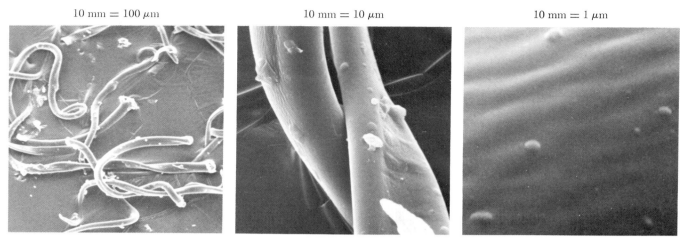

655 Catalpa Trichomes—These hairs range from cylindrical to flattened, frequently twisted ribbons. Their width is uniform (approximately 20–30 μm) over most of their length. They are sharply flared at their bases and taper to a point over the last 100 μm of their length (100X). Their surfaces are gently wrinkled (1000X and 10,000X).

656 Honey Locust Trichomes—These rough-textured hairs are about 10 μm wide and about 250–500 μm long. The ends are gently pointed and their bases flared (100X). The surface is highly rugose with bumps (1000X) and striated wrinkles (10,000X).

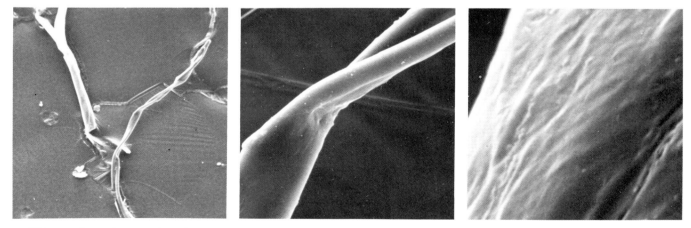

657 Peach Trichomes—These hairs are flattened, twisted ribbons, tapering to a point and with truncated bases. Morphologically rather similar to *cotton* (59), the two may be distinguished by their surface textures (10,000X). The ribbons are approximately 6–10 μm thick and 20–30 μm wide.

10 mm = 100 μm   10 mm = 10 μm   10 mm = 1 μm

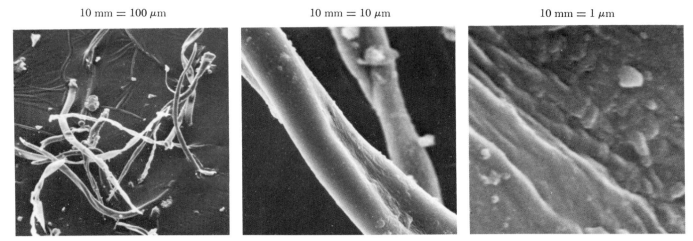

658 Plum Trichomes—These hairs vary in transverse section from near cylindrical to flattened, collapsed cylinders with diameters from about 5 to 25 μm. The hairs, which flare slightly at their roots and taper at their tips, are about 0.5 mm long and are frequently twisted and curved.

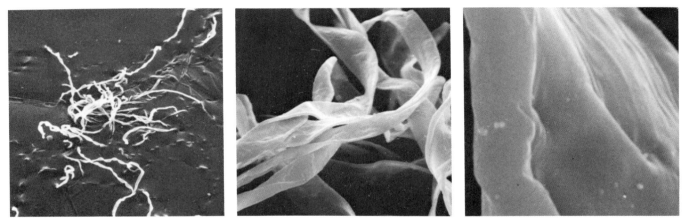

659 Poplar (*Bolleana*) Trichomes—Strongly kinked and highly twisted, these hairs are flat ribbons about 5–10 μm wide and 0.5–1 μm thick. The ribbons are frequently split and branched (100X and 1000X). The surface shows a striated texture at high magnification.

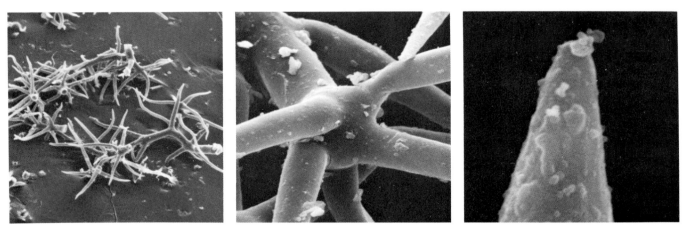

660 Sycamore Trichomes—A multiplicity of tapering fibers 100–200 μm long and 5–10 μm wide radiate from thickened nodes on a central stem about 15–25 μm in diameter. Several nodes are usually present on one stem. The individual fibers taper sharply (10,000X) and are, for the most part, smooth surfaced.

10 mm = 100 μm　　　　　　10 mm = 10 μm　　　　　　10 mm = 1 μm

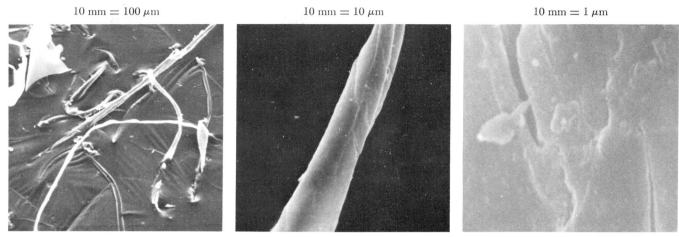

661　Tree of Heaven Trichomes—Generally straight to slightly curved fibers are characteristic. The width is about 10–15 μm with a slightly flattened transverse section. The surface is smooth with traces of the transverse septa just discernible at 1000X.

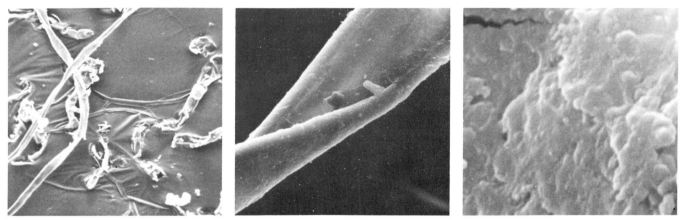

662　Yellow Poplar Trichomes—These hairs are ribbonlike with widths of about 25 μm. They vary in length from short fragments about 150 μm long to several hundred micrometers. The surface structure is somewhat rough (10,000X), but no evidence is visible on the surface of the striae observed by light microscopy.

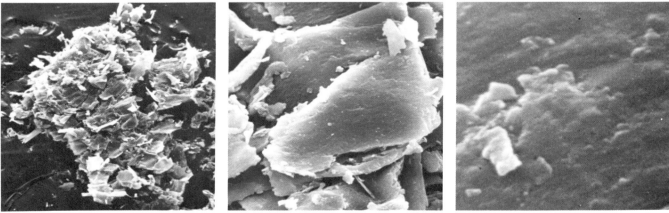

663　Bark Dust—These fragments of bark dust consist of flakes or sheets varying in diameter from a few micrometers to 30–40 μm. The surfaces of the flakes are slightly rugose (1000X and 10,000X). There are few diagnostic features observable by SEM.

10 mm = 100 μm   10 mm = 10 μm   10 mm = 1 μm

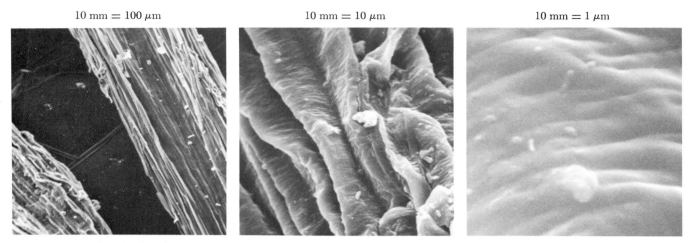

664   Corn Silk—The broad, 200–300 μm fibers are actually bundles of parallel fibrils about 10–20 μm wide (100X). At higher magnifications these fibrils are seen to be irregular ribbons striated at right angles to their length (1000X and 10,000X).

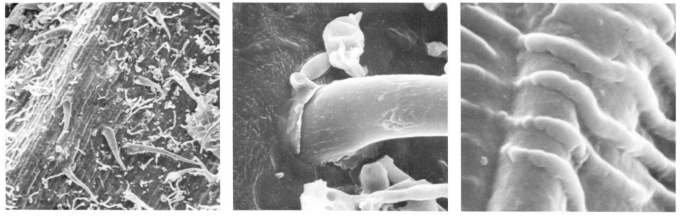

665   Corn Tassel—These massive fibers are longitudinally striated (100X) and have numerous tapering hairs, approximately 100–200 μm, distributed over their surface. At their bases these hairs have a diameter of approximately 2 μm. The rugose texture noted at 1000X can be seen at 10,000X to be due to near parallel ridges running at 90° to the coarser, longitudinal striations.

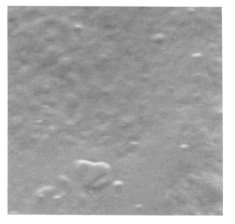

666   Milkweed Fibers—These 10–30 μm wide "fibers" (seed hairs) are, in fact, cylindrical tubes with walls about 1–2 μm thick. Surface texture of the tubes is fairly smooth but modified with numerous flattened hemispherical features about 0.2–0.4 μm in diameter (10,000X).

10 mm = 100 μm   10 mm = 10 μm   10 mm = 1 μm

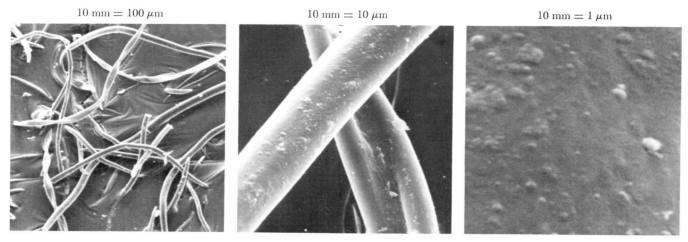

667   Peach Fuzz—These fibers, approximately 10–15 μm wide, may be either cylindrical or flattened ribbons and vary in length from about 100 μm to a few millimeters. The flattened ribbons are generally twisted. Surface texture is smooth with randomly scattered protuberances, generally hemispherical and varying in size from 0.1 to 0.4 μm.

668   Pussy Willow Fibers—These fibers are cylindrical with diameters of 5–10 μm, and taper gradually and smoothly to a point (100X). Surface structure, visible only at the highest magnification, is due to a multitude of longitudinally aligned rods or wrinkles about 0.1–0.2 μm wide and 0.3–1.0 μm long.

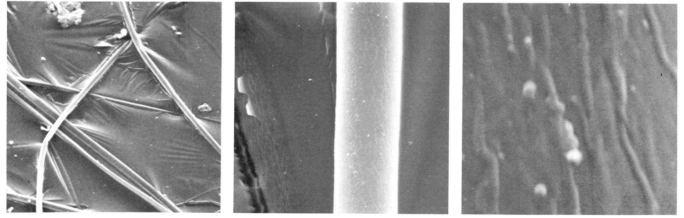

669   Sugar Cane Tassel—These long, cylindrical fibers exhibit a very uniform diameter (about 10–15 μm) along their entire length. Some evidence of surface striations is visible even at 1000X and is clearly visible at 10,000X.

10 mm = 100 μm   10 mm = 10 μm   10 mm = 1 μm

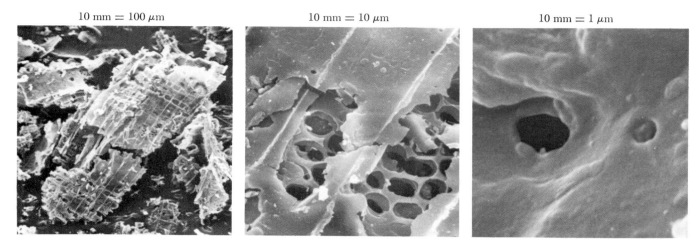

670 Wood, Decayed—Little evidence remains of the original fibrous structure of this wood. The structure and placement of the vessel elements, however, remain clearly visible (10,000X) and indicate the nonconiferous nature of the wood. This sample should be compared with *nonconiferous mechanical wood* (*70*).

671 Actinolite,
Ca$_2$(Mg,Fe)$_5$Si$_8$O$_{22}$(OH,F)$_2$
JCPDS #25-157

The characteristic amphibole cleavage is well illustrated in the SEM photograph of this monoclinic amphibole. Actinolite is the middle member of the continuous series, *tremolite* (*205*) - actinolite - ferroactinolite. The EDXRA shows Mg, Si, Ca and Fe as the principal peaks. The composition within this solid solution series can be estimated from the relative areas of the Mg and Fe peaks. Like those of all amphiboles, the SAED pattern is characterized by densely populated layer lines corresponding to an interatomic spacing of ~5.3 Å. This spacing, however, is frequently encountered in other mineral families, thus is not diagnostic of the amphiboles.

10 mm = 1 μm   17 mm = 1 μm

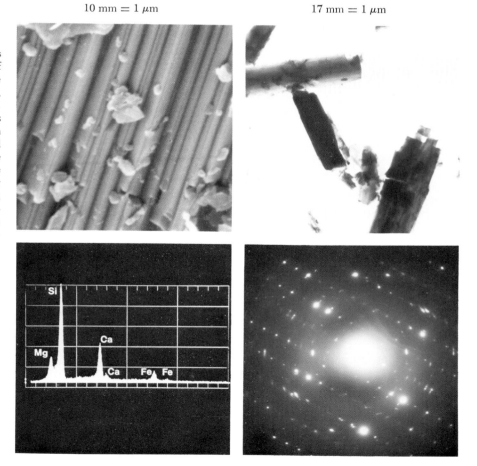

10 mm = 100 μm   17 mm = 1 μm

672 Anatase, TiO$_2$
JCPDS #21-1272

Anatase is one of the polymorphs of TiO$_2$, the commoner natural polymorph being *rutile (186)*. Although the mineral has perfect cleavages on {001} and {011}, it is brittle and tends to fracture conchoidally as shown in the SEM micrograph. EDXRA shows Ti with Al and Fe appearing as instrumental artifacts, while the SAED patterns indicate the tetragonal symmetry of the mineral. The particle size and morphology should be compared with that of the synthetic product used as a pigment, *anatase (925)*.

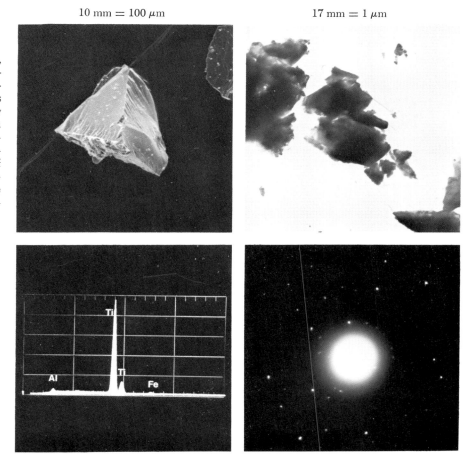

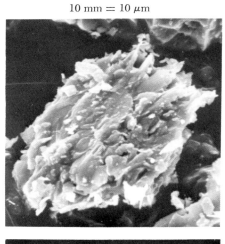

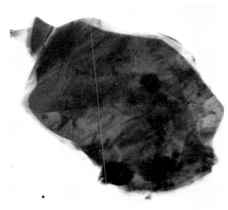

10 mm = 10 μm   16 mm = 1 μm

673 Andalusite, Al$_2$SiO$_5$
JCPDS #13-122

A common constituent of argillaceous schists and slates, this aluminum silicate may form both at low grades of metamorphism from the decomposition of kaolin, and at medium grades of metamorphism when it is the by-product of the conversion of muscovite to orthoclase. As a result, the morphology ranges from prismatic of near square crossection to columnar, fibrous or massive aggregates. This sample appears somewhat platy as evidenced both by SEM morphology and TEM electron transparency. EDXRA shows traces of K and Ca in addition to the major Al and Si.

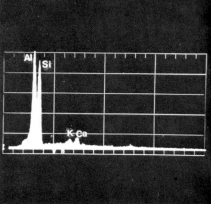

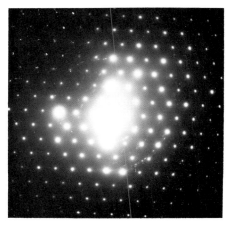

10 mm = 100 μm   17 mm = 1 μm

674   Andesine, (Ca,Na)(Al,Si)AlSi₂O₈
      JCPDS #10-359

Andesine is an intermediate member of the
triclinic plagioclase feldspar series, *albite*
(Ab) (*113*)-anorthite (An) and falls in
the composition range Ab₇An₃ to Ab₅An₅.
The fragments shown here are generally
equant with a somewhat conchoidal fracture. Some particles visible in the SEM
photograph show evidence of a developed
cleavage, tending to give tabular particles.

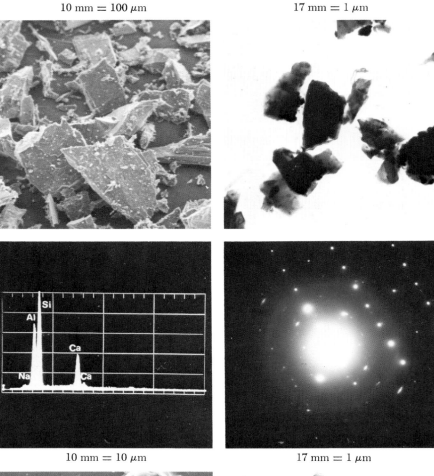

10 mm = 10 μm   17 mm = 1 μm

675   Apophyllite,
      KCa₄Si₈O₂₀(OH,F)·8H₂O
      JCPDS #19-944

This hydrated silicate of calcium and potassium was often classed with the zeolites
because of its similarity in occurrence and
somewhat similar dehydration-rehydration
behavior. Unlike the zeolites, however, apophyllite does not contain Al (see EDXRA).
The perfect basal cleavage of this tetragonal mineral is clearly seen in the SEM
photograph. TEM shows thin, bladelike
crystals. EDXRA shows Si, K and Ca.

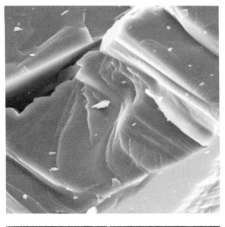

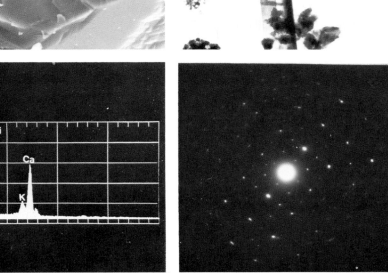

676 Arsenopyrite, FeAsS
JCPDS #14-218, 25-1230

Arsenopyrite, the monoclinic sulfide of iron and arsenic formerly known as mispickel, occurs as equant, often prismatic, grains. Striations are occasionally observed. The EDXRA, Fe, As and S only, identifies this variety as pure arsenopyrite. The cobalt-rich variety glaucodot(e) is differentiated by its composition and its higher symmetry (orthorhombic).

677 Atacamite, $Cu_2(OH)_3Cl$
JCPDS #25-269

This secondary copper mineral fractures into angular, nearly equant grains. The fracture is generally conchoidal with occasional evidence of the perfect {010} cleavage. Crystal symmetry is orthorhombic, and EDXRA shows Cu and Cl with Al and Fe probably instrumental artifacts.

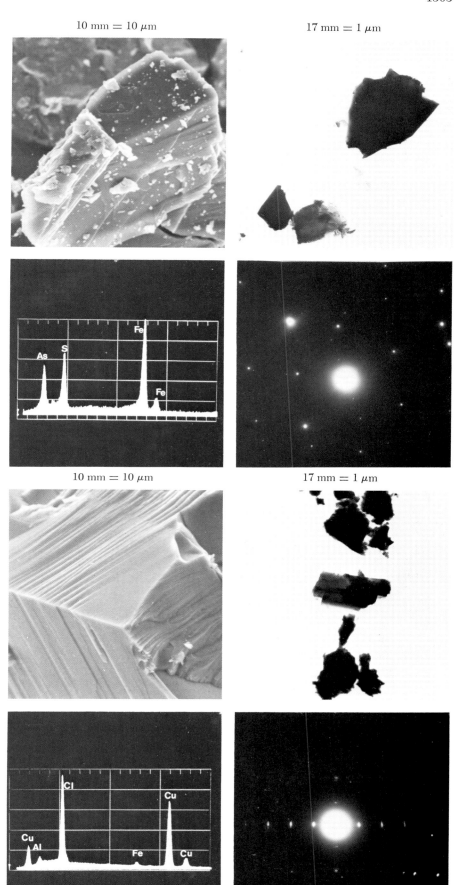

10 mm = 10 μm   17 mm = 1 μm

10 mm = 10 μm   17 mm = 1 μm

10 mm = 100 μm

17 mm = 1 μm

678 Bornite, Cu₅FeS₄
JCPDS #14-323

Formerly thought to be cubic, this iron-containing sulfide of copper is shown by diffraction to be tetragonal. The mineral cleaves poorly, tending rather to show uneven to conchoidal fracture. Twinning can occur on {111} and may account for the striated appearance in the TEM. The EDXRA shows Cu, Fe and S. Bulk samples may show variation in the Cu:Fe ratio due to intergrowth with *chalcocite (684)*.

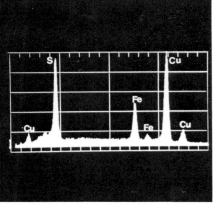

10 mm = 10 μm

17 mm = 1 μm

679 Braunite, Mn(Mn,Fe)₆SiO₁₂
JCPDS #8-78, 19-180

The irregular surface texture of this tetragonal manganese mineral is suggestive of its weathered origin. TEM shows opaque masses with a suggestion of polycrystalline aggregates. EDXRA shows a predominant Mn peak, the Si constituting only about 4–5% by weight of the mineral.

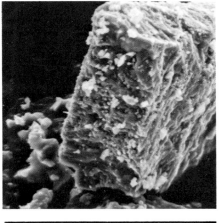

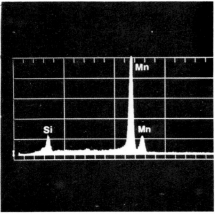

680 Brookite, TiO$_2$
     JCPDS #16-617

Brookite is the orthorhombic polymorph of TiO$_2$. The other polymorphs, *rutile* (*186*) and *anatase* (*672*), are both tetragonal. Of the electron beam methods, only diffraction can separate these trimorphs since all exhibit conchoidal to subconchoidal fracture and all show only Ti in their EDXRA spectra.

681 Celestite, SrSO$_4$
     JCPDS #5-593

The perfect {001} and good {210} cleavages of celestite (celestine) tend to give rise to regular, tabular to lathlike grains. This is reflected, to some extent, in the TEM where many of the grains appear thin and flakelike. EDXRA shows only Sr and S. Crystal symmetry is orthorhombic.

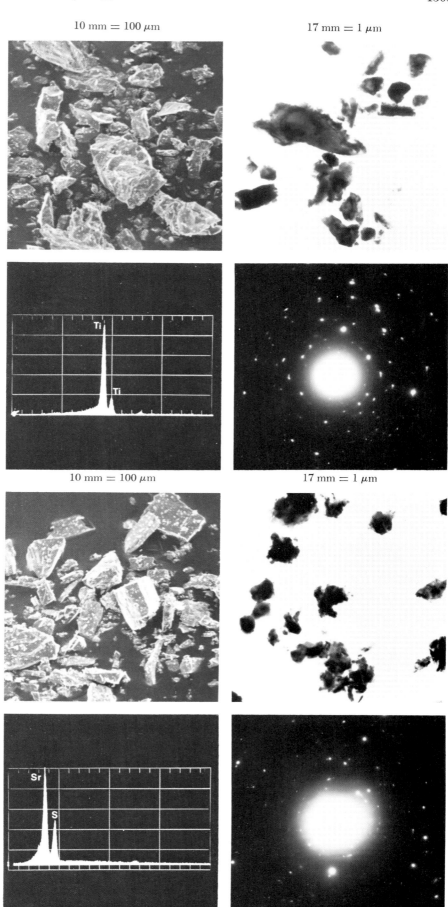

10 mm = 100 µm   17 mm = 1 µm

10 mm = 100 µm   17 mm = 1 µm

682 Celsian, BaAl₂Si₂O₈
    JCPDS #18-153, 21-812, 19-90 (syn)

These angular fragments of the barium
analog of anorthite show some evidence of
the {001} and {010} cleavages. Many fragments, however, tend to fracture conchoidally. The crystal symmetry of celsian is
monoclinic, unlike that of anorthite which
is triclinic. A further distinguishing feature
is the presence of Ba in the EDXRA spectrum which shows Al, Si and Ba only.

10 mm = 100 μm

16 mm = 1 μm

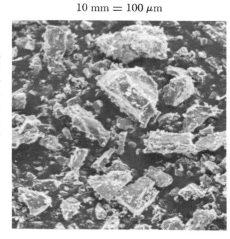

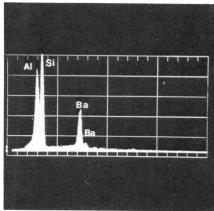

683 Chalcocite, Cu₂S
    JCPDS #24-57, 23-961 (syn)

The conchoidal fracture of this copper ore
is well illustrated in the SEM photograph.
Unground samples may show a variety of
crystal forms, prisms, plates, interpenetrating twins. Crystal symmetry is orthorhombic, although the prism angle of 60° may,
at least morphologically, give rise to a
pseudohexagonal symmetry. EDXRA shows
only Cu and S.

10 mm = 10 μm

17 mm = 1 μm

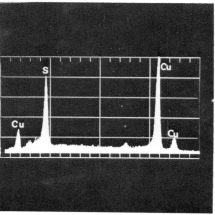

684 Chalcopyrite, CuFeS₂
  JCPDS #24-211, 25-288

Although mainly equant, some quite well-formed, lozenge-shaped crystals are present in this sample, with occasional interpenetrant twinning evident. Chalcopyrite is the commonest of the copper ores. EDXRA shows S, Fe and Cu only. Symmetry is tetragonal.

685 Chert
  JCPDS #5-490

Chert is a cryptocrystalline variety of *quartz (183)* characterized by a lower density than quartz. This reduced density is due to the presence of numerous small pores that are visible in the SEM. Ground samples typically show an assemblage of equant, irregular grains with no distinct cleavages. The conchoidal fracture typical of quartz is not seen, however, as fracture tends to occur between adjacent crystallites. The EDXRA shows only Si and the SAED pattern is that of quartz.

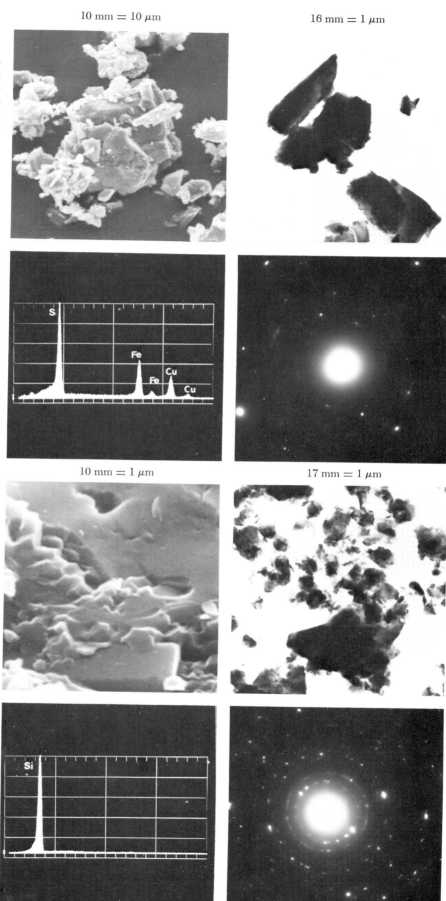

10 mm = 10 μm   16 mm = 1 μm

10 mm = 1 μm   17 mm = 1 μm

10 mm = 1 μm   17 mm = 1 μm

686   Chlorapatite, Ca₅(PO₄)₃Cl
JCPDS #12-263 (syn), 27-74 (syn),
24-214 (clino-)

Chlorapatite, the chlorine end member of
the *apatite* (*118*) group, is seldom found
in nature, although nearly pure chlorapa-
tites occur in some Norwegian metamorphic limestones. Ground fragments tend to
be angular and equant with occasional
evidence of the rather imperfect cleavages.
EDXRA shows high P, Ca and low Cl.
Chlorapatite is generally hexagonal although
a monoclinic form is also known.

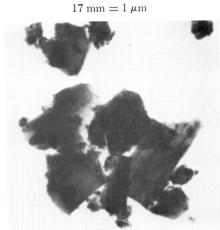

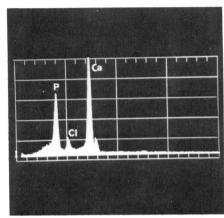

10 mm = 10 μm   17 mm = 1 μm

687   Chlorite,
(Mg,Fe,Al)₆[(Si,Al)₄O₁₀](OH)₈
JCPDS #16-362, 16-351

"Chlorite" is the generic name for a group
of commonly found metamorphic minerals
characterized by a platy habit and usually
green in color. Some twenty to thirty different species are recognized within this
group. All have a somewhat micaceous appearance and it is seldom possible to differentiate the individual species. It is thus
usually necessary simply to classify them
as chlorite. Mg-rich chlorites can be readily
differentiated from talc, with which they
frequently occur, by the presence of Al in
the EDXRA pattern.

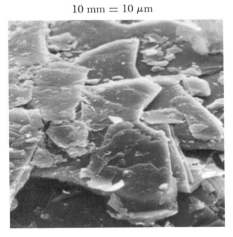

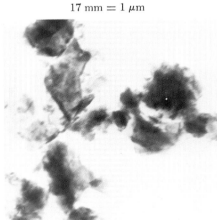

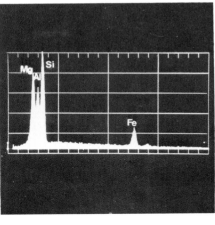

688 Chromite, (Mg,Fe)Cr₂O₄
$$\text{688 Chromite, }(Mg,Fe)Cr_2O_4$$
JCPDS #6-694

These chromite grains are typically equant and angular with occasional traces of the imperfect {111} cleavage. EDXRA shows low Mg with high Cr and moderate Fe. The diffraction pattern is that of a polycrystalline face-centered cubic structure.

10 mm = 1 μm   17 mm = 1 μm

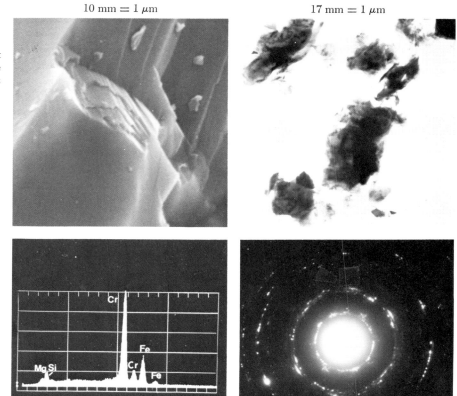

689 Cummingtonite,
$$(Mg,Fe)_7Si_8O_{22}(OH)_2$$
JCPDS #17-726 (manganoan-cummingtonite 17-727, 23-302)

The characteristic {110} cleavage of the amphiboles is well illustrated in the SEM photograph. Grinding of samples of amphiboles, as a result of this cleavage, produces prismatic rods with aspect ratios in the range of 2:1 to about 8:1. The cleavage fragments in the TEM photograph are somewhat lathlike. EDXRA indicates that this is a low Mg cummingtonite with low (~0.5–1%) Ca.

10 mm = 10 μm   17 mm = 1 μm

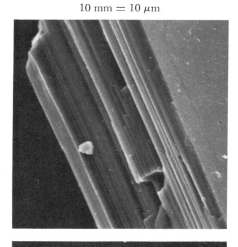

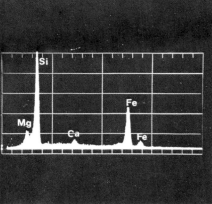

690   Dickite, $Al_2Si_2O_5(OH)_4$
JCPDS #10-446

This monoclinic clay mineral is a member of the kaolin group, trimorphous with *kaolinite* (155) and nacrite. The platy nature of the mineral is evident both in the SEM and the TEM. EDXRA of this sample shows traces of S and K in addition to the Al and Si. The K is possibly from traces of a K-rich clay contaminant. SAED shows the typical pseudohexagonal symmetry of this mineral.

10 mm = 10 μm

17 mm = 1 μm

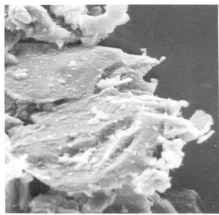

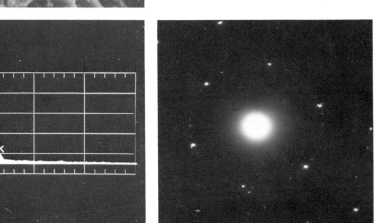

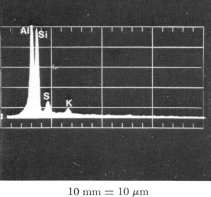

10 mm = 10 μm

17 mm = 1 μm

691   Diopside, $Ca(Mg,Fe)Si_2O_6$
JCPDS #11-654

One of the commonest of the pyroxenes, this magnesium-rich member of the diopside-hedenbergite series shows the characteristic orthogonal {110} cleavage of the pyroxenes. Diopside is a clino-pyroxene. EDXRA shows high Ca, Si, lower Mg and very low Fe.

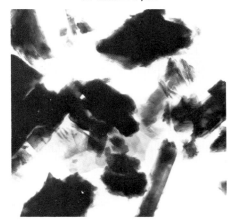

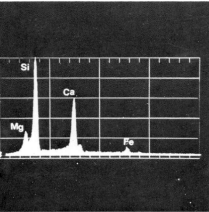

10 mm = 10 μm   17 mm = 1 μm

692 Dioptase, CuSiO$_2$(OH)$_2$
JCPDS #7-172

The rod-shaped crystal fragments of this rare copper mineral observed by light microscopy are seen by SEM to be well-formed prismatic crystals. Other fragments tend to be somewhat equant with little evidence of the reported perfect rhombohedral cleavage. EDXRA shows only Cu and Si. The crystal system is hexagonal.

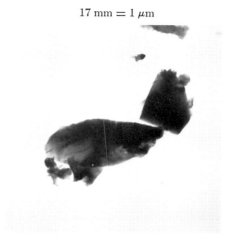

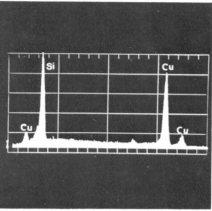

10 mm = 10 μm   17 mm = 1 μm

693 Enargite, Cu$_3$AsS$_4$
JCPDS #10-436

Angular, equant grains, some with evidence of conchoidal fracture and some with indications of one or more of the several cleavage planes of this mineral are typical. EDXRA shows Cu, As, S and a trace of Fe, the latter probably an instrumental artifact. This mineral is orthorhombic.

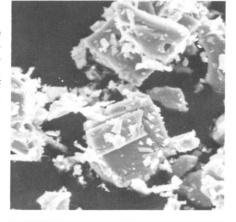

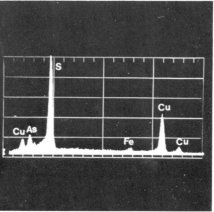

694   English Clay

English clay is generally a mixture of clay minerals with minerals of the *kaolin* (155) group predominating. Characteristically, therefore, the grains are composed of stacked, pseudohexagonal platelets. The presence of K in the EDXRA spectrum suggests incomplete transformation of the original feldspar from which the clay was derived or, possibly, the presence of an intermediate hydromuscovite.

695   Enstatite, (Mg,Fe)SiO₃
    JCPDS #22-714, 19-768 (syn)

Occurring widely as a constituent of basic and ultrabasic igneous rocks and of thermally and regionally metamorphosed rocks, enstatite is an orthorhombic pyroxene. The fragments here show well the cleavage (on {212}) which results in these elongated, lathlike particles. EDXRA shows principally Mg and Si but with a strong Fe signal suggesting that the composition of this sample is tending toward that of hypersthene with which enstatite forms a continuous solid solution.

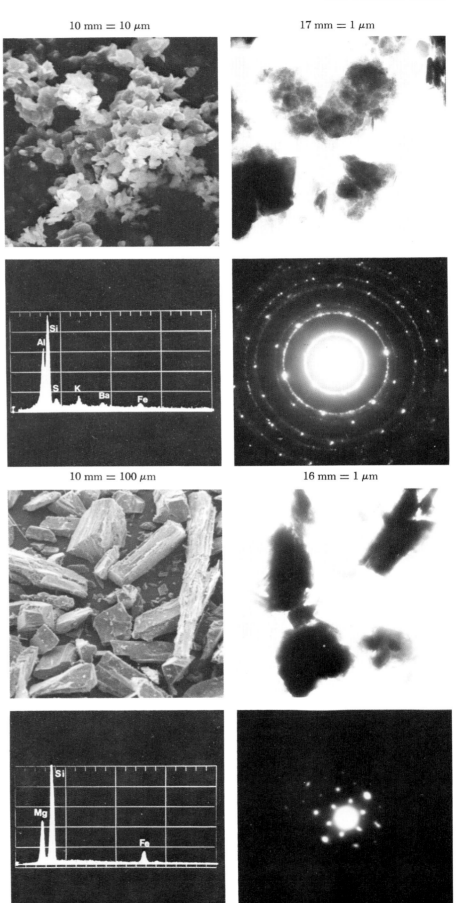

10 mm = 10 μm   17 mm = 1 μm

10 mm = 100 μm   16 mm = 1 μm

696   Forsterite, (Mg,Fe)SiO₄
JCPDS #7-74

Forsterite is the Mg-rich end member of the orthorhombic olivine solid solution series. In addition to its natural occurrence in basic and ultrabasic igneous rocks and some metamorphosed dolomitic limestones, forsterite forms by the high temperature degradation of serpentines. It is therefore a common constituent of thermally degraded *chrysotile* (*122*) asbestos products such as brake linings. EDXRA shows only Mg and Si with but a trace, probably instrumental, of Fe, indicating that this is the pure end member of the series.

697   Franklinite, (Zn,Mn,Fe)(Fe,Mn)₂O₄

One of the cubic *spinel* (*718*) family, franklinite is slightly magnetic. The mineral fractures unevenly to give angular fragments, many of them showing evidence of conchoidal fracture. EDXRA shows this particular sample to be high in both Fe and Mn.

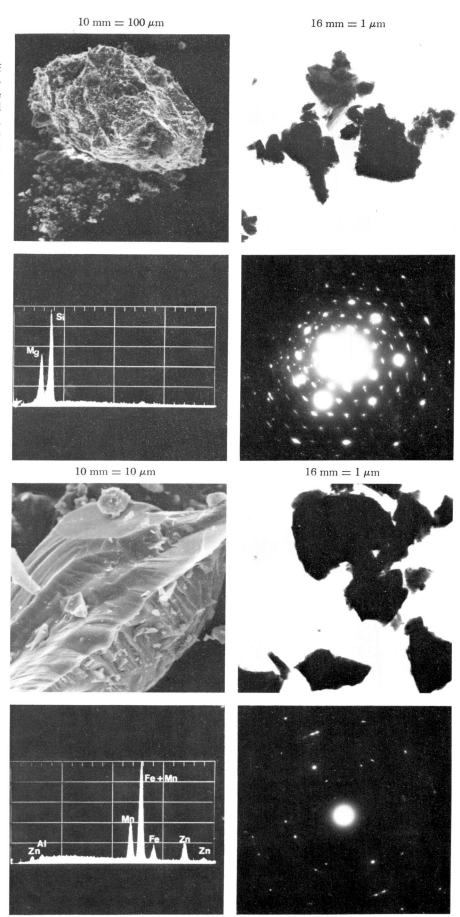

10 mm = 100 μm   16 mm = 1 μm

10 mm = 10 μm   16 mm = 1 μm

698   Gadolinite, Be₂FeY₂Si₂O₁₀

JCPDS #22-990, 22-991, 26-1139

This rare earth mineral fractures conchoidally to yield typical flakes and chips, (SEM, 100X). Be, which appears in the chemical formula, is not detectable by EDXRA. The rare elements Ce, Nd and Sn may be present through substitution for Y or may represent a rare earth inclusion. The crystal symmetry is monoclinic.

10 mm = 100 μm

17 mm = 1 μm

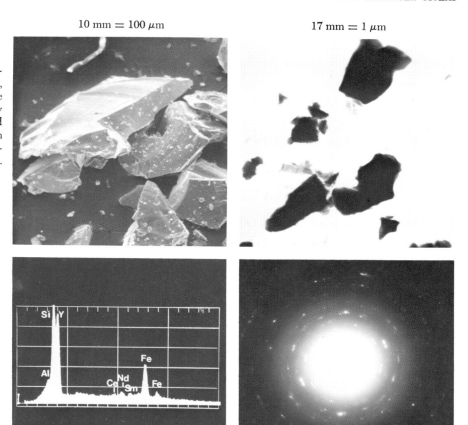

699   Galena, PbS

JCPDS #5-592

The perfect cubic {100} cleavage of galena, the principal ore of lead, is well illustrated in the SEM photograph taken at 1000X. The EDXRA spectrum shown here has a full-scale width of 20 KeV to show the Pb Lα line at 10.55 KeV. The Pb Mα line at 2.35 KeV is not resolved from the S Kα line at 2.31 KeV. Because of its high density it is electron opaque, hence the TEM micrograph shows only a "shadowgraph" picture and SAED is only possible from the edges of particles.

10 mm = 10 μm

16 mm = 1 μm

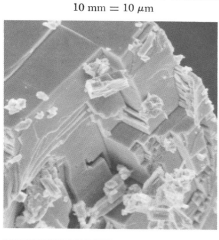

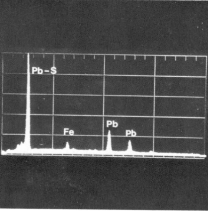

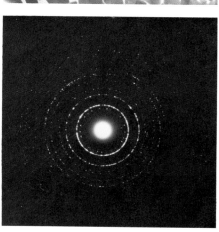

700 Gibbsite, Al(OH)₃
JCPDS #7-324, 12-460

Gibbsite is one of the hydrates of aluminum, trimorphous with bayerite and nordstrandite. The mineral is monoclinic and generally formed by the alteration of aluminum-bearing minerals. This sample is seen, by SEM, to consist of aggregates of well-formed equant crystals, each approximately 5–10 μm across. EDXRA, as expected, shows only Al. TEM shows both well-formed and feathery, somewhat platy crystals.

701 Goethite, FeO·OH
JCPDS #17-536

Goethite, a hydrated oxide of iron, is a weathering product of many iron-bearing minerals. The flattened, tabular appearance of the grains, due in part to the good {010} and {100} cleavages, is clearly seen in the SEM photograph. The EDXRA spectrum shows Fe with no other elements expected. Goethite is orthorhombic.

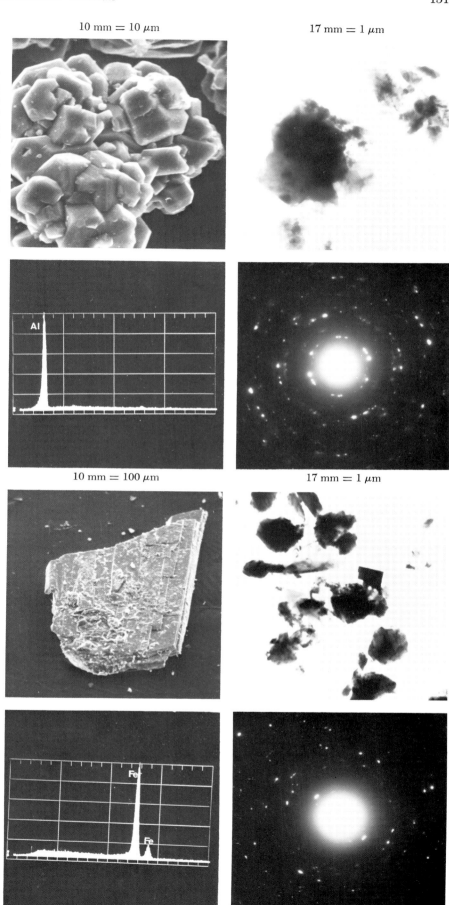

10 mm = 10 μm   17 mm = 1 μm

10 mm = 100 μm   17 mm = 1 μm

10 mm = 100 μm   17 mm = 1 μm

702   Graphite, C
     JCPDS #23-64

Both the SEM and the TEM clearly show
the platy nature of this polymorph of car-
lon). No EDXRA spectrum is presented as
eral geographically, occurring in rocks subjected to a high grade of metamorphism.
The best known commercial deposits are
the high grade graphites of Sri Lanka (Cey-
lon. No EDXRA spectrum is presented as
only a high background would be expected;
instead, a 1000X SEM is substituted. SAED
shows the typical hexagonal symmetry of a
basal flake.

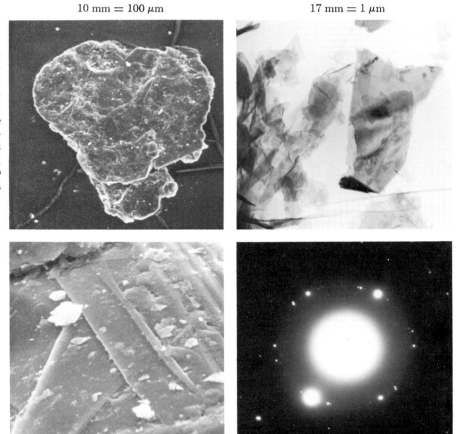

10 mm = 10 μm   17 mm = 1 μm

703   Grunerite, $(Fe,Mg)_7Si_8O_{22}(OH)_2$
     JCPDS #27-1170

Grunerite may occur in both massive and
fibrous varieties. Fibrous grunerite, as
shown here, is frequently known as *amosite (120)* when of commercial asbestos
quality. The EDXRA spectrum shows high
Fe and Si with low Mg and Al, the latter
probably an instrumental artifact. Fiber
forms invariably show a layer line SAED
pattern with interlayer spacing approximately 5.3 Å.

704 Halloysite, $Al_2Si_2O_5(OH)_4 \cdot 2H_2O$
JCPDS #9-451, 9-453

Although halloysite is typically regarded as being somewhat lath-shaped or having a tubular morphology, some exceptions to this rule do occur. The sample shown, however (from Wagon Wheel Gap, Oregon), presents the most usually encountered morphology of this clay mineral. The range of tube diameters is observed to be quite wide and may overlap with the finest diameters observed for chrysotile fibrils (*q.v.*). The diffraction pattern of halloysite also bears some similarity to that of chrysotile with some spot streaking due to curvature of the original sheet structure. The patterns, however, on close inspection can be seen to be quite clearly different.

705 Hectorite,
$Na_{0.33}(Mg,Li)_3Si_4O_{10}(F,OH)_2$
JCPDS #25-1385 (syn)

One of the *montmorillonite (711)* group of clay minerals, hectorite consists of aggregates of very fine, whispy platelets. Its morphology, EDXRA spectrum (Mg and Si only) and its diffraction pattern all distinguish hectorite from montmorillonite. Hectorite is preferred to Na-montmorillonite as a drilling mud but is less readily available, being restricted to only small deposits.

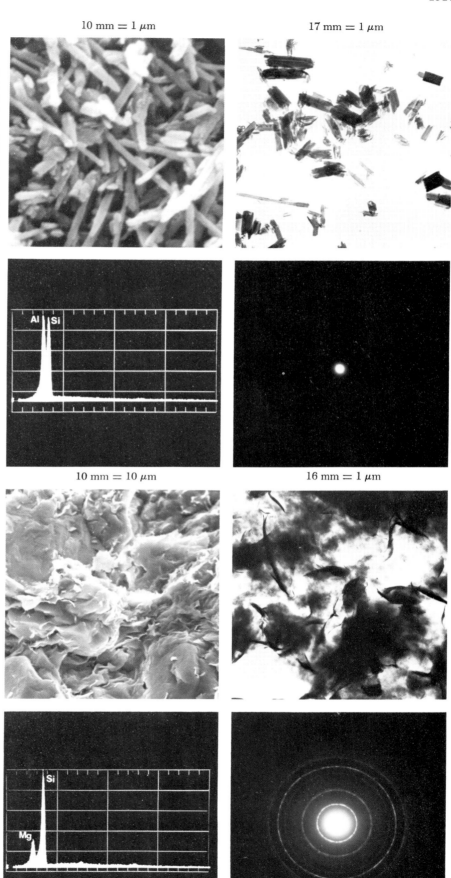

10 mm = 1 μm   17 mm = 1 μm

10 mm = 10 μm   16 mm = 1 μm

706 Hypersthene, (Mg,Fe)SiO₃
JCPDS #19-606

The SEM micrograph illustrates the good {210} cleavage of this Mg,Fe pyroxene. As a result of this cleavage, ground fragments tend to be prismatic to lathlike. The presence of Ca in the EDXRA spectrum indicates that this is not the pure orthorhombic end member but is tending toward the monoclinic pyroxene, *diopside (91)*.

10 mm = 10 µm

16 mm = 1 µm

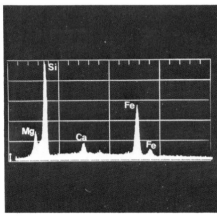

707 Illite,
K₁₋₁.₅Al₄(Si₇₋₆.₅Al₁₋₁.₅O₂₀)OH₄
JCPDS #24-495

These granular to massive fragments of illite consist of aggregates of micaceous plates, some as small as 0.1 µm across. Illite may be distinguished from other clay minerals by morphology, diffraction pattern (monoclinic, pseudohexagonal) and EDXRA spectrum in which characteristic features are the Al:Si ratio and the presence of K.

10 mm = 1 µm

16 mm = 1 µm

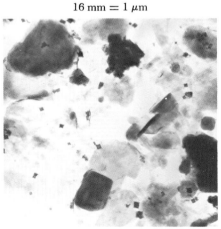

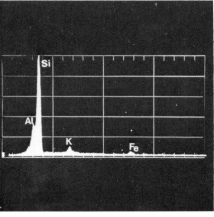

708 Jadeite, NaAl(Si$_2$O$_6$)
JCPDS #22-1338

This Na,Al clinopyroxene shows the {210} cleavage typical of all pyroxenes [*cf. hypersthene (706)* opposite]. Ground fragments of the pyroxene all show similar morphologies and substantially similar SAED patterns. It is thus necessary to use EDXRA to differentiate between them.

10 mm = 10 μm   16 mm = 1 μm

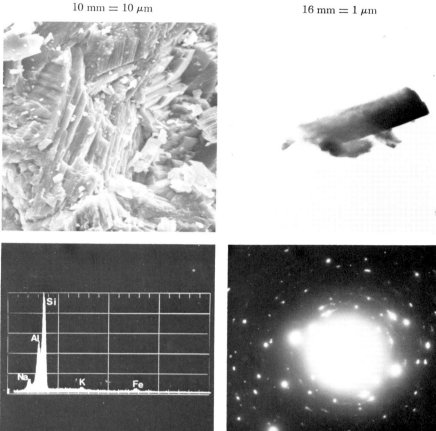

709 Lazurite,
(Na,Ca)$_8$(Al,Si)$_{12}$O$_{24}$(S,SO$_4$)
JCPDS #17-749

Lazurite, one of the *sodalite (195)* group of alkaline silicates, is cubic. The grains here are small and equant with some evidence of faceting. Agglomerates are common. EDXRA confirms the presence of Na, Al, Si, S, Ca and Fe, the latter not indicated by the ideal formula. Light microscopy had noted the presence of *forsterite (696)* as a contaminant, and this is the most likely origin of the Fe.

10 mm = 10 μm   16 mm = 1 μm

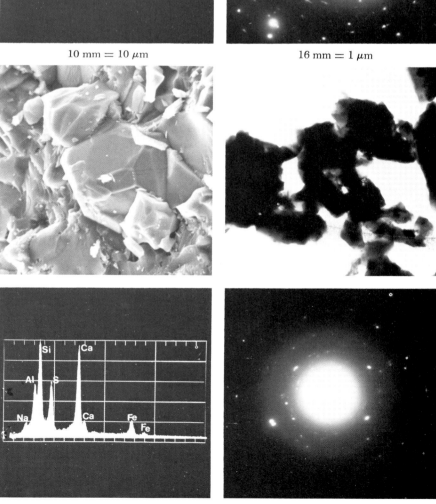

10 mm = 10 μm   16 mm = 1 μm

710   Lizardite, $Mg_3Si_2O_5(OH)_4$
        JCPDS #18-779

Lizardite is one of the three forms of serpentine, the other two being *antigorite*
(*117*) and *chrysotile* (*122*). Lizardite characteristically consists of aggregates of fine-
grained plates, many with a pseudohexagonal outline. Although structurally
monoclinic, β is 90°, and lizardite has been
described as "orthogonal-hexagonal." The
EDXRA shows Mg and Si, with Fe possibly contributed in part by the mineral
but most probably as an instrumental artifact.

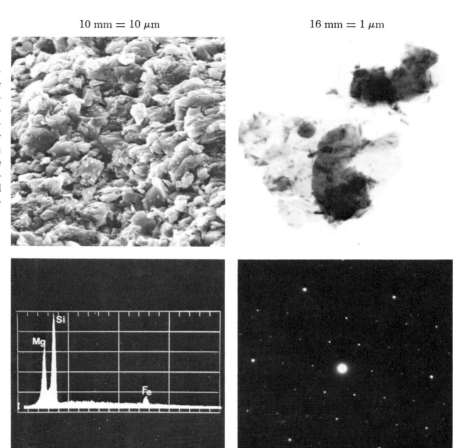

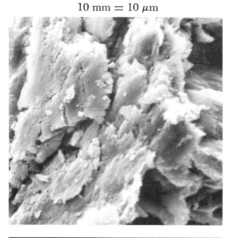

10 mm = 10 μm   16 mm = 1 μm

711   Montmorillonite,
        $(Na,Ca)_{0.33}(Al,Mg)_2Si_4O_{10}(OH)_2 \cdot$
        nH_2O

Frequently used in drilling muds to render
them thixotropic, montmorillonite is the major component of most bentonites. The particles here are aggregates of many minute
flakes. The principal elements detectable by
EDXRA in this sample are Al and Si. The
{100} spacing of montmorillonite varies
greatly with degree of hydration and the
nature of the cations.

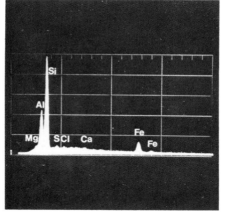

712 Pyrite, FeS$_2$
    JCPDS #24-76

Pyrite is one of the commonest and most ubiquitous of minerals and certainly the most common sulfide mineral. Pyrite is cubic, and the fragments here are angular and equant. Natural, unground crystals typically show well-developed cubic or polyhedral forms, frequently with striated faces.

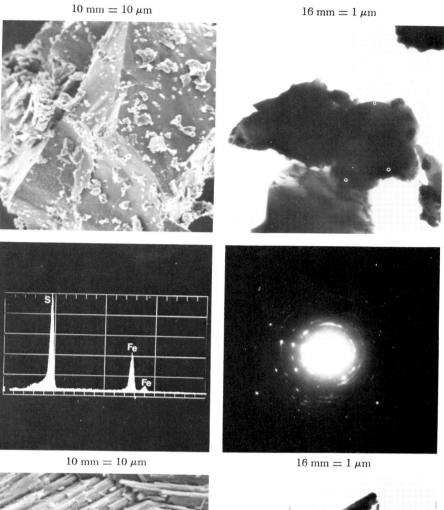

10 mm = 10 μm   16 mm = 1 μm

713 Pyrolusite, MnO$_2$
    JCPDS #12-716

The columnar to fibrous habit of these crystals is clearly visible in both micrographs. Cleavage on {110} is perfect. EDXRA shows only Mn with a trace of Si and possibly Al as contaminants. Crystal symmetry is tetragonal.

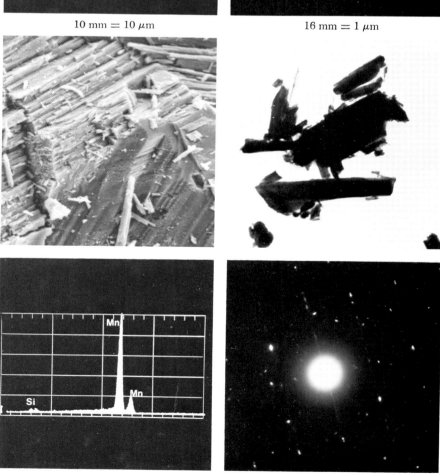

10 mm = 10 μm   16 mm = 1 μm

10 mm = 10 μm   13 mm = 1 μm

714   Pyrrhotite, Fe$_{1-x}$S
      JCPDS #17-200

A magnetic sulfide generally found associated with the other sulfide minerals *chalcopyrite* (*684*) and *pyrite* (*712*), pyrrhotite is listed in the JCPDS file as monoclinic. It is, however, crystallographically and compositionally variable with hexagonal and orthorhombic varieties also noted. Fracture is conchoidal, yielding the equant grains illustrated in the SEM photograph. EDXRA of this sample shows S and Fe.

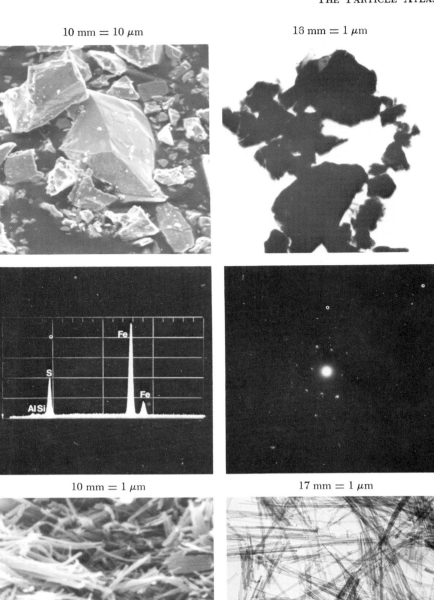

10 mm = 1 μm   17 mm = 1 μm

715   Sepiolite, Mg$_2$Si$_3$O$_8$·2H$_2$O
      JCPDS #13-595, 26-1226

Sepiolite, known in its massive form as meerschaum, generally occurs in earthy, fibrous masses as shown in the SEM photograph. Observed in the TEM, the fine fibers bear some resemblance to *chrysotile* (*122*) (see also Vol. III, p. 486, Figure 8) and palygorskite (*attapulgite* [*126*]). All three, however, are readily differentiated by SAED. EDXRA shows Mg and Si and, in bulk specimens, may be used to differentiate between sepiolite and chrysotile. Individual fibers may not be so readily differentiated by EDXRA due to geometric effects.

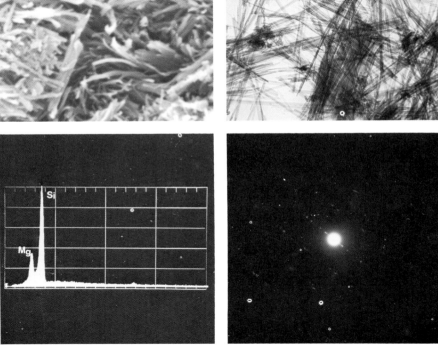

716   Smithsonite, ZnCO$_3$
          JCPDS #8-449

One of the *calcite* (*133*) group of minerals, smithsonite fragments typically show the well-developed rhombohedral cleavage, although irregular fragmentation is also common. As would be expected, EDXRA shows only Zn.

717   Soapstone

Soapstone is a rock rather than a mineral. The mineral assemblage consists principally of *talc* (*198, 199, 724, 725, 726, 727, 728*) and *chlorite* (*687*). *Steatite* (*199*) is another name for soapstone. As would be expected, fragments show platy morphology, Mg and Si in their EDXRA spectra and a monoclinic, pseudohexagonal SAED single crystal pattern. The pattern shown here is polycrystalline.

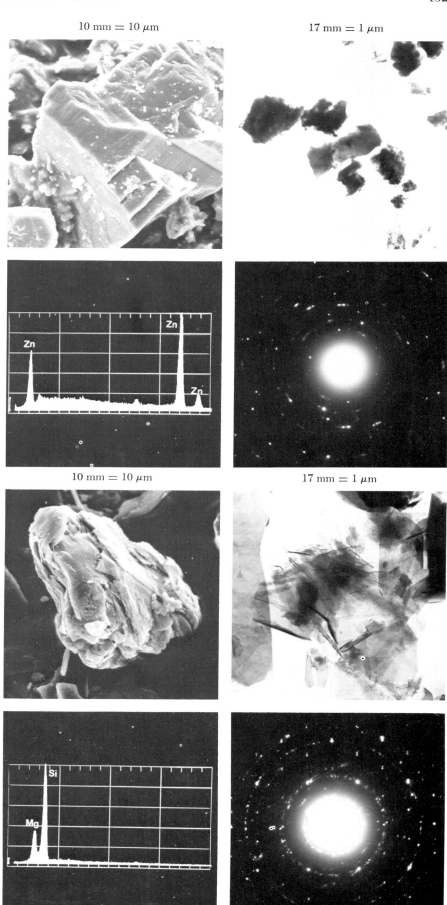

10 mm = 10 μm   17 mm = 1 μm

10 mm = 10 μm   17 mm = 1 μm

718   Spinel, MgAl$_2$O$_4$
      JCPDS #21-1152

This magnesium aluminate is the type mineral of the spinel group which also includes *chromite* (*688*), *franklinite* (*697*) and *magnetite* (*165*). Grinding has produced equant, angular fragments with classic conchoidal fracture. EDXRA shows Mg and Al with traces of Cr, probably substitutional, and Fe, most probably of instrumental origin. Crystal symmetry is cubic.

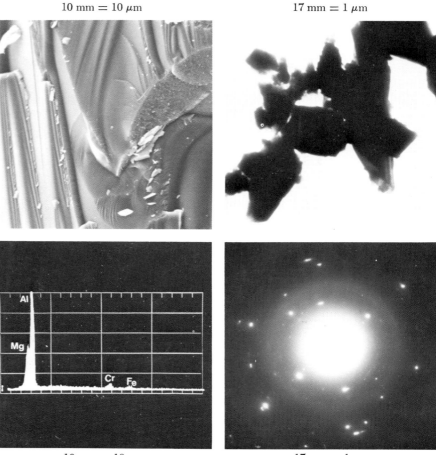

10 mm = 10 μm   17 mm = 1 μm

719   Staurolite, Fe$_2$Al$_9$Si$_4$O$_{22}$(OH)$_2$
      JCPDS #15-397

These angular fragments, equant to elongated, show an uneven, conchoidal fracture in the SEM. Typically occurring in schists and gneisses produced by regional metamorphism, the mineral is common and widespread. EDXRA shows Al, Si and Fe. The crystal symmetry is monoclinic but pseudoorthorhombic.

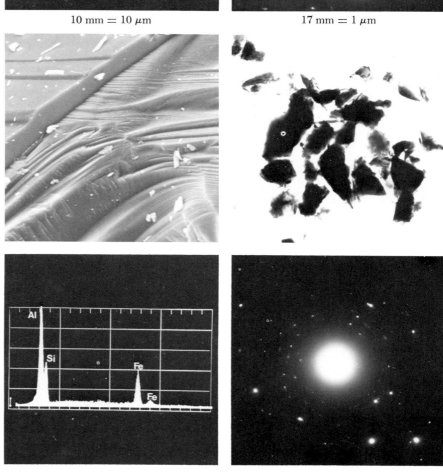

10 mm = 10 μm   17 mm = 1 μm

720 Stibnite, Sb₂S₃
JCPDS #6-474 (syn)

This antimony ore fractures into equant to prismatic forms with a perfect {010} cleavage. EDXRA shows only S and Sb (the Fe is an instrument artifact). Crystal symmetry is orthorhombic.

10 mm = 10 μm

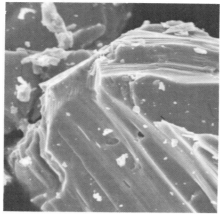

16 mm = 1 μm

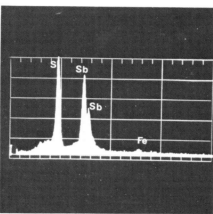

721 Stilpnomelane,
(K,Na,Ca)
(Fe,Mg,Al,Mn)₃Si₄O₁₀(OH)₂·
nH₂O
JCPDS #18-634

Occurring commonly in schists and some iron-ore deposits, stilpnomelane is a platy, micaceous mineral. EDXRA shows principally Si, Fe and Mn with traces of K and Ca and possibly also (unlabeled) Mg and Al. The crystal symmetry is triclinic.

10 mm = 10 μm

17 mm = 1 μm

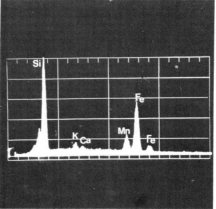

722 Strontianite, (Sr,Ca)CO₃
    JCPDS #5-418

Strontianite, belonging to the orthorhombic
aragonite (119) group of carbonates, has a
nearly perfect {110} cleavage which yields
the short, prismatic fragments seen in the
SEM photograph. EDXRA shows principally Sr with about 1–2% Ca present in
this sample.

723 Szaibelyite, (Mg,Mn)BO₃H
    JCPDS #12-179

This boron-rich mineral is frequently found
intergrown with or coating serpentine minerals. The particles in this sample, found
associated with chrysotile asbestos, are
fibers but are differentiated from the chrysotile fibers by their EDXRA spectrum and
their diffraction pattern.

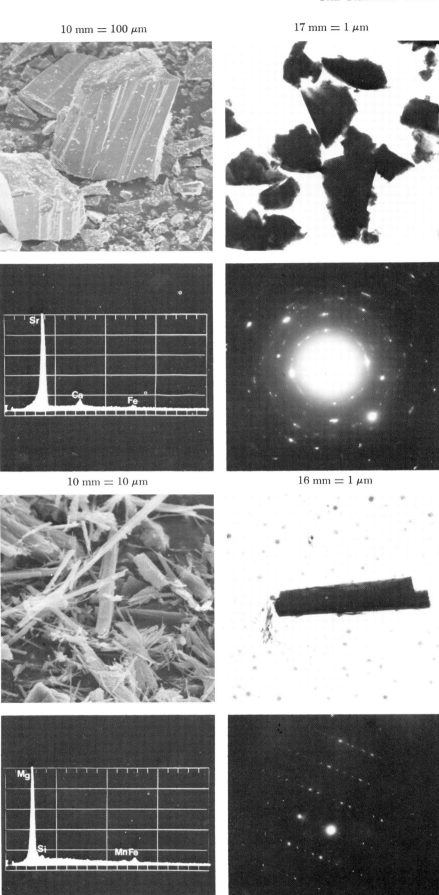

10 mm = 100 μm

17 mm = 1 μm

10 mm = 10 μm

16 mm = 1 μm

724   Talc, $Mg_3Si_4O_{10}(OH)_2$
JCPDS #13-558, 19-770

This sample from Vermont has been obtained by grinding crystals of talc hand-picked from an ore of cosmetic grade talc. The mineral here is characteristically platy, the plates having a large diameter but very low thickness, as evidenced by their electron transparency. EDXRA shows Mg and Si with Fe present as an instrument artifact. Almost all talc SAED patterns are pseudo-hexagonal as shown, due to the tendency of the plates to lie on their basal planes.

725   Talc, $Mg_3Si_4O_{10}(OH)_2$
JCPDS #13-558, 19-770

This talc sample is also from Vermont but represents the mineral as found in the ore body. The talc has been isolated in these photographs from the *magnesite* (*164*), *dolomite* (*140*), *chlorite* (*687*) and trace *quartz* (*183*) which accompany it in this ore. The extremely thin plates are well illustrated in the TEM photograph; the pseudo-hexagonal pattern is shown by SAED.

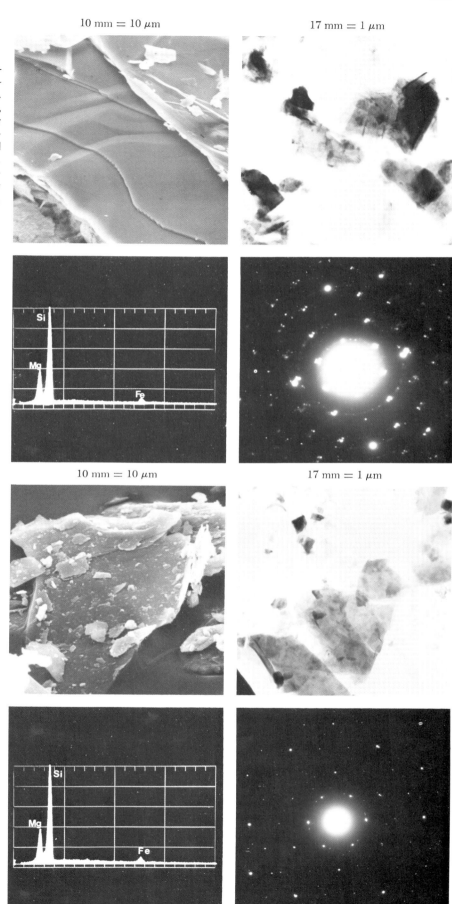

10 mm = 10 μm   17 mm = 1 μm

10 mm = 10 μm   17 mm = 1 μm

10 mm = 10 μm

16 mm = 1 μm

726 Talc, $Mg_3Si_4O_{10}(OH)_2$
JCPDS #13-558, 19-770

This talc, from New York, is typical of many of the industrial "talcs" used in the paint and ceramic industries. The mineral talc itself constitutes only 40–50% of this talc, the balance being composed of *tremolite* (*205*), *lizardite* (*710*) and *anthophyllite* (*121*). The Ca peak in the EDXRA spectrum is derived from the tremolite which comprised about one-third of the sample. Although many talc plates are observed, some talc particles are more granular in nature, as evidenced by their electron density in transmission.

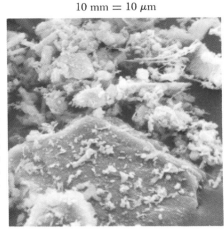

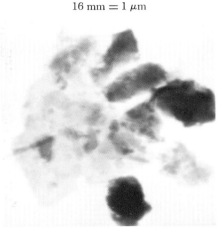

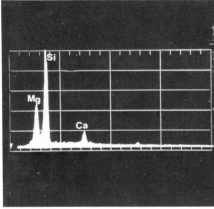

10 mm = 10 μm

17 mm = 1 μm

727 Talc, $Mg_3Si_4O_{10}(OH)_2$
JCPDS #13-558, 19-770

From Texas, this talc is very much less platy than those previously described. This ore has about 70–75% of the mineral talc present, but the plates are small and somewhat splintery. Ca in the EDXRA spectrum results from about 5–10% *dolomite* (*140*) and 2% *calcite* (*133*) detected by x-ray diffraction (XRD) of this sample. XRD also indicated an anomalous association of *forsterite* (*696*) and *quartz* (*183*) in this sample.

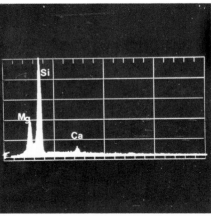

728   Talc, $Mg_3Si_4O_{10}(OH)_2$
JCPDS #13-558, 19-770

This Georgian talc, in addition to containing the mineral talc (50–60%), contains significant amounts of *chlorite* (*687*), *lizardite* (*710*), each about 10–15%, and minor amounts, approximately 5% each, of *dolomite* (*140*), *biotite* (*167*) and a *tremolite* (*205*)-*actinolite* (*671*) amphibole. As a result, the material seen in the corresponding SEM indicates a wide range of morphologies. A correspondingly diverse range should be expected in a TEM preparation. Here we show thin, platy talc particles, identifiable by their SAED pattern. EDXRA shows Mg, Si and a trace of Fe.

10 mm = 10 μm

16 mm = 1 μm

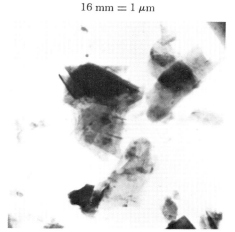

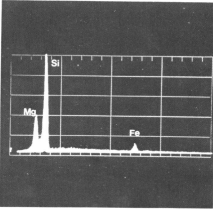

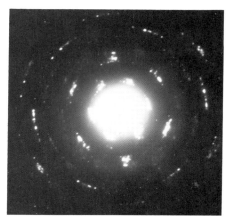

729   Tephroite, Mn_2SiO_4
JCPDS #19-788

Although macroscopically and light microscopically identified as tephroite, the EDXRA spectrum of this sample indicates a composition closer to knebelite, the intermediate member of the fayalite-knebelite-tephroite solid solution series. The particles fragment in a brittle manner to give equant grains with conchoidal fracture faces. The crystal symmetry is orthorhombic.

10 mm = 10 μm

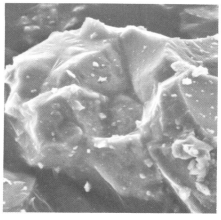

17 mm = 1 μm

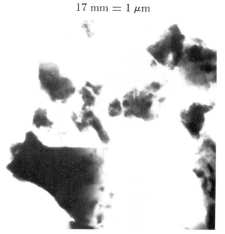

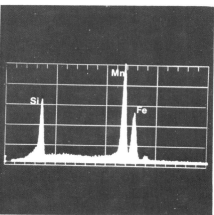

730 Tetrahedrite, $Cu_{12}Sb_4S_{13}$
JCPDS #24-1318

This cubic mineral breaks unevenly to give angular, equant to elongate grains. EDXRA shows traces of Zn, prominent Fe and Al, the latter possibly an instrumental artifact, in addition to the Cu, Sb and S expected from the formula.

10 mm = 10 μm   17 mm = 1 μm

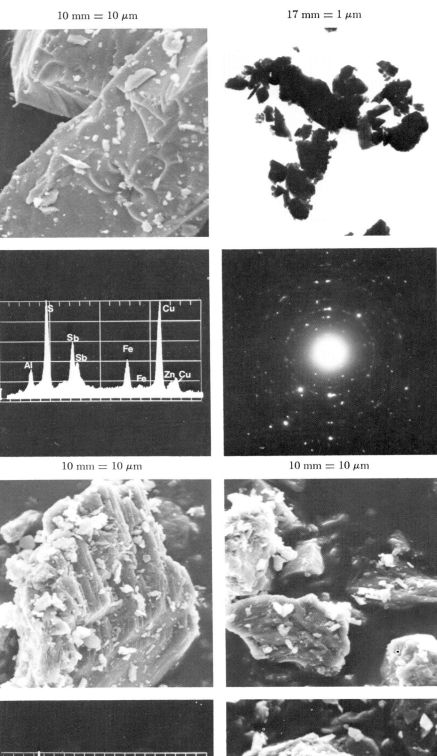

10 mm = 10 μm   10 mm = 10 μm

731 Trap Rock

Trap rock is a generic term which has been used in the mineral exploitation industries. In hard-rock mining the term was generally applied to any fine-grained, dark-colored rock. In petroleum exploitation it was applied to structural formations conducive to the retention of oil or gas. The mineral content, therefore, can be extremely varied, depending on the rock types present. These SEM photographs at 1000X magnification show the typical variations encountered in this sample which consists principally of plagioclase feldspar.

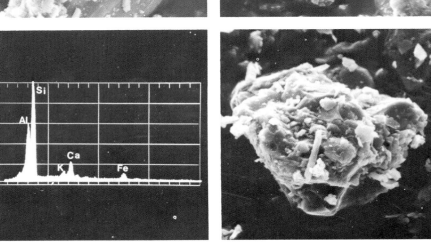

732 Uraninite, UO₂
JCPDS #13-225

These angular grains range from massive material to apparently agglomerated forms, with individuals in the agglomerates being platelike. These plates may, however, be the yellow alteration product observed by light microscopy. EDXRA shows Al, Si and Fe in addition to the U.

733 Witherite, BaCO₃
JCPDS #5-378

Witherite, like *strontianite* (722), belongs to the orthorhombic *aragonite* (119) group of carbonates. The cleavage of witherite, however, is imperfect, the crystals breaking unevenly to give the irregular fragments seen in the SEM micrograph. EDXRA shows the multiple peaks of Ba with Al and Fe most probably instrument artifacts. TEM again shows angular fragments and SAED here shows a polycrystalline ring pattern.

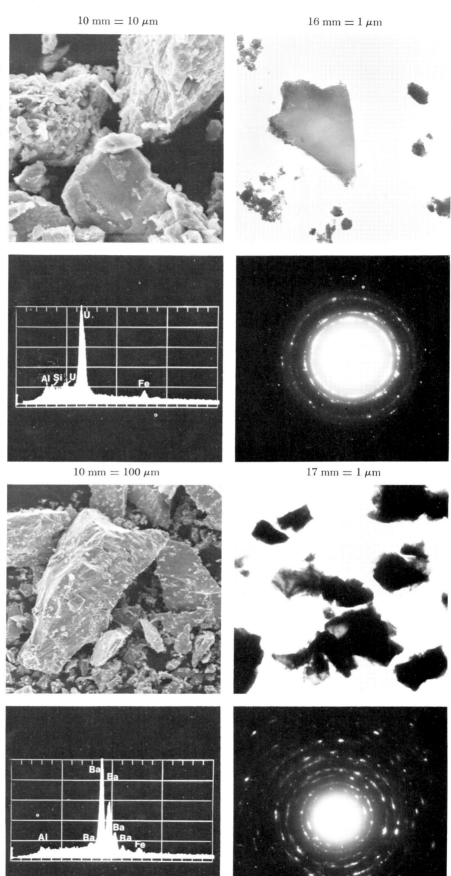

10 mm = 10 μm   16 mm = 1 μm

10 mm = 100 μm   17 mm = 1 μm

734   Wolframite, $(Mn,Fe)WO_4$
      JCPDS #11-591

This tungstate of manganese and iron tends to fracture unevenly to give irregular equant grains, although occasionally traces of the perfect {010} cleavage may be observed. EDXRA here shows a trace of S, possibly from an associated sulfide, with the expected W, Mn and Fe lines. Symmetry is monoclinic but approximates closely to orthorhombic, with $\beta = 89°34'$.

735   Wollastonite, $CaSiO_3$
      JCPDS #19-249, 27-88

This fibrous calcium silicate has been suggested as a possible substitute for asbestos in some applications. Electron optically, it may be distinguished from the asbestos minerals both by its diffraction pattern and its EDXRA spectrum which shows only Ca and Si.

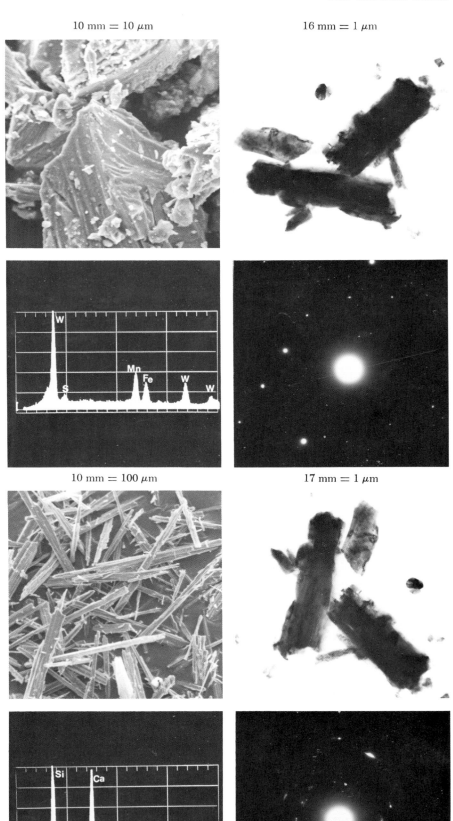

10 mm = 10 μm   16 mm = 1 μm

10 mm = 100 μm   17 mm = 1 μm

736 Aluminum Silicate, Al₂O₃·SiO₂

736 Aluminum Silicate, $Al_2O_3 \cdot SiO_2$
    JCPDS (sillimanite) #10-369, 22-18
The small 0.2–1.0 μm diameter platelets which make up the larger agglomerated masses of this sample are clearly shown by SEM. Their platy habit is confirmed by their electron transparency in the TEM. EDXRA shows traces of Ti and Fe in this sample, the former probably from traces of TiO₂, the latter probably an instrument artifact.

10 mm = 1 μm   15 mm = 1 μm

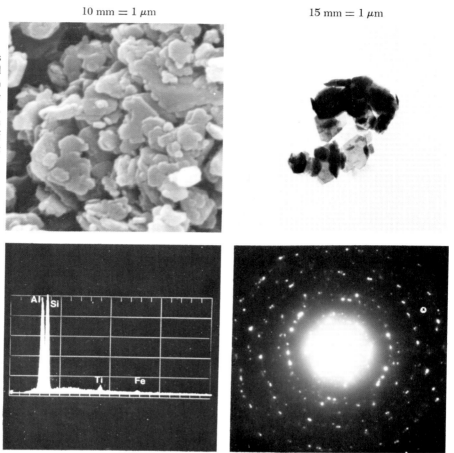

10 mm = 10 μm   10 mm = 1 μm

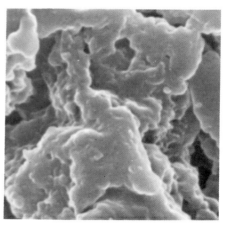

737 Aluminum Stearate—Small 0.1–0.8 μm crystals make up these granular aggregates of aluminum stearate. At high magnification the margins of many of these crystals appear to merge into each other possibly due to a solution effect. EDXRA shows traces of S and Fe in addition to the major Al peak.

10 mm = 100 μm 10 mm = 10 μm   10 mm = 1 μm

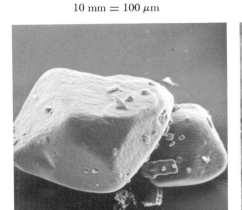  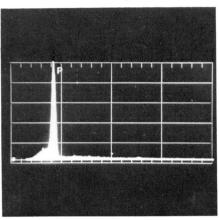

738   Diammonium Phosphate—These equant bipyramids show solution effects in the form of rounded edges and apices, seen at 100X, and extensive etch pitting, visible at 1000X. As would be expected, phosphorus is the only element visible in the EDXRA spectrum.

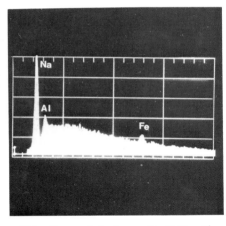 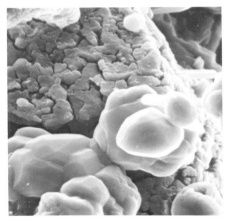 

739   Borax, Anhydrous, $Na_2B_4O_7$—These near spherical particles appear faceted, suggesting that they are crystalline rather than the true, glassy anhydrous form. The typical monoclinic needle shown at 10,000X is most probably the fully hydrated decahydrate. As would be expected, EDXRA shows only Na other than the instrumental Al and Fe.

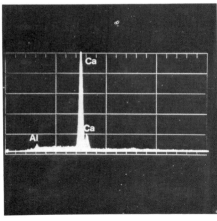  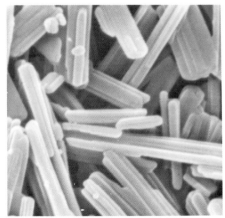

740   Calcium Citrate, $Ca_3(C_6H_5O_7)_2·4H_2O$—The individual acicular crystals making up these agglomerates are 0.2–1.0 μm wide and up to 10 μm long. Parallel growths and longitudinally striated crystals are common. Ca is the only element of the formula expected in the EDXRA spectrum. The Al trace is an instrument artifact.

10 mm = 1 μm   17 mm = 1 μm

741 Carbon, C
     JCPDS #23-64, 25-284 (syn)

These agglomerates of carbon black are composed of individual carbon particles about 0.1 to 0.2 μm in diameter. SAED rings are distinct although broadened, indicating a well-crystallized material of small crystallite size (*cf. 742*). EDXRA shows a high background with Al and S prominent and minor Si and Fe. Compare also *carbon (soft black) (371)* and *carbon (channel black) (372)*.

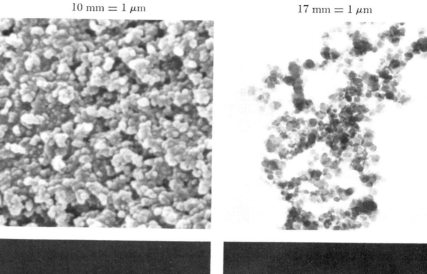

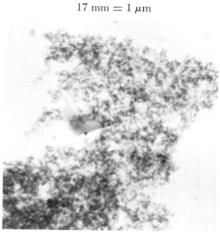

10 mm = 1 μm   17 mm = 1 μm

742 Carbon, C
     JCPDS #23-64, 25-284 (syn)

Although SEM suggests a similar size for individual carbon particles as was observed for *741*, TEM shows that the individual crystallites are considerably smaller. This is evidenced both by the morphological appearance and by the diffuseness of the diffraction rings. EDXRA is similar to that of *741*.

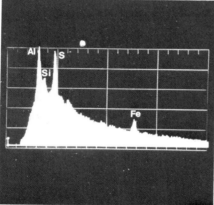

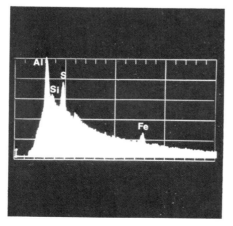

10 mm = 10 μm   10 mm = 1 μm

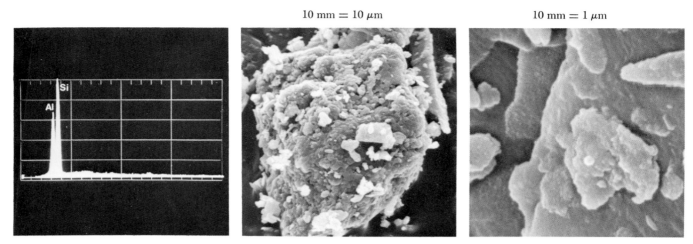

743 China (porcelain)—This sample of dust from a porcelain factory was shown by light microscopy to consist of the unfired raw materials. The material shown here is principally a clay aggregate; EDXRA shows it rich in Al and Si with no evidence of Na, K or Ca which would be expected if feldspars were present.

744 Denitrogenation and Desulfurization Catalyst—These irregular, somewhat rounded particles appear at high magnification to be aggregates of small 0.1–0.2 μm spheres. EDXRA shows high Si with traces of S, Ca and Co (the Fe in the spectrum is believed to be an instrument artifact).

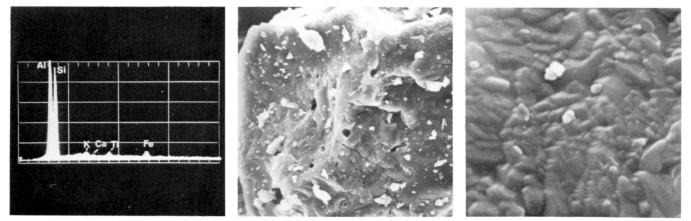

745 Firebrick—Firebrick is a term applied to any brick made from a clay that will withstand high temperatures without fusing or deforming. Its composition generally approaches that of *kaolin* (*155*). The high Al signal seen by EDXRA indicates that this is a high-grade firebrick.

746 Lead Monoxide, PbO
JCPDS #5-570

This sample of lead monoxide is composed of aggregates of small particles of 0.1–0.5 μm diameter. Their mean particle size and morphology thus differ from the other *massicot* (*406*) sample. EDXRA shows Pb as the principal peak with traces of Al, Si and Fe. Electron density is very high, thus yielding only shadowgraphs by TEM and poor SAED patterns. The crystal symmetry is orthorhombic.

10 mm = 1 μm   15 mm = 1 μm

747 Lead Tetroxide, Pb$_3$O$_4$
JCPDS #8-19

Individual particles within these aggregates of lead superoxide range in size from 0.1 to 1–2 μm. Morphologies range from near spherical in the small size ranges to angular and possibly tabular forms. EDXRA shows traces of Al, Si and Fe in addition to the strong Pb peak. The high electron density results in poor SAED patterns and only particle shadows in the TEM micrograph.

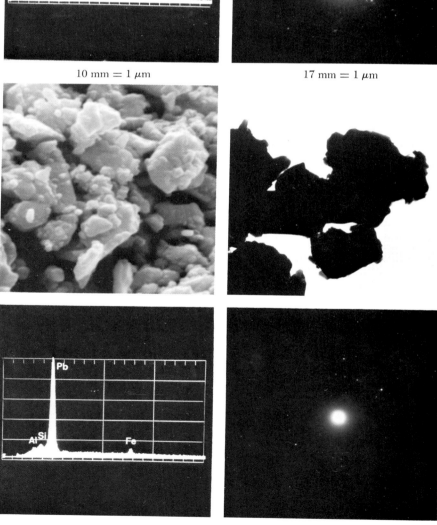

10 mm = 1 μm   17 mm = 1 μm

748 Lime Flue Dust
This sample consists of aggregates and single particles, 0.5–300 μm in diameter, of calcium carbonate (*calcite* [*133*]). Some flyash spheres are also observed. As would be expected, EDXRA shows only Ca. The diffraction pattern is that of calcite (JCPDS #24-27, 5-586 [syn]).

10 mm = 10 μm   15 mm = 1 μm

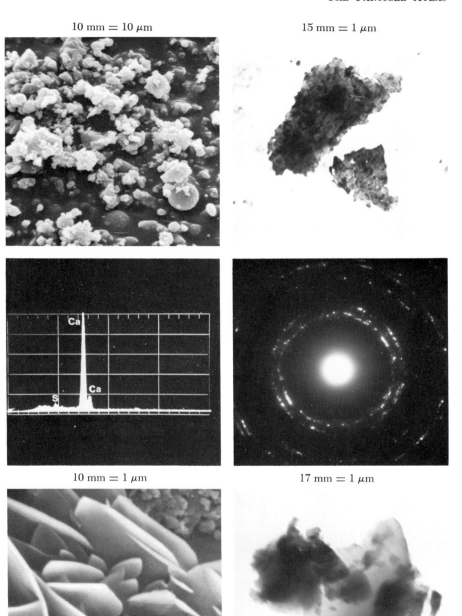

749 Magnesium Oxide, Hydrated
JCPDS #7-239

Aggregates of crystal flakes constitute this brucite sample. Flake diameters vary widely from submicrometer to several micrometers. Their thinness is indicated by their electron transparency in the TEM. EDXRA shows only Mg. The crystal symmetry is rhombohedral.

10 mm = 1 μm   17 mm = 1 μm

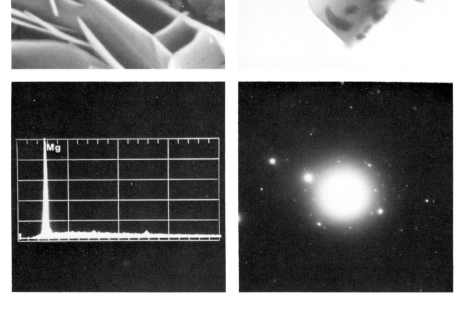

10 mm = 100 μm   10 mm = 10 μm   10 mm = 1 μm

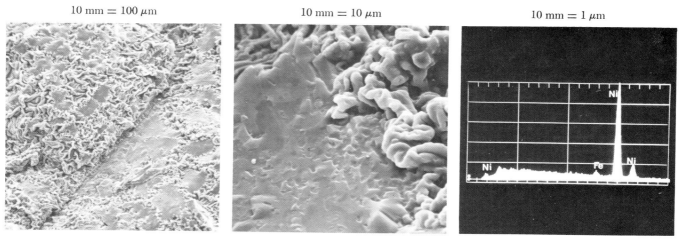

750 Nickel Nitrate—These concretionary aggregates are most probably the anhydrous nitrate, formed as water has been removed from the deliquescent hexahydrate in the vacuum of the microscope. As would be expected, only Ni is present in the EDXRA spectrum.

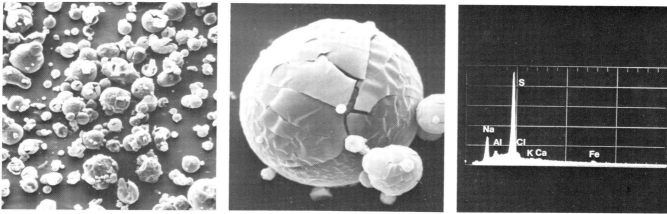

751 Oil Drilling Mud—This lubricant added to oil drilling muds consists of spherical and near spherical grains. Several of these are cracked and split. The spalling effect observed at 1000X is due to the presence of a liquid phase in the lubricant which has prevented good adherence of the gold film evaporated on the surface. It is this film which is flaking off. This phenomenon is not observed on uncoated samples.

752 Ottawa Sand—Consisting of both *quartz* (*183*) and *feldspars* (*157*), Ottawa sand shows both the conchoidally fractured, irregular quartz grains and the more tabular feldspars with good cleavage. EDXRA indicates that this sample is predominantly quartz, and that the feldspar is a potassium feldspar.

10 mm = 100 μm   10 mm = 10 μm   10 mm = 1 μm

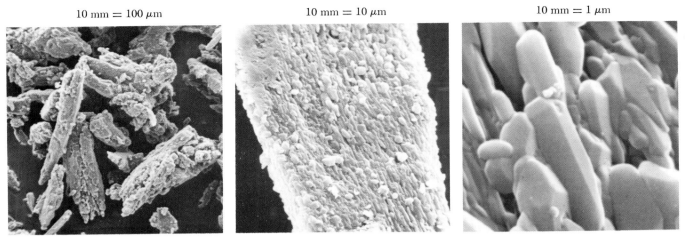

753   Phthalic Anhydride, $C_6H_4(CO_2)O$—These granular, elongated masses are seen at high magnification to consist of aggregates of acicular to prismatic crystals. Individual crystals are well formed and frequently in parallel growth, with their prismatic edges aligned parallel to the long axis of the aggregate.

754   Porcelain—This sample of porcelain raw materials is similar in composition to *china* (*743*). The predominant mineral present is a clay, probably *kaolin* (*155*), typified by the pseudohexagonal platelets shown at 10,000X. EDXRA shows principally Al and Si with traces of K and Ca, presumably from feldspars.

755   Sodium Carbonate, $Na_2CO_3 \cdot 10H_2O$—Na is the only element detectable in the EDXRA spectrum of sodium carbonate. Crystals range from granular to plates and blades. Skeletal forms are common.

10 mm = 1 μm

15 mm = 1 μm

756 Silica Flour

EDXRA of this ground sand shows evidence of the *limestone* (*161*) (Ca) and *iron oxide* (*391*) (Fe) observed by light microscopy. The high Al in combination with K, and perhaps some of the Ca, suggests a feldspar may also be present. The principal component is *quartz* (*183*), SiO$_2$. The particles are sharp, angular fragments. The fine dust shown here ranges from about 0.2 μm upward and is resting on the conchoidally fractured face of a larger quartz grain.

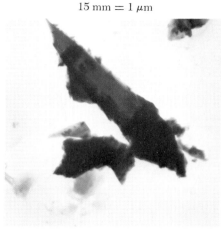

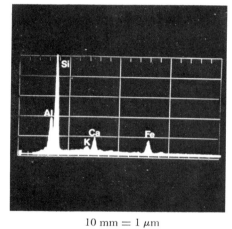

10 mm = 1 μm

17 mm = 1 μm

757 Silica Fumes

Mineralogically these fumes consist principally of *quartz* (*183*). Individual grains from about 0.1 μm upward are agglomerated to give larger aggregates. EDXRA is almost identical to that of *silica flour* (*756*).

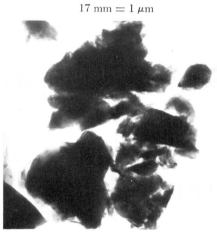

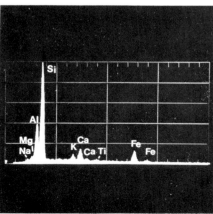

10 mm = 100 μm   10 mm = 10 μm   10 mm = 1 μm

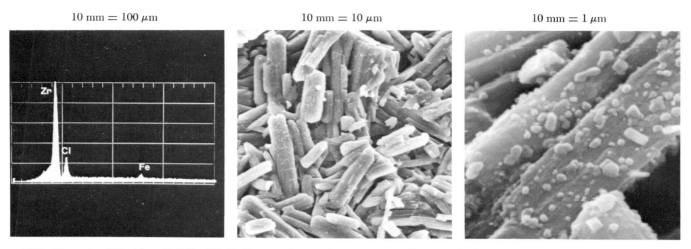

758 Zirconyl Chloride, ZrOCl₂·8H₂O—These elongated, somewhat tabular crystals, ranging in width from 0.5 to 5.0 μm, are seen at high magnification to be decorated with numerous smaller crystals from 0.1 to 0.5 μm across and generally equant. EDXRA shows Zr and Cl with Fe as an artifact.

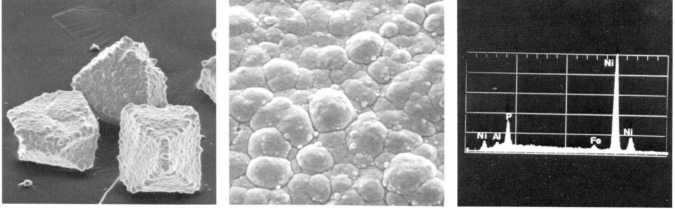

759 Borazon®, Nickel-coated—The nickel coating on these 200–300 μm octahedra has a rough, orange-peel texture which totally obscures the original Borazon surface. EDXRA would not be expected to show the B and N of the Borazon. The presence of a substantial P peak, in addition to the high Ni, indicates the presence of residues from the nickel deposition process.

760 Borazon®—A number of crystalline forms is shown in the 100X micrograph of this boron-nitride abrasive, with octahedral forms predominating. Growth striations are common on the pyramidal faces and are shown in more detail at 1000X and 10,000X.

10 mm = 100 μm   10 mm = 10 μm   10 mm = 1 μm

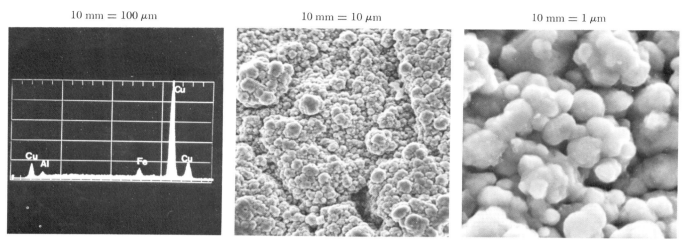

761 Diamond, Copper-coated—The granular structures shown here are of the copper coating. Individual grains are approximately 0.3–1.0 μm across. The coating is continuous with no evidence of the *diamond (222)* substrate visible.

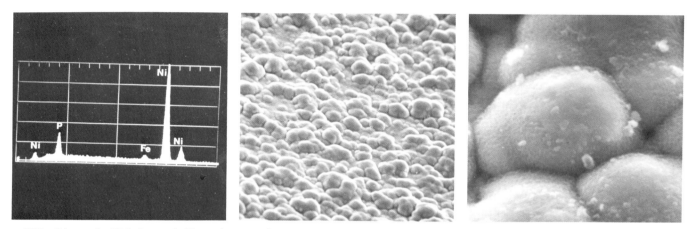

762 Diamond, Nickel-coated—Here the granular texture is due to the nickel coating. Phosphorus in the EDXRA spectrum is a result of residues from the deposition process [*cf. Borazon®, Nickel-coated (759)*].

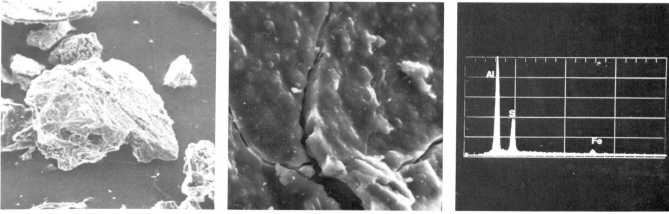

763 Aluminum Oxides, Hydrated—This scaly deposit is somewhat typical of many hydrated corrosion products. A fairly featureless matrix encloses individual grains which range in size from 1 to 5 μm. EDXRA identifies the original metal as aluminum, while the S in the spectrum suggests a sulfate attack.

764   Copper Oxides (dark)

Another corrosion product, this one origi-
nates from Cu as evidenced by the EDXRA
spectrum. The deposit is a mixture of copper oxides (SAED) and forms aggregates
of 0.1–5 μm crystals. The presence of Ca
and Cl in the deposit suggests contact with
a water supply, the Ca originating from
carbonate deposits and the Cl from chlorination of the water.

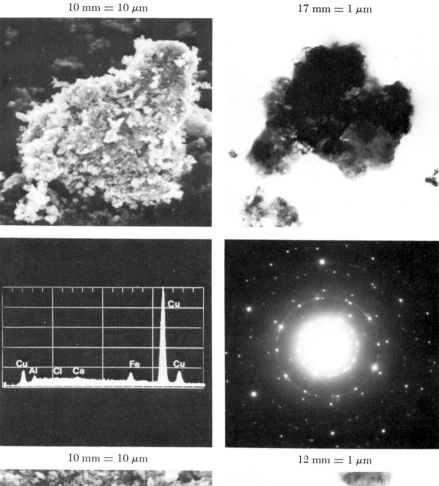

10 mm = 10 μm   17 mm = 1 μm

765   Copper Oxide (light)

A loose aggregate of small crystals ranging
in size from <0.1 to 5 μm, this corrosion
deposit is not only higher in Cu_2O than
the previous sample (764) but also contains a substantial amount of mineral debris. As a result, Al, Si, K, Ca and Fe all
show as major elements in the EDXRA
spectrum.

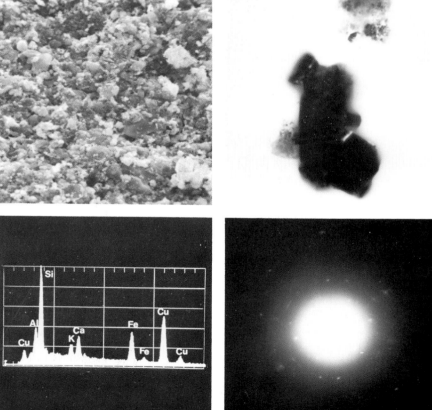

10 mm = 10 μm   12 mm = 1 μm

766 Iron Scale

This iron corrosion product is again an aggregate of many small crystals, ranging in size from <0.1 to >5 μm. Like many hydrated corrosion products, it yields an almost amorphous SAED pattern. EDXRA indicates iron as the base metal. Phosphorus, sulfur, calcium and copper are also noted in the spectrum.

10 mm = 10 μm   17 mm = 1 μm

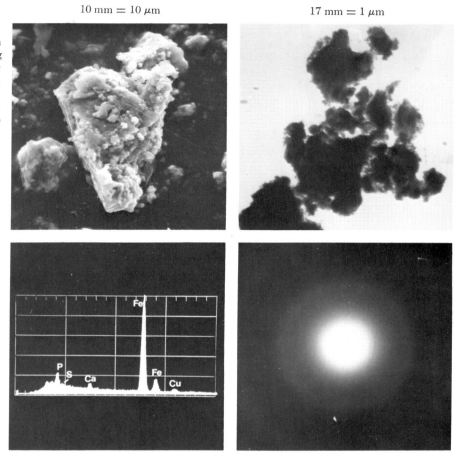

10 mm = 100 μm   10 mm = 10 μm

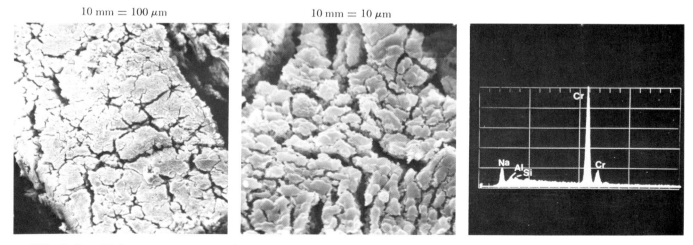

767 Sodium Dichromate, $Na_2Cr_2O_7 \cdot 2H_2O$—The large "slab" seen at 100X is composed of many small segments each about 1–2 μm across. Whether these are individual crystallites or the result of rapid drying of the material is not clear. Light microscopy suggests many aggregated masses with individuals in the aggregates of the same order of size as the segments observed here. EDXRA shows Na and Cr with traces of Al and Si.

10 mm = 100 μm 10 mm = 10 μm 10 mm = 1 μm

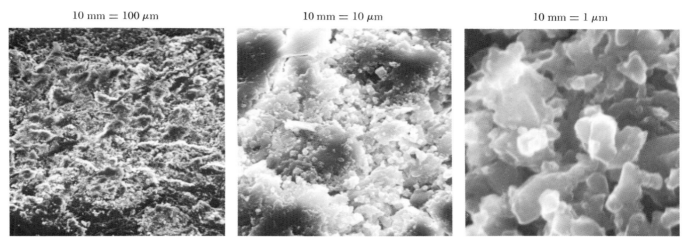

768 Benzocaine—Although benzocaine appears as square tablets by light microscopy, this is a result of a recrystallization from the mounting medium. By SEM, no clear crystalline forms are discernible at magnifications less than 1000X. At this and higher magnifications the crystals are platy and somewhat irregular in outline although an occasional square outline may be seen.

769 Cocaine Hydrochloride, Mexico—This sample consists of large, 100–150 μm equant grains together with numerous smaller, <10 μm particles. The surfaces of the large grains appear rough, and this may be due to adhering smaller grains, surface pitting or etching. The smaller particles may be derived by fracture of some of the surface asperities. EDXRA shows Cl from the hydrochloride. Al and Fe are instrument artifacts.

770 Heroin Hydrochloride, Germany—Irregularly shaped aggregates of platy to tabular crystals characterize this material. Individual crystals in these aggregates range in size from <2 to >20 μm. Cl is detected by EDXRA. Al and Fe are instrument artifacts.

10 mm = 100 μm   10 mm = 10 μm

  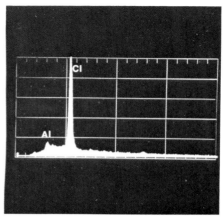

771 Heroin Hydrochloride, Italy—Forming smaller aggregates than those observed in the previous sample (770), this sample is again characterized by platy to tabular crystals, with Cl detected by EDXRA. Individual crystals again show a wide size range, <2 to>20 μm.

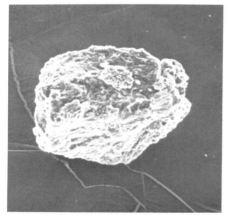  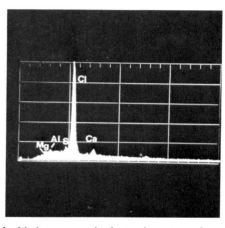

772 Heroin Hydrochloride, Mexico—The large, irregular grain shown here at 100X shows little evidence of the platy crystalline aggregate structures which characterized the two previous samples (770, 771). Instead, rod to lath-shaped crystals are barely discernible embedded in a nearly featureless striated matrix. EDXRA shows traces of Mg, Al, S and Ca in addition to the expected Cl.

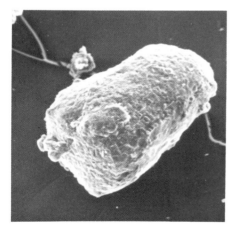 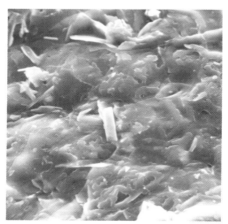 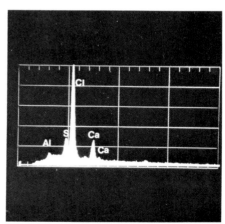

773 Heroin Hydrochloride, Rustic—Somewhat similar to 772, this sample shows even less evidence of the crystallinity observed in 770 and 771. Al, S and Ca are present as significant impurities presumably associated with the amorphous matrix.

10 mm = 100 μm   10 mm = 10 μm

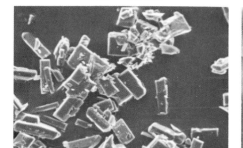  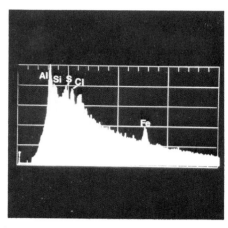

774 Heroin Base, Purified—Crystals vary from prismatic rods to near tabular and cover a wide size range. The crystal faces are generally featureless although some striated forms may be present. Although traces of Al, Si, S, Cl and Fe are noted in the EDXRA, very long count times are necessary to show them, as evidenced by the high background. Al and Fe show the most significant signals, and these are most probably instrument artifacts.

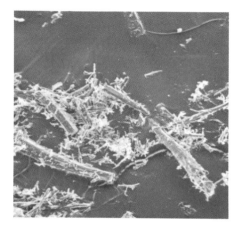  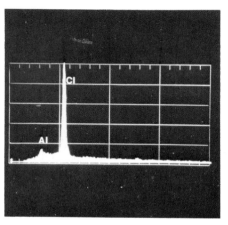

775 Morphine Hydrochloride—Fibers, with an apparent bimodal width distribution, form fluffy aggregates. The fibers appear rectangular in transverse section and are occasionally flattened. EDXRA shows Cl with trace Al and Fe.

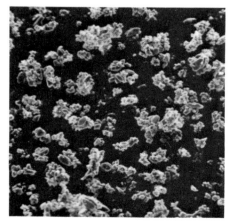  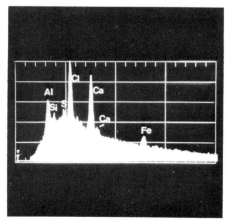

776 Morphine Base, Crude—Small grains and aggregates in the range 5 to 50 μm characterize this sample. Many of the apparent aggregates are spherulitic (1000X) and are probably the *calcite* (133) observed by light microscopy. EXDRA shows a high, organic background with Ca and Cl as the most significant elements.

10 mm = 100 μm   10 mm = 10 μm

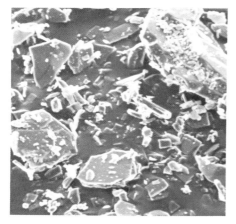

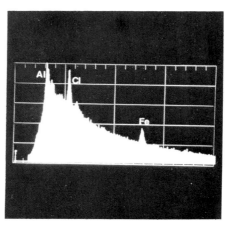

777 Morphine Base, Purified—This material is typified by aggregates and intergrowths of platy to tabular crystals. Individual crystals range in size from <1 to >20 μm, with aggregates >100 μm common. EDXRA shows Al, Cl and Fe with a high background count.

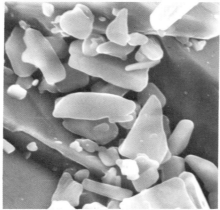
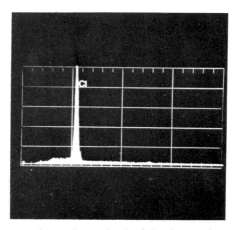

788 Norephedrine Hydrochloride—Large tabular crystals, >200–300 μm across, are common. The edges of both large and small tablets are irregular with no clearly defined crystal faces; EDXRA shows only Cl.

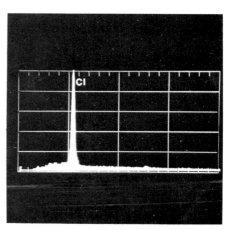

779 Novacaine Hydrochloride—Fragments range from platy to equant, are irregular in outline and show a conchoidal fracture. Sizes range from <1 to >200 μm. EDXRA shows only Cl.

10 mm = 100 μm   10 mm = 10 μm   10 mm = 1 μm

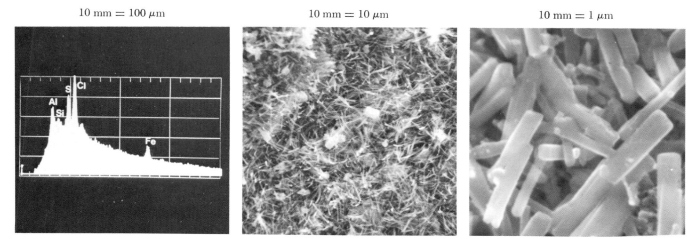

780 Quinine—This fine, felted mass is made up of fine, approximately 0.2–0.5 μm diameter needles, rods and laths. Occasional 5 μm grains, possibly impurities, are visible within the felt. EDXRA shows a high background with peaks for Al, Si (tr.), S, Cl and Fe.

781 Streptomycin A—This sample of streptomycin consists principally of a mass of fine granules each approximately 1–2 μm in diameter. Occasional larger plates, 4–5 μm across, are present. S is the only element detectable by EDXRA, indicating that this sample is probably streptomycin sulfate.

782 Strychnine, $C_{21}H_{22}N_2O_2$—Grains ranging from 20 to 500 μm across are composed of individual crystals ranging from equant to tabular. EDXRA shows a high background with peaks for Al and Fe, both probably instrument artifacts, and traces of Si, S and Cl.

10 mm = 100 µm   10 mm = 10 µm

783   Sulfaguanidine, $C_7H_{10}N_4SO_2$—Large, prismatic rods are "decorated" with many small plates or tablets about 1–10 µm across. Aggregates of these smaller crystals are also common. S is the only element detected by EDXRA.

784   Sulfanilamide, $C_6H_8SN_2O_2$—These irregular, equant grains contrast with the well-formed crystals that can be prepared from aqueous solution. Many of the grains observable at 100X are seen, at higher magnification, to be aggregates of small crystals. Only S is detectable by EDXRA.

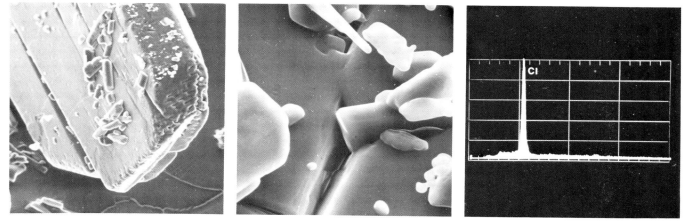

785   Xylocaine Hydrochloride, $C_{14}H_{22}N_2O \cdot HCl$—Large tabular to prismatic crystals characterize xylocaine (lidocaine) hydrochloride. Smaller crystals adhere to, or are intergrown with, the larger ones. Cl is the only element detectable by EDXRA.

10 mm = 100 μm   10 mm = 10 μm   10 mm = 1 μm

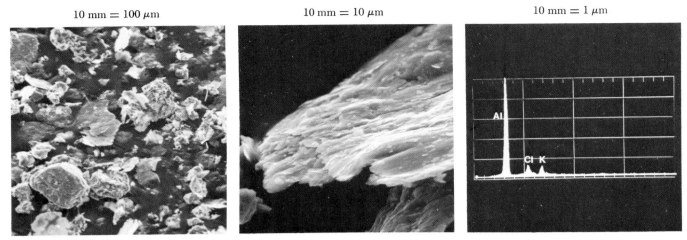

786   Aluminum Powder—This aluminum powder consists primarily of thin flakes ranging in diameter from <10 to >100 μm. Some large (100–200 μm) equant grains are also present.

EDXRA shows Al, with a small percentage of K and Cl from potassium chlorate also observed by light microscopy.

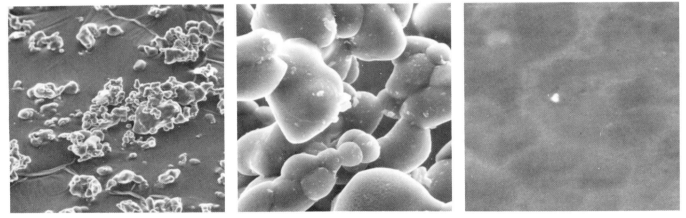

787   Ammonium Nitrate—Individual grains are equant and somewhat rounded, with diameters from 5 to 50 μm. Aggregates and conglomerates are common. Surfaces are slightly mottled at high magnification.

788   Ammonium Perchlorate—These 300 μm diameter spheres have a rough surface texture with some porosity. Some spheres have an indication of angularity, suggesting that they are rounded crystals. EDXRA shows traces of K and Ca in addition to the expected Cl.

10 mm = 100 μm   10 mm = 10 μm   10 mm = 1 μm

789 HMX, Form 1—These prismatic crystals, ranging in size from 5 to 50 μm, show frequent interpenetrant twins (1000X). Although several face forms are illustrated, most exhibit a typical monoclinic morphology.

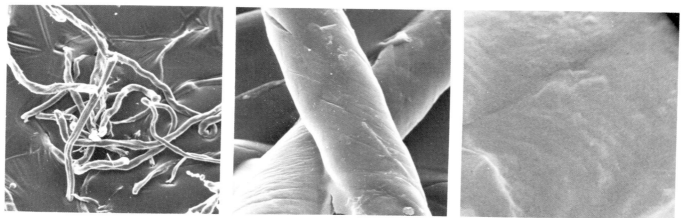

790 Nitrocellulose—Nitrocellulose is produced by the nitration of *cotton linters* (*61*). The morphology observed, therefore, is substantially the same as that observed on the original linters. Note, however, degradation of the striated surface structure observed on the original linters. See also *cellulose nitrate* (*457*).

791 Pentaerythritol Tetranitrate (PETN)—Crystals of PETN range in size from <10 to >300 μm and in shape from tabular to prismatic, although some near equant crystals are observed. Crystal faces are well developed and nearly featureless.

10 mm = 100 μm   10 mm = 10 μm   10 mm = 1 μm

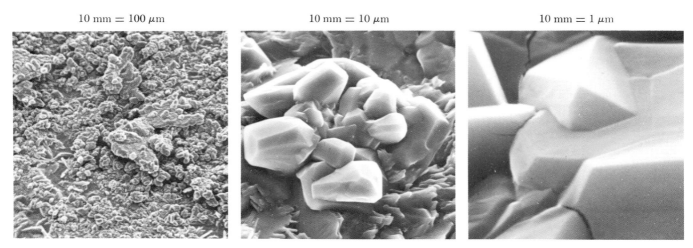

792 Picric Acid—The somewhat granular-looking masses observed at 100X are seen, at higher magnifications, to consist of intergrowths of well-formed crystals of about 2–20 μm diameter. Interpenetrating growths are frequent and may be twinned.

793 Potassium Nitrate—These equant, irregular fragments of KNO$_3$ range in size from <10 to >300 μm. Some exhibit conchoidal fracture. EDXRA shows K with trace Al, the latter probably an instrumental artifact.

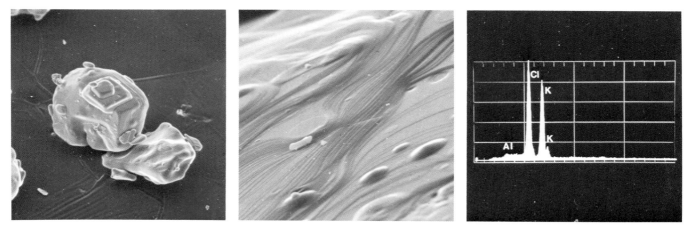

794 Potassium Chlorate—These equant crystals of potassium chlorate show evidence of solution with severe rounding of the crystal edges and typical solution striae on the faces (1000X). EDXRA shows a trace of Al in addition to the K and Cl expected.

10 mm = 100 μm   10 mm = 10 μm   10 mm = 10 μm

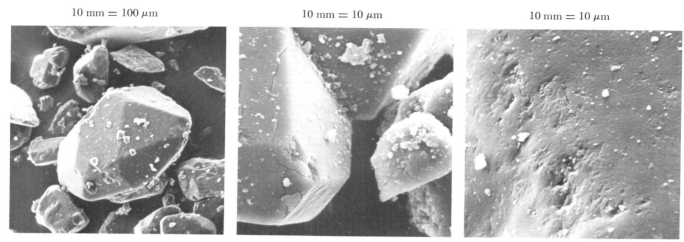

795 RDX—These well-formed crystals of cylotrimethylene trinitramine are generally prismatic with pyramidal terminations. The crystals tend to be slightly flattened, giving a nearly tabular appearance to many of them. Sizes may range up to several hundred micrometers. Degradation in the electron beam prevented obtaining a good 10,000X photograph. The right-hand photograph, therefore, is also at 1000X.

796 Sodium Chlorate—These rounded grains appear to have suffered some solution. Aggregates are frequent, and many individuals show evidence of having broken from such aggregates. At higher magnification the contact plane between intergrown crystals is frequently evident. EDXRA shows only Na and Cl.

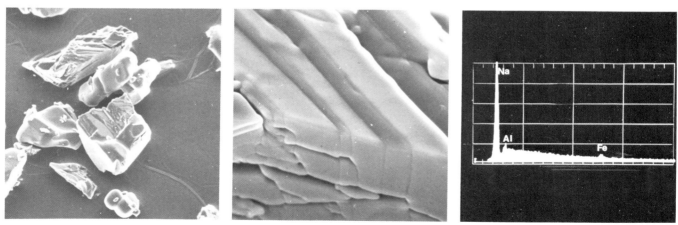

797 Sodium Nitrate—Sodium nitrate is isomorphous with *calcite* (*133*); indeed, a drop of NaNO$_3$ solution placed on freshly cleaved calcite will grow NaNO$_3$ rhombohedra epitaxially related to the calcite. As a result, the two crystals are indistinguishable morphologically. They are, of course, readily differentiated by EDXRA, which shows Na for sodium nitrate and Ca for calcite.

10 mm = 100 μm   10 mm = 10 μm   10 mm = 1 μm

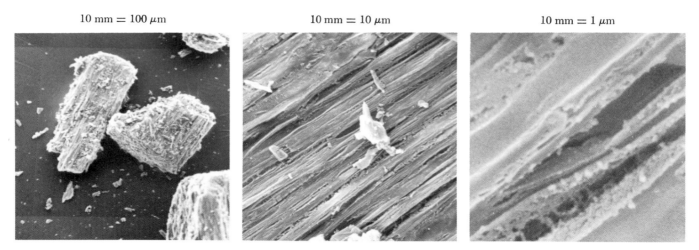

798 2,4,6-Trinitrotoluene (TNT)—This sample of TNT, mechanically ground, appears to consist of equant to rod-shaped aggregates of fibers. At higher magnification these fibers appear split or torn longitudinally, presumably as a result of the mechanical degradation.

799 Pocatello Fertilizer Plant—This and the following four samples all originate from a fertilizer plant in Pocatello, Idaho, an area rich in *phosphate rock (284)*. This particular sample is from the acidulation scrubber and consists of masses of fine, approximately 1–5 μm particles, rich in Si and Ca with lower levels of Al, P, S, K, Ba and Fe.

800 Pocatello Fertilizer Plant—This sample is taken from a stock pile of curing *triple superphosphate (290)*. Note the beneficiation of Ca and P evident in the EDXRA pattern. The crystals are blade-shaped and frequently in rosettelike clusters.

10 mm = 100 μm   10 mm = 10 μm   10 mm = 1 μm

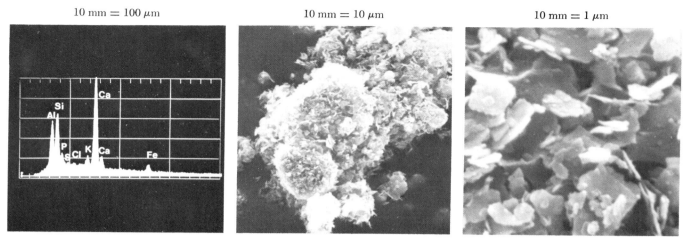

801 Pocatello Fertilizer Plant—Taken from the scrubber waste ponds, this sample contains aggregates of assorted debris; most are fine and platy. EDXRA, combined with the morphology, indicates possibly a high clay content (high Al and Si) with Ca also high.

802 Pocatello Fertilizer Plant—This sample of settled dust taken from a girder over the furnace slag tapper is high in Ca, Si and P with significant K, Al and Fe also. The sample is a mixture of mineral types with equant conchoidally fractured grains (possibly *quartz* [183]), granular aggregates and fine needles.

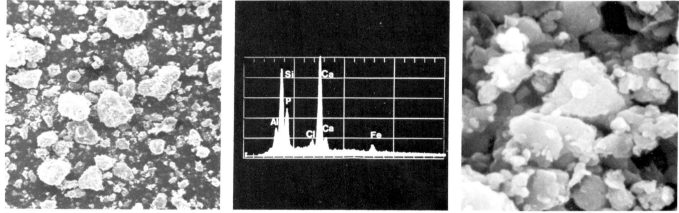

803 Pocatello Fertilizer Plant—This kiln product sample appears at 100X very similar to *799*. EDXRA, however, shows it higher in Ca, P and Al. Some platy material, resembling that seen in *802* at 10,000X, is present, and an occasional spherical particle is observed (100X).

10 mm = 100 µm   10 mm = 10 µm   10 mm = 1 µm

804 Organic Nitrogen (20%) Fertilizer—The rounded, 200–300 µm agglomerates are composed of small rod-shaped crystals approximately 1×10 µm and frequent 10 µm equant grains. The large featureless grains (seen in the upper half of the 100X micrograph) are quartz (hence the high Si peak in the EDXRA), probably sand used as a carrier or diluent for the fertilizer.

805 Organic Nitrogen (40%) Fertilizer—These large, equant to subspherical grains are aggregates of an assortment of particle types, including spheres, platelets and irregularly shaped particles with some suggestion of a featureless amorphous cement. EDXRA shows a high background with Al, Si, P, S, Cl, K, Ca and Fe all prominent.

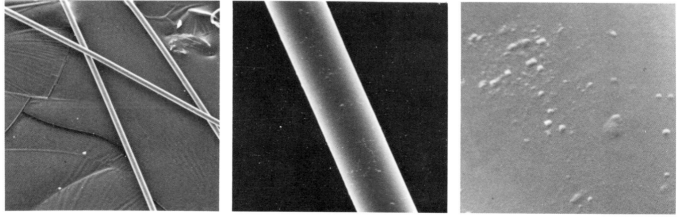

806 Fortrel®—This polyester filament, manufactured by Fibre Industries, is formed as continuous cylinders. The cylinder diameters in this sample are about 15 µm. The surface, as shown at 1000X and 10,000X, is very smooth.

10 mm = 100 µm   10 mm = 10 µm   10 mm = 1 µm

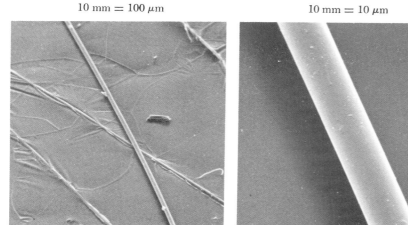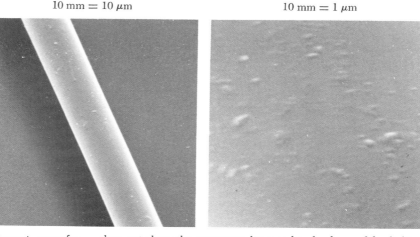

807 Kevlar® Aramid—Kevlar, or Aramid filament, manufactured by duPont, is cylindrical and has an 11–12 µm diameter in this sample. The surface is relatively smooth. The SEM does not show the transverse lines or bands observed by light microscopy.

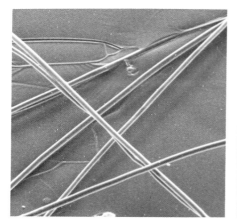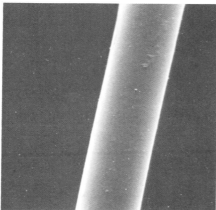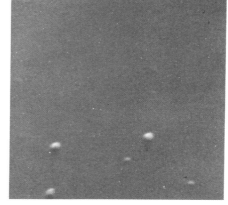

808 Kynol®—These cylindrical filaments show a range of diameters from about 10 to about 20–25 µm with some variation along the length of a single filament (100X). The surface is characteristically smooth and featureless (1000X, 10,000X).

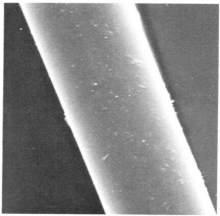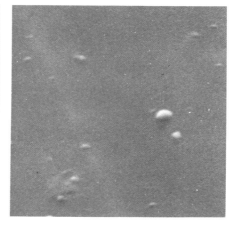

809 Lycra®—Circular to oval to dumbbell-shaped in transverse section, these polyurethane fibers manufactured by duPont vary in width from about 20 to 80 µm. The surface is smooth but contains a number of randomly distributed inclusions approximately 0.1–0.5 µm in diameter.

10 mm = 100 μm   10 mm = 10 μm   10 mm = 1 μm

810 Nylon, Caprolan®—This nylon filament, manufactured by Allied Chemical, is cylindrical in transverse section with diameters in the range of 40–45 μm. The surface is smooth with some evidence of drawing marks parallel to the fiber length (1000X).

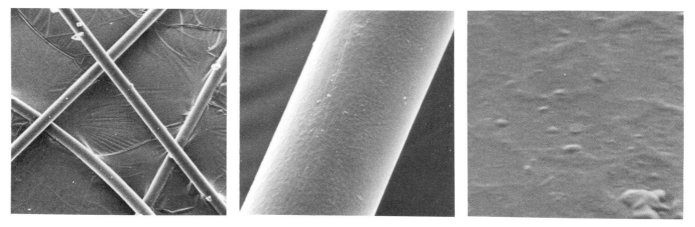

811 Nylon, Undrawn—These nylon fibers are cylindrical with diameters of about 30–35 μm. In contrast to the drawn fibers of (810), the surface is quite rough, showing almost an "orange peel" texture at 1000X.

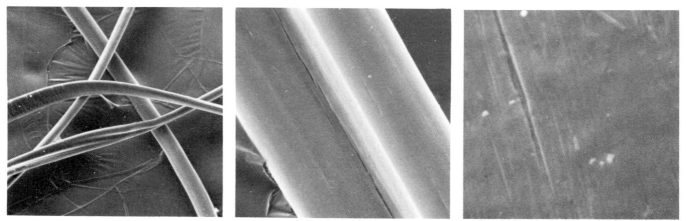

812 Teklan®—Courtalds' modacrylic, Teklan, has a crescent- or kidney-shaped crossection (100X and 1000X), about 20 × 50 μm. Striations and surface cracks parallel to the filament length are most probably die-induced during drawing or extrusion of the filament.

10 mm = 100 μm   10 mm = 10 μm   10 mm = 1 μm

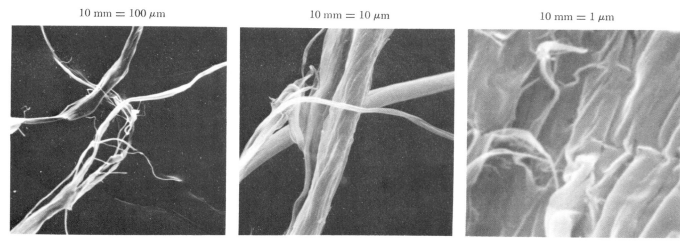

813 Tynek®—These split and frayed ribbon filaments are a nylon manufactured by duPont. The ribbons vary from about 50 μm wide to shredded fibrils less than 1 μm in diameter. The surface texture of the unshredded ribbon shows some deformation, suggesting that the shredding has been accomplished mechanically.

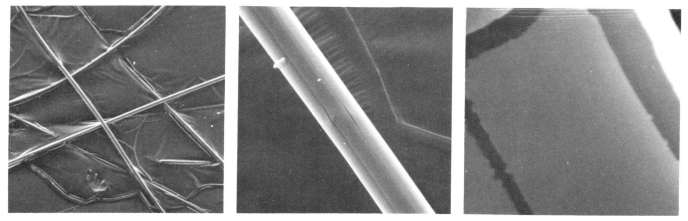

814 Viscose Rayon Tire Cord—These 10–12 μm diameter cylindrical filaments contrast markedly with conventional textile-grade *viscose rayon* (*102*). The surface is remarkably smooth, with some evidence of longitudinal die scratches. The conventional multilobate crossection is replaced by a cylindrical one. The cracking observed at 10,000X is an artifact due to electron beam damage.

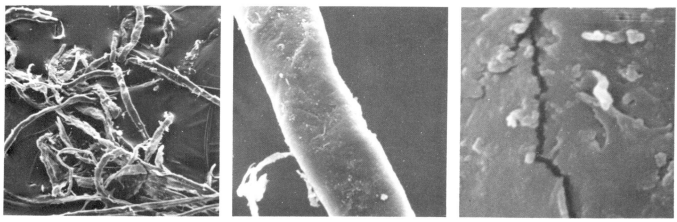

815 Vulcanized Fiber—This sample consists of *coniferous chemical wood* (*73*) paper fibers bonded with rubber. It is the morphology and surface features of the paper which predominate at low magnification. The rubber appears as isolated flakes and granules approximately 0.5–2.0 μm across. At 1000X and 10,000X much of the typical paper fibrosity is obscured, as though filmed over.

10 mm = 100 μm   10 mm = 10 μm   10 mm = 1 μm

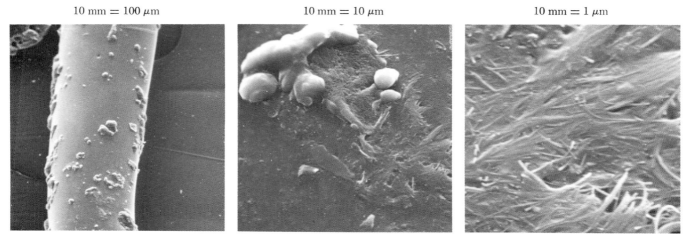

816 Vyrene®—This polyurethane fiber, manufactured by U.S. Rubber and by Dunlop, U.K., is markedly different from the other polyurethane in this collection, *Lycra®* (*809*). The fibers are quite large, that shown is approximately 250 μm in diameter. The surface is pockmarked (10–20 μm diameter) and covered with protuberances, the latter often associated with the pitting. A fine, fibrous structure is evident in some of the pits (10,000X).

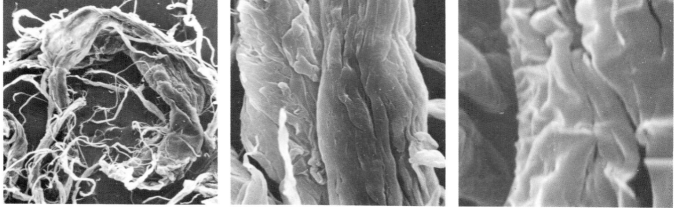

817 Crown Zellerbach® SWP—These highly tortuous polyethylene fibers, ranging in diameter from <1 μm to several tens of micrometers, show a highly complex surface texture (1000X and 10,000X). The surface is strongly fibrilated with individual fibrils, irregular both in size and shape.

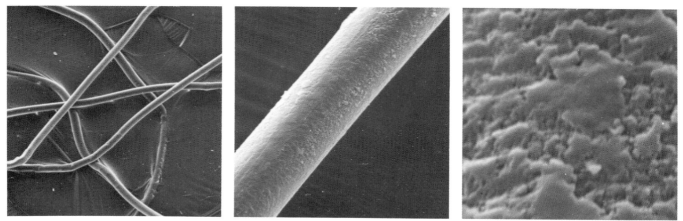

818 Zefran®—An acrylic fiber manufactured by Dow Badische, Zefran has a cylindrical crossection of about 20–25 μm in diameter. The surface is rough, almost as though etch-pitted (1000X and 10,000X). Some longitudinal striations are barely visible in the 1000X view.

10 mm = 100 μm   10 mm = 10 μm   10 mm = 1 μm

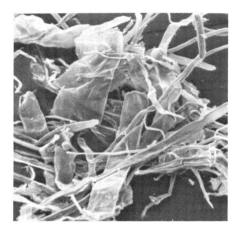 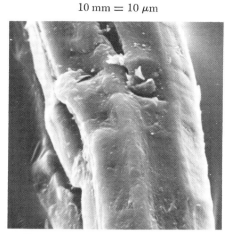 

819 Abaca (*Musa textilis*)—These coarse fibers, 50 μm in diameter, appear at low magnification to be bundles of thinner fibers. At higher magnification (1000X) it is apparent that this bundle effect is due, at least in part, to the irregular crossection of the fiber which shows longitudinal grooves with occasional splitting along the groove. The surface is reticulated in some areas, smooth in others (10,000X).

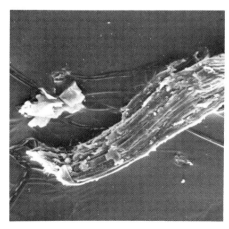 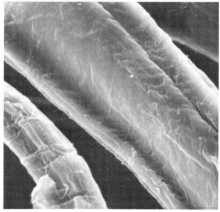 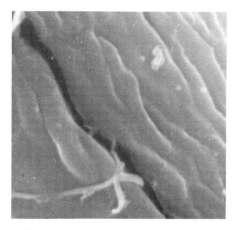

820 Bagasse—These sugar cane fibers show a variety of shapes ranging from segmented cylinders to wide ribbons. At 1000X the transverse grooving which gives rise to the segmented appearance is clearly seen in the left-hand fiber. Longitudinal striations are also visible, both at 1000X and 10,000X.

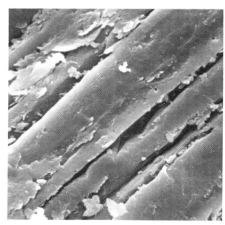 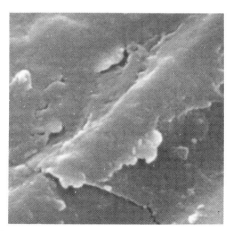

821 Coir—Typically short and stubby, these fiber bundles are composed of dense aggregates of ribbonlike fibers, 10–25 μm wide. The edges of these ribbons are irregular, and their surfaces appear scaly (1000X and 10,000X). The bundles are likewise irregular in outline and seldom exceed 1 mm in length.

10 mm = 100 μm   10 mm = 10 μm   10 mm = 1 μm

 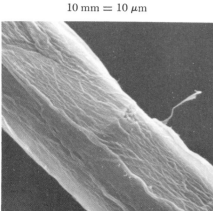 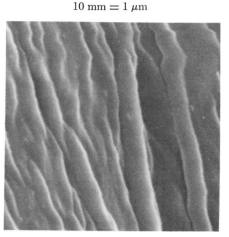

822 Gum, White (*Liquidambar styraciflua*)—Individual fibers vary in width from 10 to 30 μm, with such variations often occurring along the length of a single fiber. The surface of the fibers is reticulated, giving a striated, corded appearance. The fibers are frequently flattened and ribbonlike.

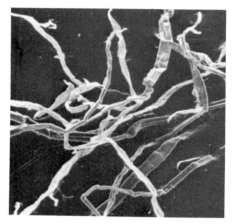 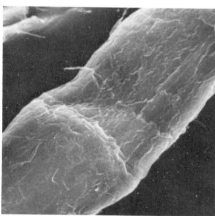 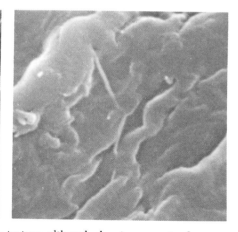

823 Fir, Balsam (*Abies balsama*)—These softwood fibers, which have been chemically separated, form ribbons about 20–30 μm wide. The ribbons are frequently kinked and twisted. The surface texture, although showing some tendency to a longitudinal alignment, is somewhat irregular (1000X and 10,000X).

 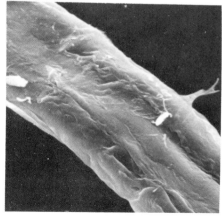 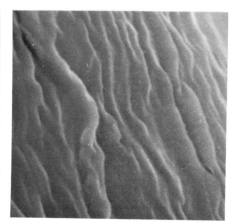

824 Fir, Western Balsam (*Abies* sp.)—This paper pulp, although morphologically similar to 823, is slightly coarser and shows less tendency to kink. The surface texture varies from smooth to striated.

10 mm = 100 μm   10 mm = 10 μm   10 mm = 1 μm

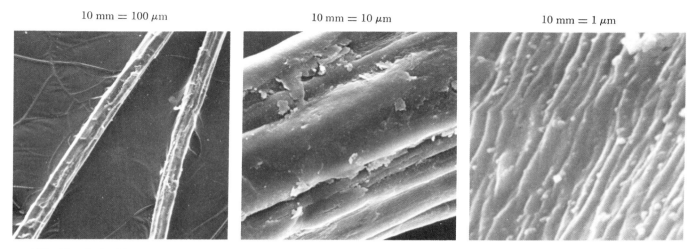

825 Kenaf (*Hibiscus cannabinus*)—The 50 μm diameter fibers observed at 100X are aggregates or intergrowths of individual 20–25 μm diameter fibers. These individual fibers have irregular outlines (1000X) and, in some areas, marked longitudinal striations (10,000X).

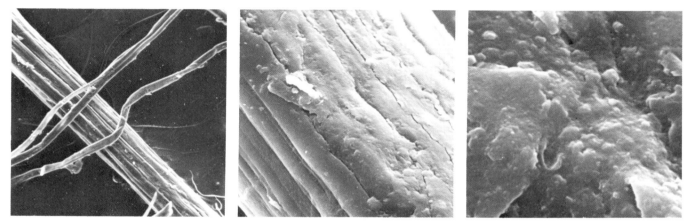

826 Manila (*Musa textilis*)—Manila is another name for *abaca* (819), *q.v.* In this sample both fine and coarse fibers (up to 150 μm wide) are observed. The morphology is similar to that described for *abaca* (819). The high magnification micrograph here shows an area of the surface with many 0.2 to 0.4 μm protuberances.

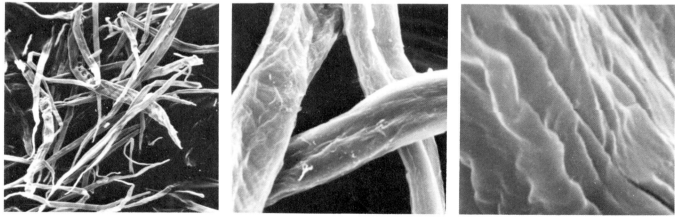

827 Maple, Sugar (*Acer saccharum*)—These chemically separated, hardwood fibers are flattened and ribbonlike with widths from 5 to 50 μm. The ribbons are frequently kinked and twisted. The surface frequently shows a crosshatching at 45° to the fiber length (1000X) and perforations may be observed (100X).

10 mm = 100 μm   10 mm = 10 μm   10 mm = 1 μm

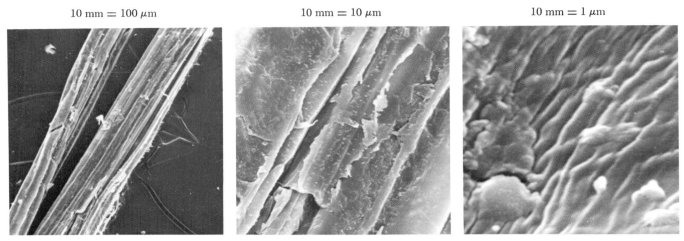

828 Mauritius (*Furcraea gigantea*)—These fiber bundles are made up of individual fibers approximately 20–30 μm in diameter. The surface of the individual fibers is frequenty damaged (1000X), exposing a reticulate subsurface (10,000X).

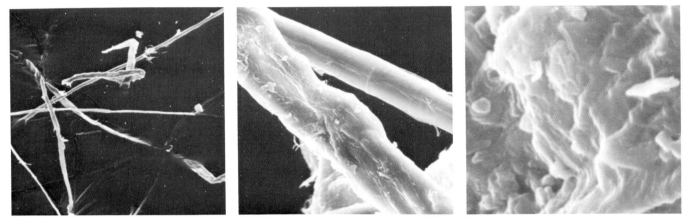

829 Mitsumata (*Edgeworthia papyrifera*)—Two fiber types are evident here. The first is a ribbonlike typical paper fiber 15–20 μm wide. The second is a comparatively smooth fiber, somewhat nodular and resembling a bamboo cane in miniature (1000X). The surface texture of the ribbons is variable, as shown at 1000X.

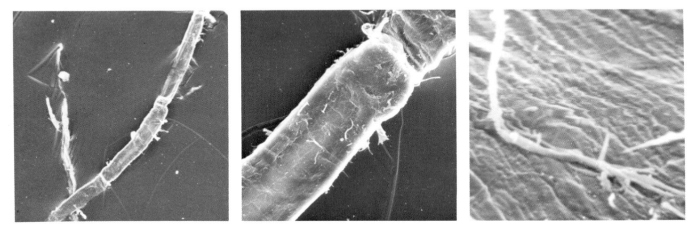

830 Mulberry (*Broussonetia papyrifera*)—Theses fibers, from the inner bark of the kozo tree, are flat and ribbonlike. Transverse kinks or segments are common. Ribbon widths are about 20–50 μm. The surfaces of the ribbons are striated and generally decorated with thin, short fibers, frequently branched.

10 mm = 100 μm   10 mm = 10 μm   10 mm = 1 μm

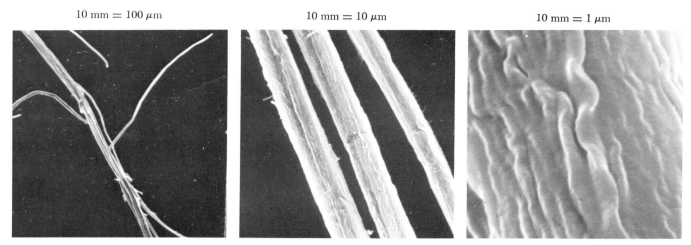

831 Oak, White (*Quercus alba*)—These wood fibers are about 10 μm in diameter and frequently are in parallel aggregates. The individual fibers are longitudinally striated (1000X), this striation being due to a longitudinally oriented reticulation (10,000X).

832 Phormium (*Phormium tenax*)—Individual fibers are typically 5–15 μm in diameter with a cylindrical or near-cylindrical crossection. The fibers range from straight, through curved, to highly convoluted. The surfaces appear striated due to a longitudinally oriented reticulation (1000X, 10,000X).

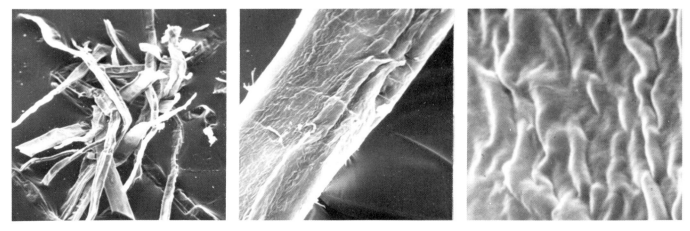

833 Pine, Scotch (*Pinus silvestris*)—This paper pulp typically forms ribbons 20–50 μm wide. The ribbons are not so markedly kinked as those of the firs, *balsam* (823) and *Western balsam* (824). At higher magnifications (1000X, 10,000X) the surface of the fibers is seen to be striated due to a longitudinal reticulation.

10 mm = 100 μm   10 mm = 10 μm   10 mm = 1 μm

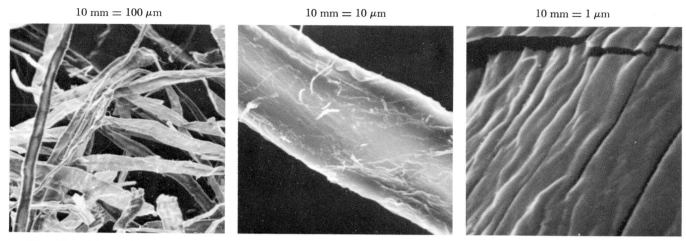

834 Sisal (*Agare sisalana*)—These flat fibers range in width from about 10 to 50 μm. Their surfaces are reticulated, giving the appearance of longitudinal striations (1000X and 10,000X). Some light, transverse markings are seen at 1000X.

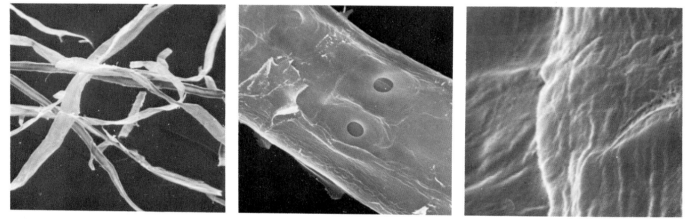

835 Spruce, Black (*Picea mariana*)—These paper pulp fibers are ribbonlike and range in width from about 25 to 50 μm. Surface pits approximately 5 μm in diameter are prominent. A slightly reticulate surface gives the appearance of longitudinal striations.

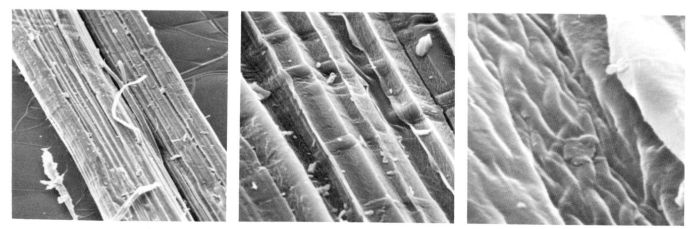

836 Tow, Brazilian—Tow is a short, broken fiber from *flax* (*63*), *hemp* (*64*) or *jute* (*65*) used for yarn, twine or stuffing. The fibers in this sample are polygonal in transverse section and about 10–15 μm in diameter. Morphologically they most closely resemble those of *hemp* (*64*), *q.v.*

10 mm = 100 μm   10 mm = 10 μm   10 mm = 1 μm

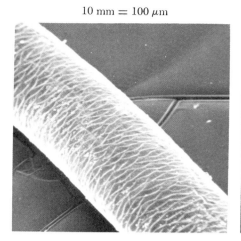 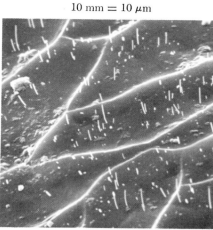 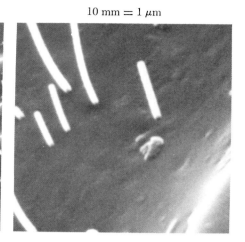

837 Antelope Hair—This cylindrical hair is about 100 μm in diameter, and scale widths are about 25–30 μm. The scales form a mosaic pattern and, unlike most hairs, do not seem to overlap. The 0.2 μm diameter "whiskers" observable at 1000X and 10,000X may be crystalline growths from the scale surface (*cf. elk [844]* in which similar crystalline whisker growths are prevalent).

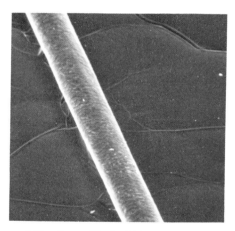 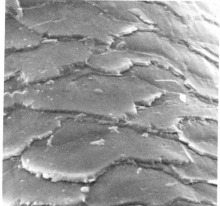 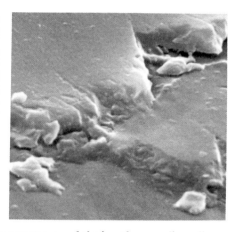

838 Bear, Black (*Ursus americanus cinnamomum*)—These 100 μm diameter cylindrical hairs show a pattern of irregular, overlapping scales with approximately 10 scales per 100 μm length. The scales are prominent and thick with generally well-defined margins as shown at 1000X and 10,000X.

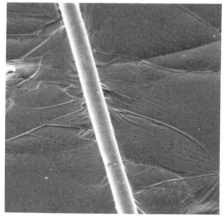 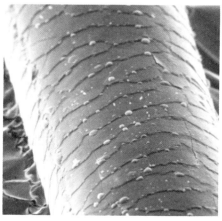 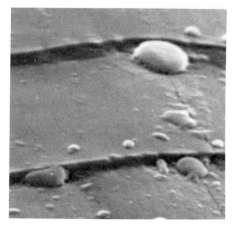

839 Bobcat Hair (*Lynx rufus pallescens*)—This 50 μm cylindrical hair shows a scale pattern resembling overlapping hoops. There are 12–15 scales per 100 μm of length. The scales are thin and have prominent edges between longitudinally adjacent scales but show little differentiation between circumferentially adjacent scales (1000X, 10,000X).

10 mm = 100 μm   10 mm = 10 μm   10 mm = 1 μm

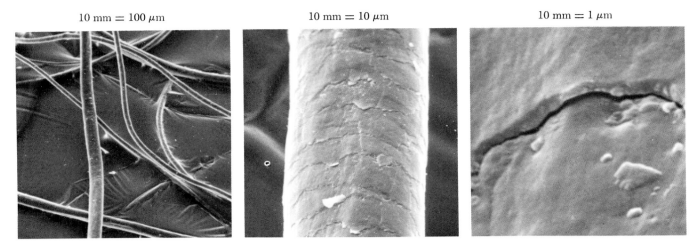

840 Camel Hair—These 20–50 μm diameter hairs are cylindrical to flattened in crossection. The scales and scale margins are somewhat indistinct even at 1000X. The overlapping scales, approximately 9–10 per 100 μm, are irregular in shape.

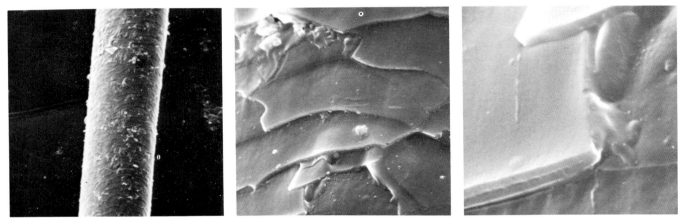

841 Caribou Hair—These coarse-textured hairs, approximately 200 μm in diameter, are covered with prominent, angular scales. There are about 6 scales per 100 μm length of the hair. The thick, sharply angular nature of the scales is well shown in the 10,000X micrograph.

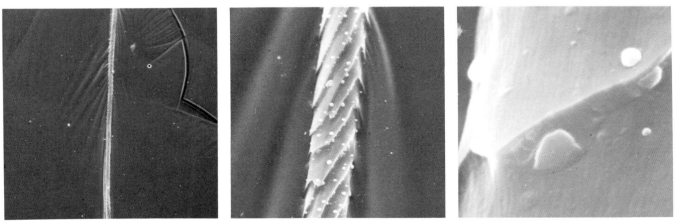

842 Chinchilla Hair—These fine, 10–15 μm diameter hairs have a unique scale arrangement which distinguishes them from those of other rodents. The scale pattern (1000X) resembles a set of nested cones truncated at about 30° to their axes. The scales are comparatively thick, and their margins are sharply defined (10,000X).

10 mm = 100 μm   10 mm = 10 μm   10 mm = 1 μm

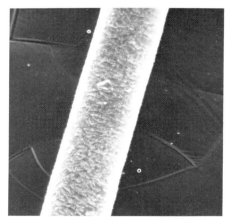 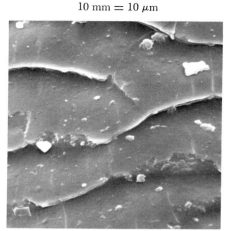 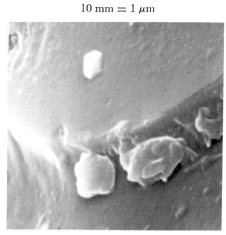

843 Deer, White-Tailed (*Odocoileus virginianus*)—These 250 μm diameter cylindrical hairs have polygonal scales arranged to give a wavelike edge between longitudinally adjacent scales. The boundary between circumferentially adjacent scales is not very distinct. There are about 4–5 scales per 100 μm.

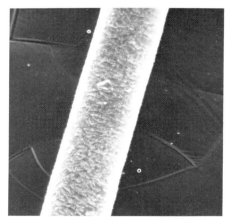 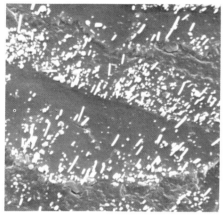 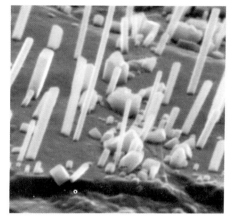

844 Elk Hair (*Cervus canadensis nelsoni*)—This cylindrical hair, approximately 175 μm in diameter, shows a very indistinct, irregular scale pattern. The surface of the hair is, however, characterized by numerous prismatic "whiskers" growing from the scale surface. The prismatic nature of these whiskers and the poorly defined scale margins differentiate these hairs from those of the *antelope* (*837*) which they superficially resemble.

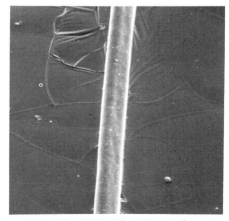 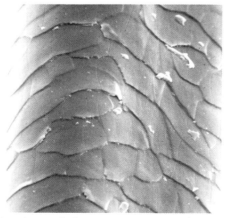 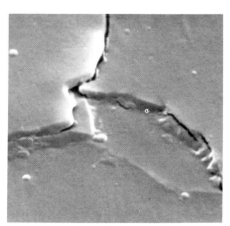

845 Fox Hair—This 70 μm diameter hair has a slight concavity or flattening to its crossection. The scales are wide and closely spaced with somewhat serrated margins (1000X). This serration is best seen at 1000X. The scale pattern otherwise resembles that of the small *dog* (*44*).

10 mm = 100 μm   10 mm = 10 μm   10 mm = 1 μm

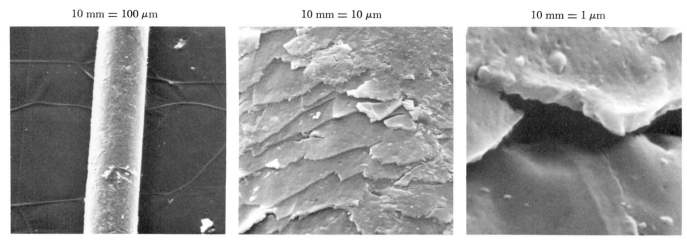

846 Horse Hair (*Equus caballus*)—A wavelike, mosaic scale pattern is observed with sharply defined, crenate scale edges. Boundaries between circumferentially adjacent scales are indistinct but can be observed at high magnification. The hair shown at 100X is approximately 150 μm wide, toward the high end of the range observed for this sample, and there are about 100 scales per millimeter of length.

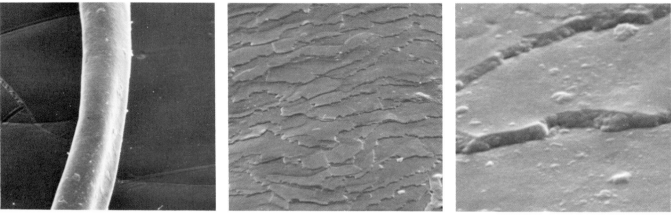

847 Human, Pubic Hair (*Caucasian male*)—Slightly coarser than hair from other parts of the body, pubic hair differs in few other physical properties. The description given in *human hair* (*Caucasian*) (*49*), applies equally to this sample, and indeed the diameter of the hair shown here lies within the size range given in (*49*).

848 Mink Hair (*Mustela vision*)—These fine, 40–50 μm diameter hairs are characterized by their regular, lanceolate scale structure. Individual "teeth" are 7–8 μm wide at their bases and taper to a rounded point over a length of 20–25 μm.

10 mm = 100 μm   10 mm = 10 μm   10 mm = 1 μm

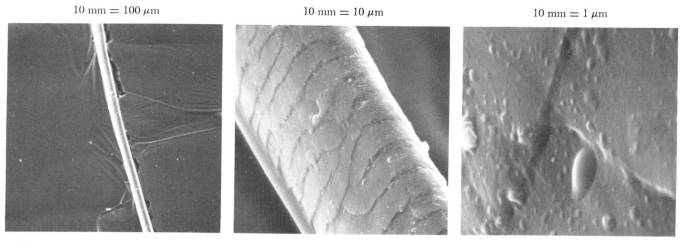

849   Opossum Hair—These near cylindrical hairs show an irregular, waved mosaic scale pattern. There are about 12–15 scales per 100 μm. The scale margins are smooth to crenate, as shown at 1000X and 10,000X.

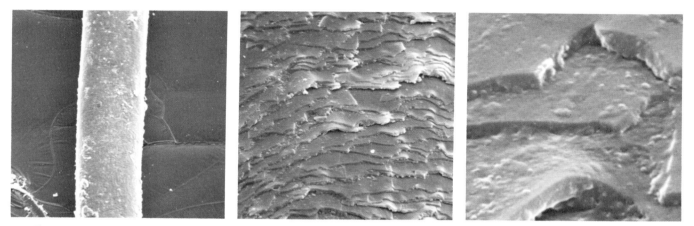

850   Pig (Hog) Hair—These hog bristles are scaly cylinders, about 175 μm in diameter for the hair shown at 100X. The scale pattern shows a closely spaced, irregular wave form. The scale margins are close and somewhat crenate.

851   Vicuña Hair (*Llama vicuña*)—This fine, about 15 μm diameter, near cylindrical hair shows some variation in diameter along its length. The scale pattern is irregular waved mosaic to coronal, the individual scales having smooth to rippled margins (1000X).

10 mm = 100 μm   10 mm = 10 μm   10 mm = 1 μm

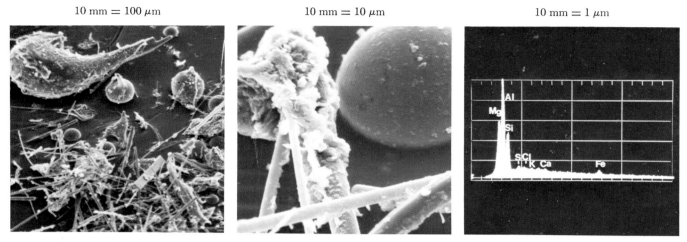

852   **Ban Rock D®**—This synthetic mineral wool shows a combination of fibers, spheroids and irregular particles. The fibers show a wide range of widths, from about 1 to 20 or 30 μm. Occasional fibers have globular ends. EDXRA shows principally Mg, Al and Si with traces of S, Cl, K, Ca and Fe.

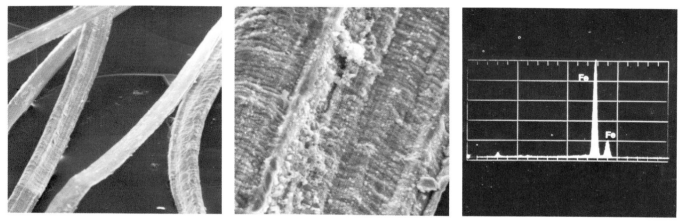

853   **Metal Fibers (Brillo)**—These fibers are irregular in cross-section, tending toward flattened ribbons 50–100 μm wide. They are striated both longitudinally and transversely. EDXRA shows the parent metal from which they were cut to be iron or steel.

854   **α-Alanine, CH₃CH(NH₂)CO₂H**—α-Alanine (2-aminopropanoic acid) is soluble in both water and alcohol. These aggregates are composed of well-formed crystals showing a pyramidal form and a well-developed basal plane. The pyramidal faces are striated parallel to the basal plane.

10 mm = 100 μm   10 mm = 10 μm   10 mm = 1 μm

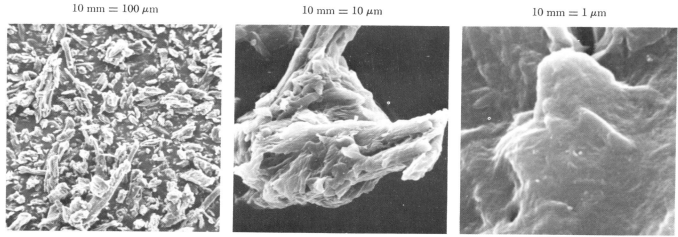

855 Avicel—Avicel is microcrystalline cellulose and therefore exhibits many of the morphological characteristics of the other cellulosics. The crystals tend to be rods or fibers with longitudinal striations. See also *alpha-cellulose dust* (*455*).

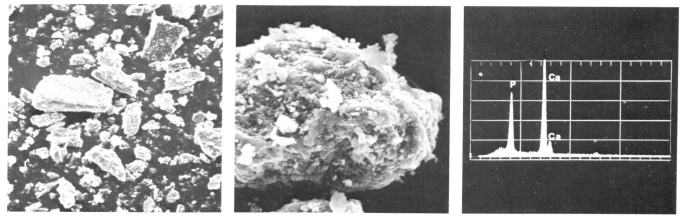

856 Bone Meal, steamed—These irregular-shaped grains are aggregates of 1–5 μm crystals, some platy and some nearly spherical. Unlike *bone dust* (*298*), few of the histological features remain. EDXRA shows only Ca and P.

857 Brewer's Grain—These granular residues extracted from cereal products of a brewing process are of somewhat indefinite shape but frequently show some evidence of the original cellular structure. EDXRA shows Mg, Al, Si, Fe, P, S, Cl, K and Ca. The last five are frequently characteristic of cellular material.

10 mm = 100 μm   10 mm = 10 μm

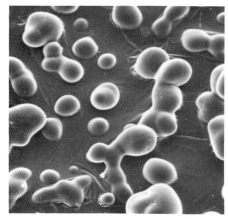 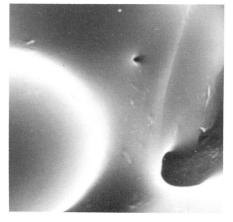 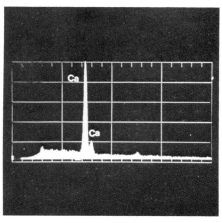

858 Calcium Pantothenate—No evidence is seen in this sample of the acicular crystals observed by light microscopy. Instead, the material appears almost as liquid droplets approximately 20–100 μm in diameter and frequently coalesced to give chainlike structures. EDXRA shows only Ca.

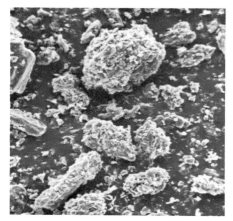 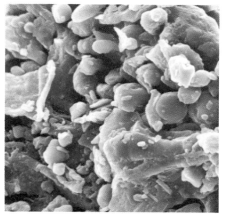 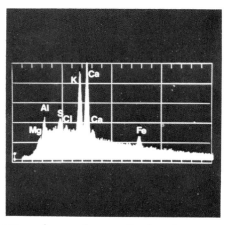

859 Cinnamon—The granular aggregates observed at 100X are seen at higher magnification to consist of several phases. Rounded grains, probably starch, are about 8 μm across. Thin shards of tissue and other, thicker, cellular material are frequent. Some small, <10 μm long, rod or needle-shaped crystals are present. EDXRA shows Mg, Al, S, Cl and Fe with abundant K and Ca and a prominent, organic background.

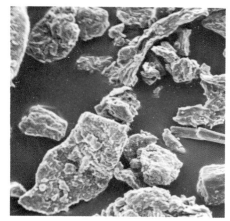 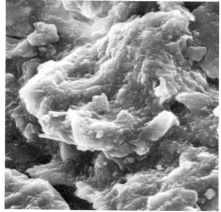 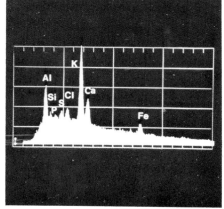

860 Cloves—Particles in this crushed sample range from rod-shaped to equant with rough, frequently angular outlines. Even at higher magnification there is little evidence on the undulose, rough-textured surface of any cellular structure. EDXRA shows Al, Si, P, S, Cl, K, Ca and Fe with a high, organic background.

10 mm = 100 μm   10 mm = 10 μm   10 mm = 1 μm

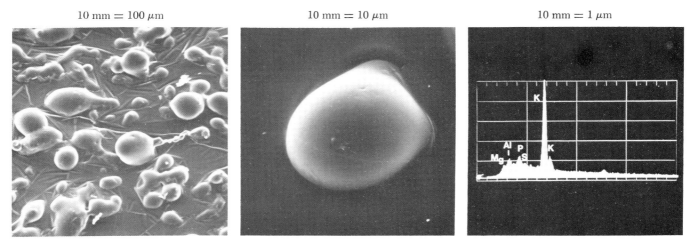

861 Coffee, Instant—These rounded grains vary in size from 20 to 100 μm and appear almost as liquid droplets. They are virtually featureless at higher magnification. EDXRA shows Mg, Al, P and S in addition to high K.

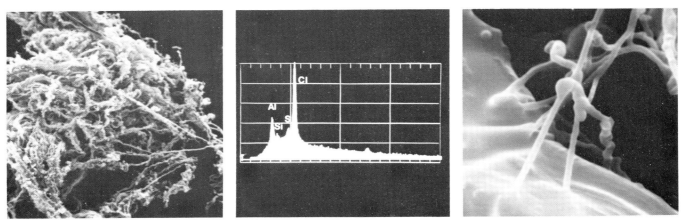

862 Collagen Fibers—These bundles of collagen fibers are composed of individual fibrils approximately 0.2 μm in diameter. The individuals range from straight, parallel-sided fibrils to twisted, branching fibrils with frequent nodes. EDXRA shows Al, Si, S and Cl.

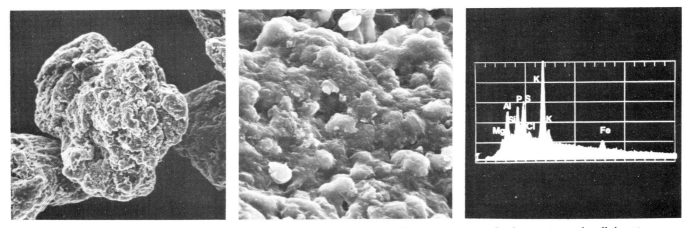

863 Distillers Dried Grain—These granular aggregates are the dried residues obtained by passing corn liquor through a screen. They are composed of a variety of cellular tissues. EDXRA shows Mg, Al, Si, P, S, Cl, K and Fe.

10 mm = 100 μm   10 mm = 10 μm   10 mm = 1 μm

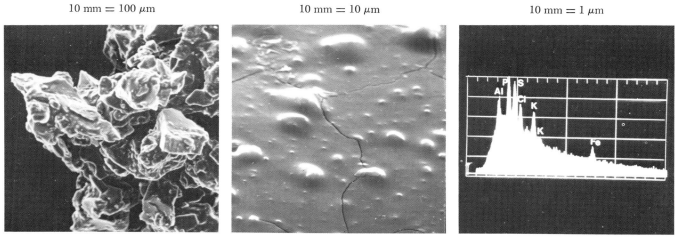

864   Fish Eggs, Freeze-dried—This sample shows the typical features of most freeze-dried products when examined by SEM. Particles are angular and irregular both in size and shape. Surfaces are smooth and crazed. Some rounded pro-tuberances, possibly the original, spherical eggs are seen. EDXRA shows Al, P, S, Cl, K and Fe with a high, organic background.

865   Folic Acid, $C_{19}H_{19}N_7O_6$—Plates, laths and ribbons are the crystal morphologies observed in this sample of folic acid. Crystal sizes range from submicrometer to several micrometers across with some laths 50 to 100 μm long.

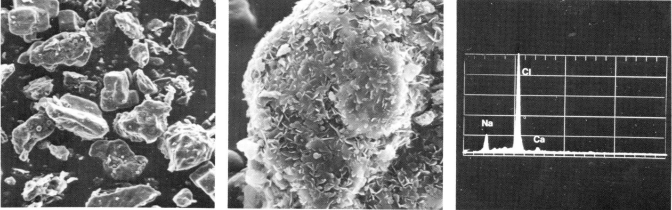

866   Garlic Salt—At low magnification, the basic feature observed is the cubic morphology of the base, common salt (*salt dust* [336]), frequently with rounded corners and other evidence of partial solution. At 1000X tiny platelets and needles are seen to cover the surface of the salt; these are particles of the garlic extract. EDXRA shows only Na, Cl and a trace of Ca.

10 mm = 100 μm   10 mm = 10 μm   10 mm = 1 μm

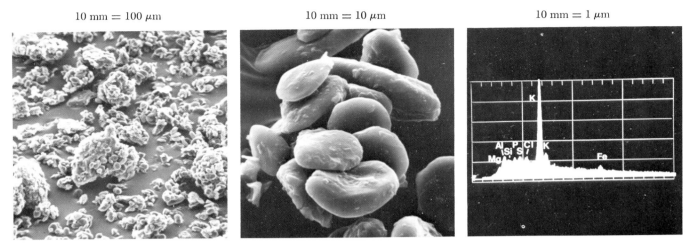

867   Ginger—These rounded grains are almost entirely aggregates of individual starch grains ranging in size from 15 to 25 μm across. Most of these starch grains appear flattened or collapsed (1000X). EDXRA shows a strong K peak with traces of Mg, Al, Si, P, S, Cl and Fe.

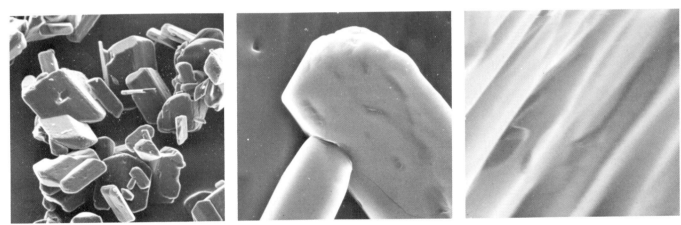

868   Glycine, $C_2H_5NO_2$—These well-formed crystals of aminoacetic acid exhibit the prismatic forms typical of many monoclinic crystals. Crystal sizes range from about 20 to almost 200 μm. Longitudinal striations are visible on some prism faces.

869   Jello®, Lime—The large, tabular crystal seen at 100X is even more typical of *sucrose* (*351*) than the ground crystals shown in *351*. The surfaces of the sucrose here are covered with many small crystals, some of which undoubtedly originate from colorants and flavorings.

10 mm = 100 μm   10 mm = 10 μm

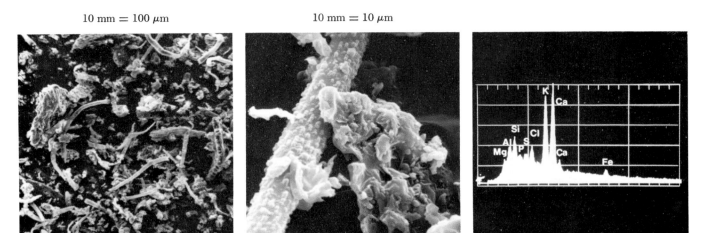

870   Marjoram—Derived by grinding of the leaves, this aromatic mint shows a variety of leaf tissue fragments, including trichomes, conductive tissue fibers and collapsed cells. EDXRA shows high K and Ca with Mg, Al, Si, P, S, Cl and Fe also present.

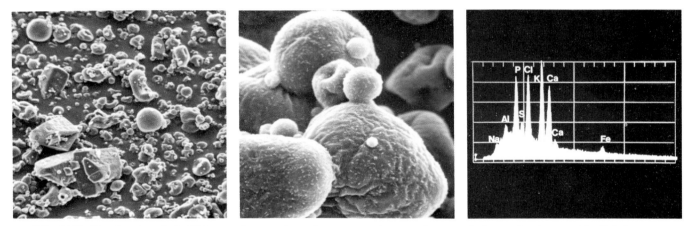

871   Milk Powder (nonfat)—This powder consists of two phases readily separated on the basis of morphology. The first consists of large, angular fragments and occasional tablets of *lactose* (322). The second is a typical spray-dried product occurring as spheres and distorted spheres with slightly rugose surfaces. EDXRA shows major P, Cl, K and Ca with lesser amounts of Na, Al, S and Fe.

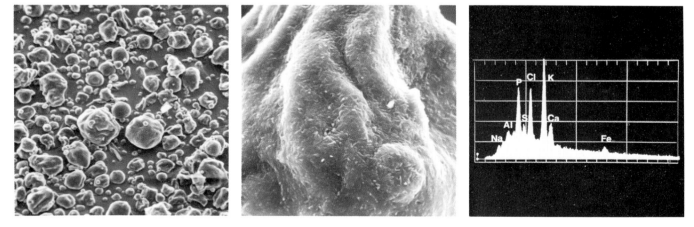

872   Milk Substitute—Almost identical in appearance to *milk powder* (871), this milk substitute shows fewer angular *lactose* (322) particles. EDXRA is similar in elemental makeup to that of milk powder but with a much lower Ca content.

10 mm = 100 μm   10 mm = 10 μm   10 mm = 1 μm

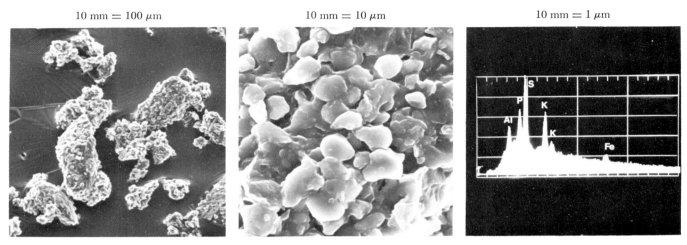

873 Mustard Seed—These irregular masses are composed of aggregates of small, 2–10 μm particles, some rounded, some irregular platelets. These are smaller than the collapsed cells seen in the powdered yellow mustard (*mustard* [329]). EDXRA shows Al, P, S, K and Fe.

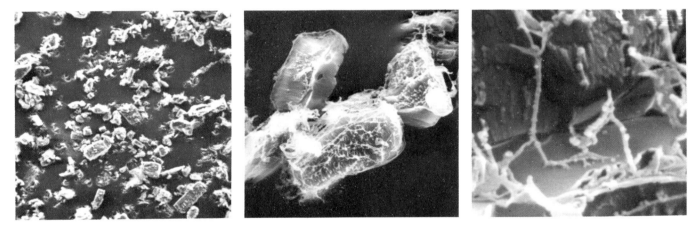

874 Niacin, $C_5H_4 \cdot NCOOH$—These niacin grains vary from sharply angular, almost tabular, to rounded in outline. When fractured they tend to do so conchoidally. The grains are covered with wispy nodular stringers, frequently branching. These stringers may be growths resulting from sublimation and recrystallization in the electron beam.

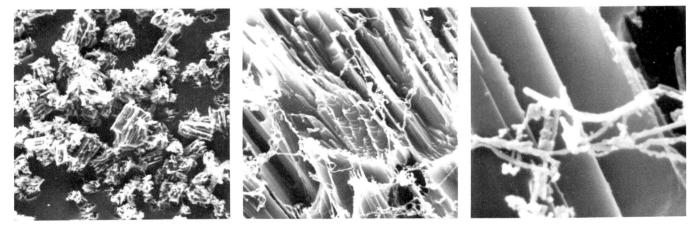

875 Niacinamide, $C_5H_4N \cdot CO \cdot CH_2$—Niacinamide is polymorphous, with four known polymorphs. The stable room temperature form gives the prismatic rods and tablets shown here. As with *niacin* (*874*), the surface stringers may be a sublimation-regrowth phenomenon induced by the electron beam as niacin sublimes at 150–160°C at a vacuum of 5×10^{-4} mm Hg.

10 mm = 100 μm   10 mm = 10 μm

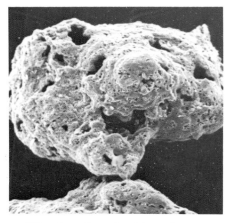 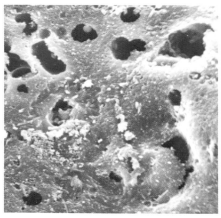 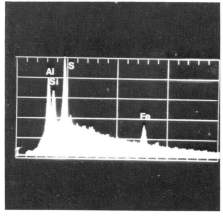

876 Oven Deposits—These deposits are typical of carbonized materials. Their irregular shape, relative abundance of vesicles and absence of V in the EDXRA spectrum help distinguish them from *oil soot* (556). The presence of high S indicates these deposits are from a gas oven.

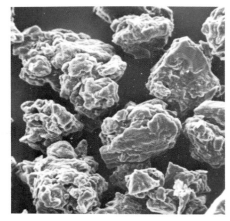 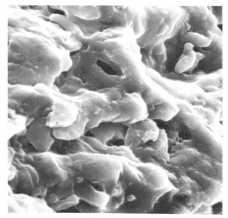 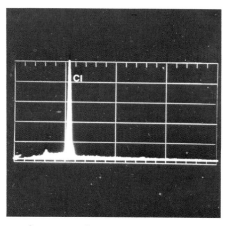

877 Paprika—These irregular masses derived from the *Capsicum* pepper show little evidence of their biological origin. Some evidence of cellular structure may be evident at higher magnifications, but no diagnostic features are observed. EDXRA shows high Cl.

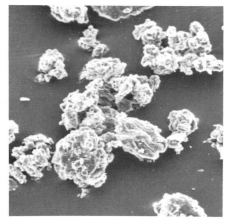 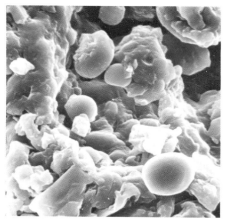 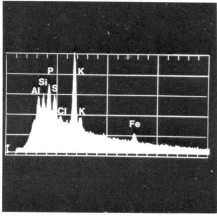

878 Peanut Meal—These aggregates derived from peanut kernels consist of spherical and near spherical starch grains, approximately 7–20 μm across, together with cellular tissue. EDXRA shows a high, organic background with high K and significant Al, Si, P and S peaks. Traces of Cl and Fe are also observed.

10 mm = 100 µm   10 mm = 10 µm

  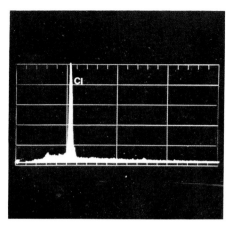

879 Pyridoxine Hydrochloride, $C_8H_{11}O_3N \cdot HCl$—Equant to tabular crystals, together with irregular aggregates of crystal fragments, make up this sample of vitamin B_6 (5-hydroxy-6- methyl-3,4-pyridinedicarbinol hydrochloride). As would be expected, Cl is the only significant element detected by EDXRA.

 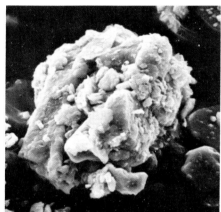 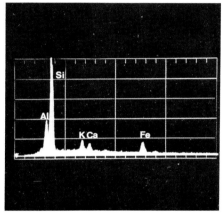

880 Raisin Cleaning Dust—Only by the fact that the source of this sample is known is it possible to identify this material as "raisin cleaning" dust. The sample is an assemblage of silicate minerals. Both morphology and chemistry, as indicated by EDXRA, suggests *quartz* (*183*), *feldspars* (*113, 176*), micas and/or clays. Such an assemblage might more correctly be identified as a soil.

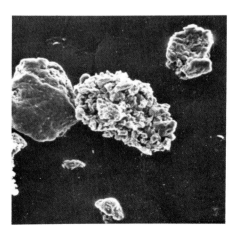 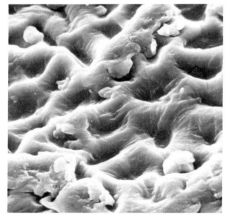 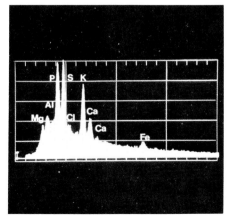

881 Rape Seed (*Brassica napus L.*)—These large masses are aggregate of cells from the inner seed. At 1000X, details of the reticulated cell walls are clearly seen. EDXRA shows high P, S and K with lower levels of Mg, Al, Cl and Fe superimposed on a high, organic background.

1584

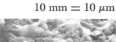
10 mm = 100 μm   10 mm = 10 μm

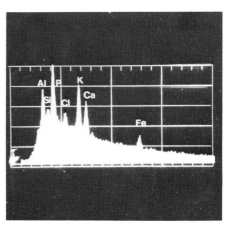

882 Rice Bran—The large, often ribbed fragments of *rice hull* (335) observed at 100X are seen at higher magnification to be covered with individual, spherical *starch grains* (346) about 2–4 μm diameter and larger granular aggregates. Some of the angular particles observed at 1000X are probably the *calcium carbonate* (133, 485) particles observed by light microscopy. EDXRA shows high P, K and Ca with significant Al, Si, Cl and Fe, superimposed on a high organic background.

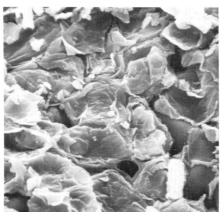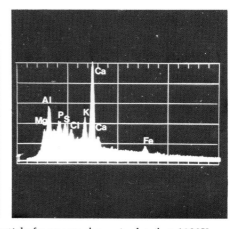

883 Savory—Derived from one of the aromatic mints, the ground particles of this spice show a variety of leaf parts, from the blocky, lignified fibers dominating the 100X micrograph to the fleshy cuticle fragments shown in detail at 1000X. EDXRA shows Mg, Al, P, S, Cl, K, high Ca and Fe on a high, organic background.

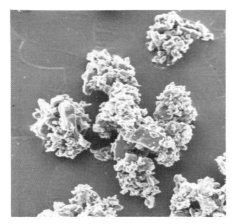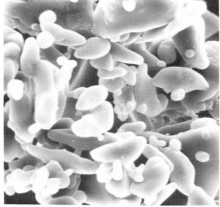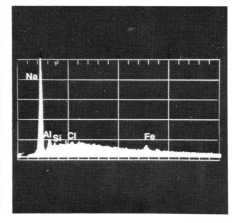

884 Sodium Citrate, $C_6H_5O_7Na_3 \cdot 2H_2O$—These 100–200 μm diameter aggregates are composed of individual crystals ranging in size from 2 to 20 μm. The individuals are generally rounded and tend to be platy. The rounding may be due to partial solution. EDXRA shows Na as the principal element, with traces of Al, Si, Cl and Fe probably instrumental or preparation artifacts.

10 mm = 100 μm   10 mm = 10 μm

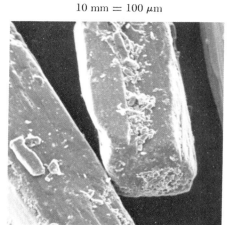  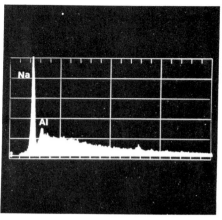

885 Monosodium Glutamate, $C_5H_8NNaO_4 \cdot H_2O$—These massive, monoclinic prisms show evidence of the perfect {001} and less perfect {100} cleavages of this flavor additive. EDXRA shows only Na other than instrumental artifacts.

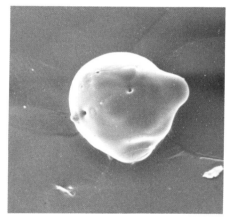 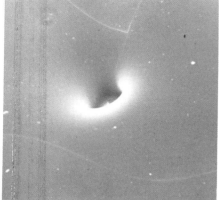 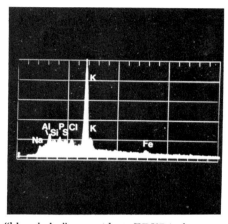

886 Tea, Instant—Morphologically similar to other spray-dried products, this sample is best compared to *instant coffee* (*861*). Here the particle size is larger and the shape more nearly spherical. Gas "blow-holes" are evident. EDXRA shows high K, as did the coffee. There are, however, differences in the trace elements observed.

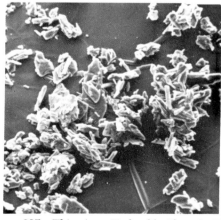  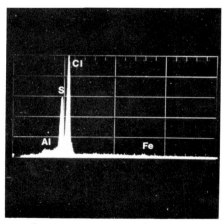

887 Thiamine Hydrochloride, $C_{12}H_{17}ON_4SCl \cdot HCl \cdot H_2O$—Prismatic and tabular crystals ranging in size from 5 to 50 μm constitute this vitamin B$_1$ sample. Longitudinal striations, possibly reflecting a cleavage plane, are common on the prismatic forms. EDXRA shows only S and Cl, as would be expected from the formula. The Al and Fe are instrumental artifacts.

10 mm = 100 μm

10 mm = 10 μm

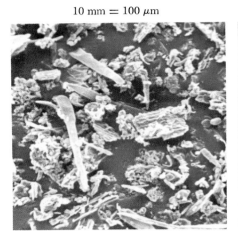

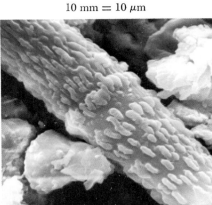

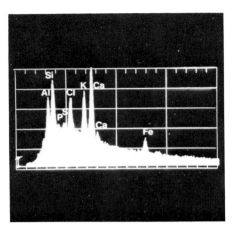

888 Thyme—The most characteristic feature of this crushed herb is the appearance of the decorated trichomes. As shown at 1000X, the 20 μm diameter trichomes are covered with an array of small, 1.5 × 5 μm spikes. In addition to the trichomes, the sample contains other leaf parts, identifiable by their histological features. EDXRA shows a high background with peaks for Al, Si, Cl, K, Ca, Fe and traces of P and S.

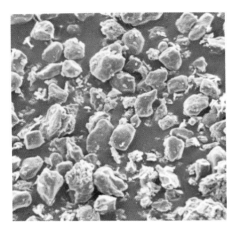

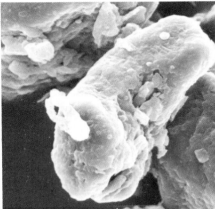

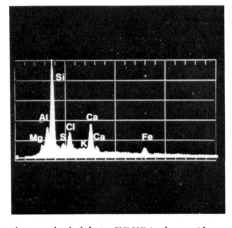

889 Turmeric—This condiment and colorant derives its intense, yellow coloration from the rhizome of the plant *Curcuma longa* which is crushed to make this product. Few histological features are visible in this crushed debris. EDXRA shows Al, high Si, Cl, Ca and traces of Mg, S, K and Fe.

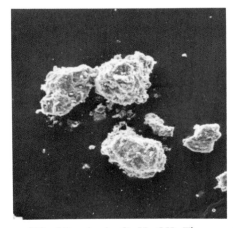

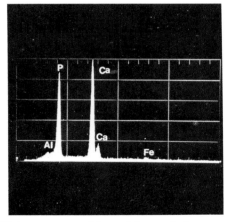

890 Vitamin A, $C_{20}H_{29}OH$—These grains are composed of both large and small crystal fragments. Many of these are irregular in outline but some, predominantly those less than about 5 μm, are angular and well formed. The presence of Ca and P in the EDXRA is unexpected but might result from dibasic calcium phosphate, used therapeutically as a calcium replenisher.

10 mm = 100 μm   10 mm = 10 μm   10 mm = 1 μm

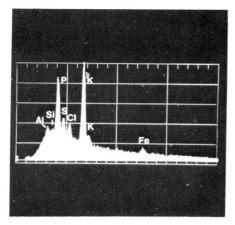 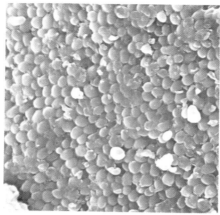 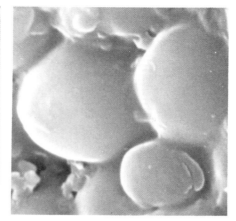

891 Nutritional Yeast—These yeast aggregates are composed of a multitude of spherical and oval particles with diameters in the 2–5 μm range. The particles have virtually featureless surfaces and appear to be bonded to each other (10,000X). EDXRA shows high K and P peaks with traces of Al, Si, S, Cl and Fe on a high, organic background.

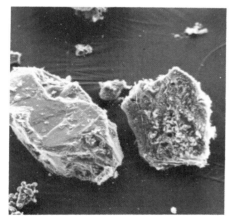 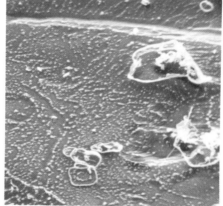 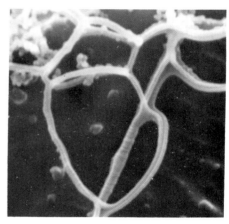

892 Aldrin—Produced in this case as a 1% solution in benzene and applied to an organic carrier, this Shell insecticide is 1,2,3,4,10,10-hexachloro-1,4,4a,5,8,8a-hexahydro-1,4-endo-exo-5,8-dimethanonaphthalene. As a result, the EDXRA (not shown here) shows only Cl. When applied to inorganic carriers, EDXRA would be expected to show principally the elements of those carriers. Morphologically, only the carrier is observed at low magnifications. At higher magnifications, small equant crystallites about 0.1 μm across and chains or webs of the dried insecticide may be seen on the carrier surfaces.

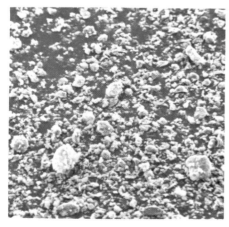  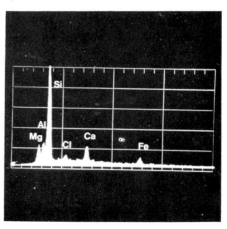

893 Chlordane—At all magnifications the inorganic carrier dominates the micrographs. Here the carrier is a mixture of *diatomaceous earth* (4–7) and unidentified clays; thus Si dominates the EDXRA spectrum, with Mg, Al and Ca also significant. Cl is present in the spectrum, but only weakly as the insecticide has been applied to the carrier as a 1% solution in benzene.

10 mm = 100 μm   10 mm = 10 μm   10 mm = 1 μm

 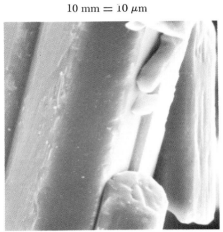 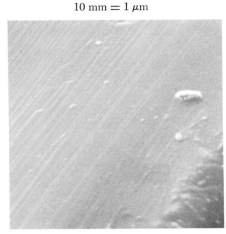

894   DDT (purified)—These elongated, orthorhombic crystals of purified DDT, 1,1,1-trichloro-2,2-bis(p-chlorophenyl)ethane, vary in size from a few micrometers to several hundred micrometers long. Striations parallel to their length are possibly traces of cleavage planes. EDXRA (not shown here) shows only Cl.

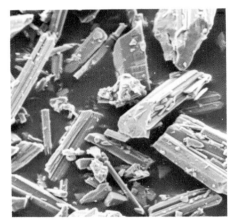  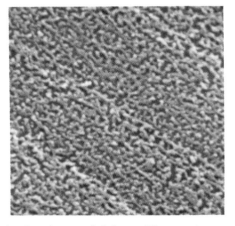

895   Dieldrin—This Shell insecticide has been applied as a 1% solution to an organic carrier. EDXRA, which is not shown here, shows only Cl, a major element of the chemical formulation, 1,2,3,4,10,10-hexachloro-6,7-epoxy-1,4,4a,5,6,7,8,8a-octahydro-1,4-endo-exo-5,8-dimethanonaphthalene. The carrier appears to be crystalline and, at high magnification, a very fine network structure can be seen in some areas, possibly of the recrystallized insecticide.

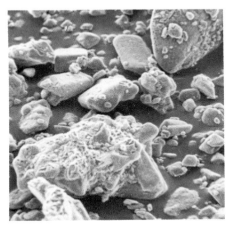 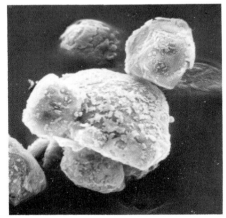 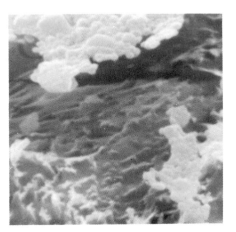

896   Endrin—Endrin, an isomer of dieldrin, is also prepared as a 1% solution in benzene applied to an organic carrier; it is the latter which dominates the micrographs. The carrier in this case is granular, ranging in size from about 10 μm to several hundred μm. Traces of a deposit, possibly the recrystallized endrin, are visible on the grain surfaces. EDXRA, not shown here, shows only Cl, the only element with atomic number higher than 11 in the chemical formula.

10 mm = 100 μm   10 mm = 10 μm   10 mm = 1 μm

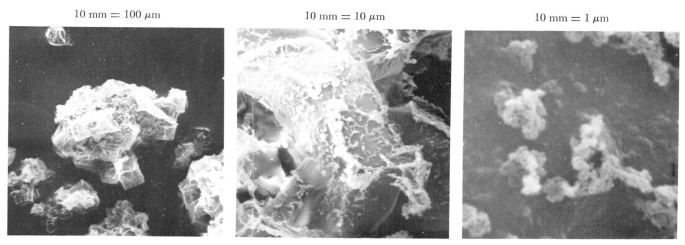

897 Heptachlor—The organic carrier to which this 1% benzene solution of heptachlor, 1,4,5,6,7,8,8a-heptachloro-3a,4,7,7a-tetrahydro-4,7-methanoindene, has been applied consists of equant, angular grains and aggregates of these grains. The surfaces of the grains at high magnification show the dried residues of the heptachlor solution. These residues are composed of aggregates of small, nearly spherical particles 0.1–0.2 μm in diameter. EDXRA, not shown here, shows only Cl.

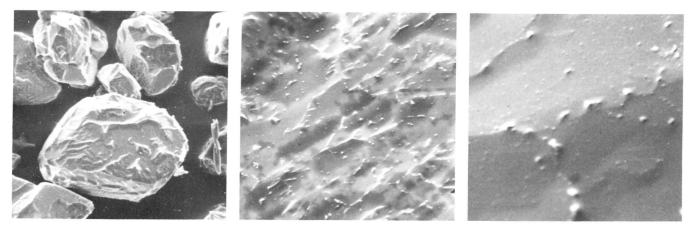

898 Lindane—This sample of lindane, γ-hexachlorocyclohexane, has again been applied as a 1% solution in benzene onto an organic carrier. The carrier in this case consists of large, 100–400 μm grains. Some traces of the lindane residue may be visible on the grain surfaces. EDXRA shows only Cl.

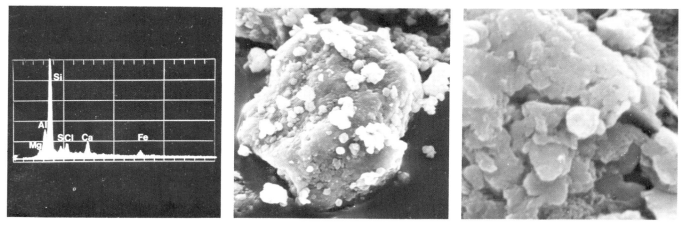

899 Malathion—The carrier to which this 1% benzene solution of S-(1,2-dicarbethoxyethyl)O,O-dimethyldithiophosphate has been applied is a clay. The typical morphology of the clay particles is thus the only feature visible in the micrographs. EDXRA is also dominated by the clay, with high Si, moderate Al and Ca and some Mg. S and Cl show in the EDXRA but P, present in the malathion formula, is barely distinguishable as a shoulder on the dominant Si peak.

10 mm = 100 μm   10 mm = 10 μm   10 mm = 1 μm

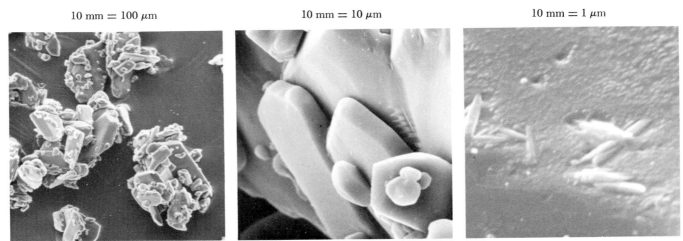

900 Methoxychlor—In this sample the methoxychlor has been applied as a 1% solution in benzene to an organic carrier; it is the morphology of this carrier which dominates these micro-graphs. At the highest magnification, thin, 1 μm long, needle-shaped crystals (which may be the methoxychlor) are seen on the surface of the tabular host crystals.

10 mm = 10 μm   15 mm = 1 μm

901 Aluminum Recovery

The large particle shown in the SEM micrograph is an agglomeration of submicrometer particles. The TEM micrograph also suggests agglomeration. The probable composition is aluminum, aluminum oxide and calcium sulfate. The calcium sulfate is from the oil soot particles that accompany the sample.

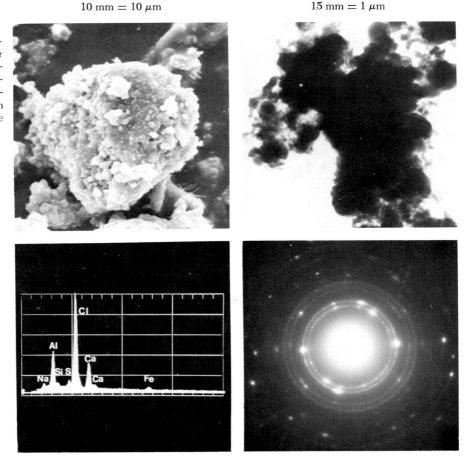

902 Brass Melting Furnace

The particles shown in the SEM micrograph
have an earthlike appearance and are made
up of submicrometer particles. The EDXRA
shows predominantly Zn, Cu, Pb or S, and
Fe. The very small particles are probably
ZnO, *zincite* (*211*), formed by precipitation.

903 Brass Pouring Dust

The particles shown in the SEM micrograph have an earthlike appearance similar
to *902* and are predominantly composed of
ZnO, *zincite* (*211*). The EDXRA shows Zn,
Al and Fe; the last two elements may be
from the instrument.

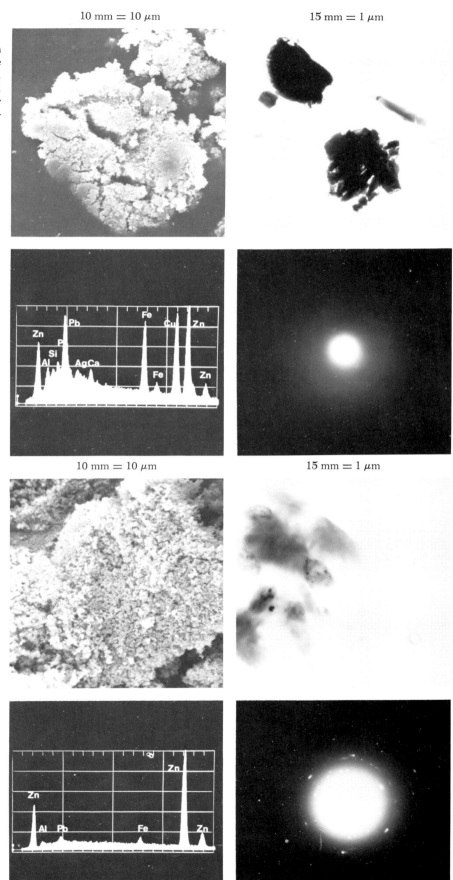

10 mm = 10 μm

15 mm = 1 μm

904 Brass Slag

Thin flakes, which can be seen in both the SEM and TEM micrographs, are characteristic of this sample. These flakes are impurities that are skimmed off the top of the molten brass. The EDXRA shows a composition of Cu, Zn, Pb and/or S and some Fe.

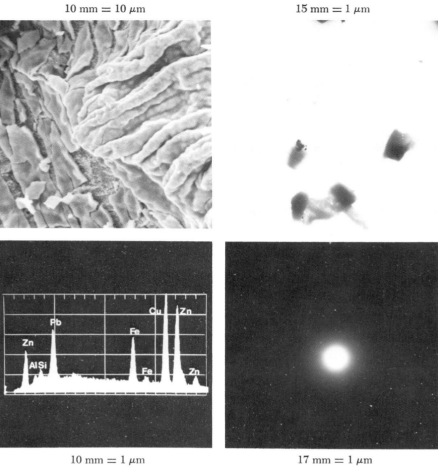

10 mm = 1 μm

17 mm = 1 μm

905 Copper Smelting

The sample shows the typical smelting assemblage of volatile metals and metal oxides. Zinc and lead sulfides commonly occur in copper sulfide ores. When smelted, these elements form volatile oxides such as ZnO and PbO. The large, flat plates are ZnO, *zincite* (211). The EDXRA shows Zn, Pb and S, and some Fe. The Fe may be an instrumental artifact.

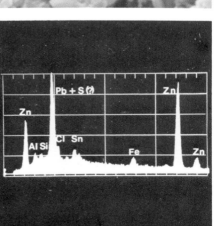

10 mm = 10 μm 12 mm = 1 μm

906 Copper Crusher Residue

The SEM shows angular fragments of quartz and also some clay mineral flakes. The minerals are typical of ore residues after crushing. Feldspars are also present as evidenced in the optical studies and EDXRA. The TEM shows angular grains which may be quartz. The EDXRA shows high Al and Si. The peak for Pb may also be S, and the Fe may be from the instrument.

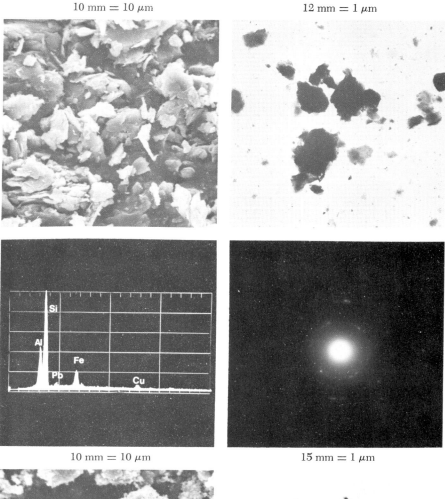

10 mm = 10 μm 15 mm = 1 μm

907 Foundry Dust

The SEM micrograph shows iron and iron oxide particles. These are made up of agglomerates of very small submicron particles that can be seen in the TEM micrograph. There is a large number of elements present in the EDXRA spectrum. Fe predominates with Al and Si. The Pb may also be S because the peaks overlap. Ca is from the calcite.

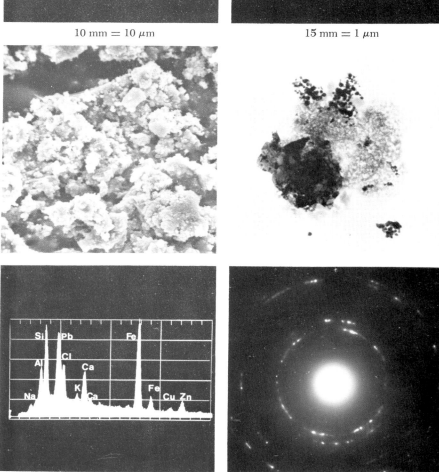

10 mm = 10 μm   12 mm = 1 μm

908   Galvanizing Kettle

This sample is from the iron kettle that is used for galvanizing steel. Euhedral crystals of zinc chloride are seen in this SEM micrograph. The chlorine comes from the NH₄Cl which is used as a flux in the process. EDXRA shows Cl, Fe and Zn.

10 mm = 1 μm   17 mm = 1 μm

909   Gray Iron Cupola

The submicrometer particles of iron oxide can readily be seen in this SEM micrograph. The EDXRA shows high Fe, Zn, Pb or S, Si and other elements typical of a foundry environment. The sample was collected above a cupola via baghouse equipment.

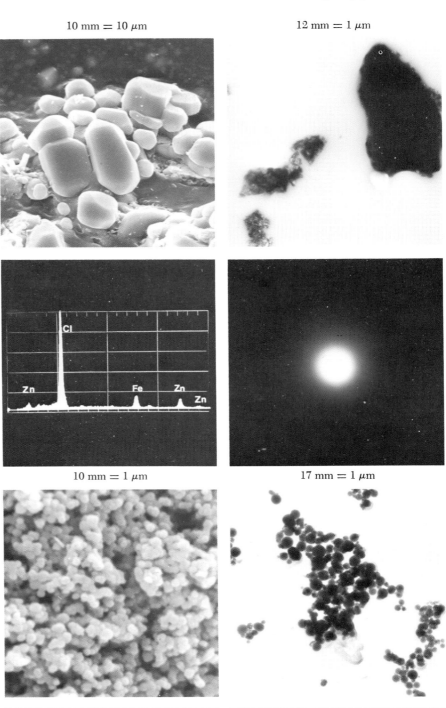

10 mm = 10 μm

15 mm = 1 μm

910   Lead Smelter #2035

The dust from a lead smelting blast furnace is seen here. The SEM micrograph shows large, irregular particles of *calcite* (*133*) and feldspar and smaller spherical particles of lead and iron oxides (*hematite* [*390*]). The EDXRA shows high Pb and S and moderate amounts of Al, Si, Ca, Fe, Cu and Zn. The Pb and S have nearly the same energy and are not resolvable in the EDXRA readout. (See page 578 of Volume III.) Previous x-ray diffraction analyses show the percentage composition was 75% PbS, 5% PbSO$_4$ and 20% ZnS.

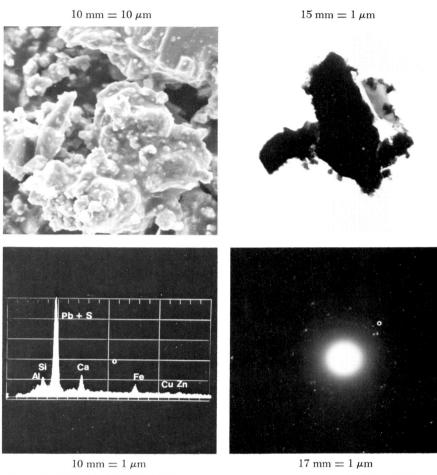

10 mm = 1 μm

17 mm = 1 μm

911   Lead Smelter #2091

The SEM micrograph shows submicrometer particles of lead and zinc oxides (*zincite* [*211*]). EDXRA shows high Pb and S, Zn and other elements typical of a smelter environment. An earlier x-ray diffraction analysis showed the percentage composition to be 10% Pb, 3% PbS, 5% PbSO$_4$, 72% ZnO and 5% ZnS.

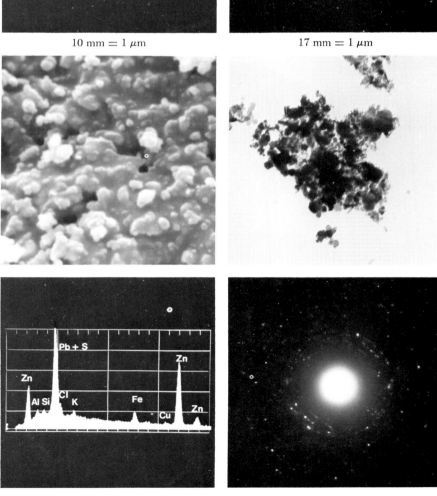

10 mm = 10 μm   15 mm = 1 μm

912   Lead Smelter #3083

Lead and lead sulfide particles are the predominant feature of this sample. Some very small calcite fragments may also be seen. The EDXRA shows high Pb and S and lesser amounts of Zn, Al, Si, Cl and K. X-ray diffraction done previously shows a percentage composition of 35% Pb and 65% PbS.

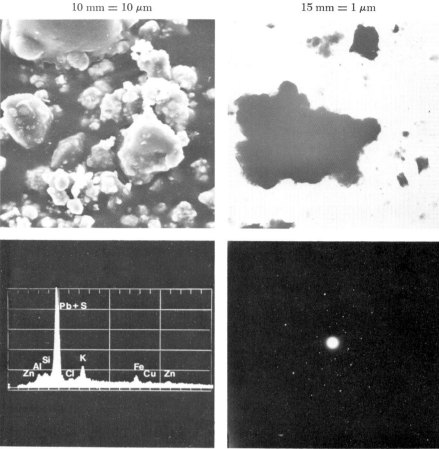

10 mm = 1 μm   15 mm = 1 μm

913   Lead Smelter #3090

The sample is predominantly Zn and ZnO plus Pb and S. Iron oxide also occurs in small amounts. EDXRA shows high Zn and moderate amounts of Al, Pb and Cl. A fibrous mineral may also be seen. Previous x-ray diffraction analysis gave a composition of 10% Pb, 5% $PbSO_4$, 55% ZnO, 5% ZnS and 25% $CaSO_4$.

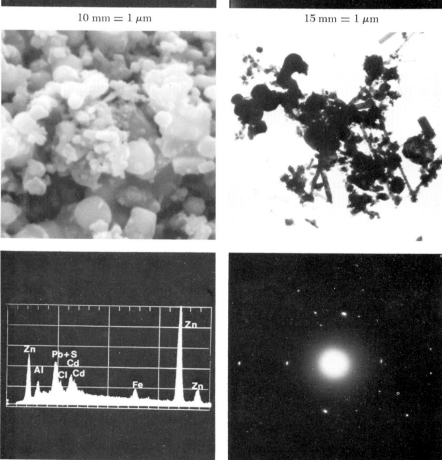

10 mm = 100 μm   10 mm = 10 μm   10 mm = 1 μm

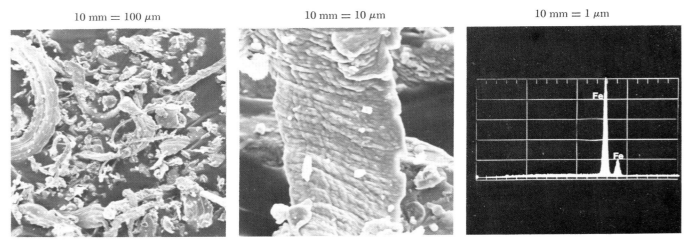

914 Metal Finish Belt Dust—The abraded nature of the iron particles in the SEM micrographs suggests a machining process. The sample is from an automobile assembly plant. The EDXRA shows only iron which indicates a malleable iron rather than a steel.

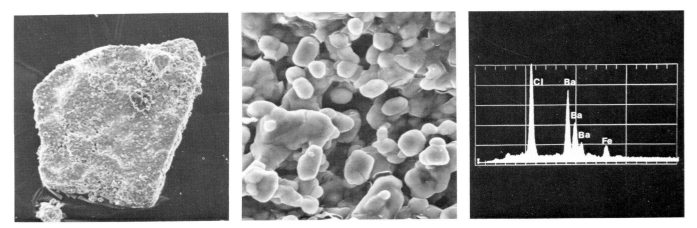

915 Metal Heat-Treating Salts—Somewhat rounded crystals of monoclinic barium chloride can be seen in the SEM micrographs. Barium chloride is used in heat-treating to control the heating and cooling rates of metal parts. The parts are immersed in a bath of molten barium chloride to control hardness and ductility. The EDXRA shows Ba, Cl and Fe.

916 Molybdenum Roaster—The two components seen in the SEM micrographs are molybdenite (MoS_2) and molybdenum oxide (Mo_2O_5). The molybdenite occurs as flat, platy crystals similar to graphite; the molybdenum oxide occurs as rod-shaped crystals. The EDXRA shows a peak for Mo; sulfur is also present but its peak is obscured by the Mo. Al and Fe are probably instrument artifacts.

917 Nickel Processing

The SEM shows a silicate mineral fragment with very small nickel particles adhering to it. The EDXRA shows a typical nickel ore assemblage where the major elements are Fe, Si and S. Nickel occurs in a relatively small amount because most of it was extracted from the residue seen here.

918 Silver Processing

The SEM shows an agglomeration of silver metal particles. The EDXRA shows a broad peak due to the superposition of other Ag lines.

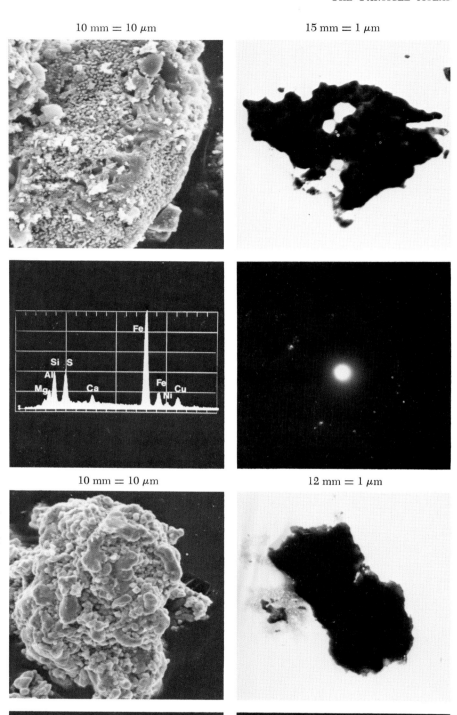

919　Smelter Stack

The SEM shows a cinderlike particle that appears to be made up of submicrometer particles that are fused together and/or sintered. The EDXRA shows a high sulfur content. This would be consistent with a sulfide smelter operation. Fe, Na, Al, Cl and K occur in smaller amounts.

920　Steel (basic oxygen process)

The SEM and TEM reveal spherical particles of iron oxide and iron metal. Calcium carbonate and/or oxide is also present. The EDXRA shows Fe, Ca and smaller amounts of Al, Cl, Mn and Zn.

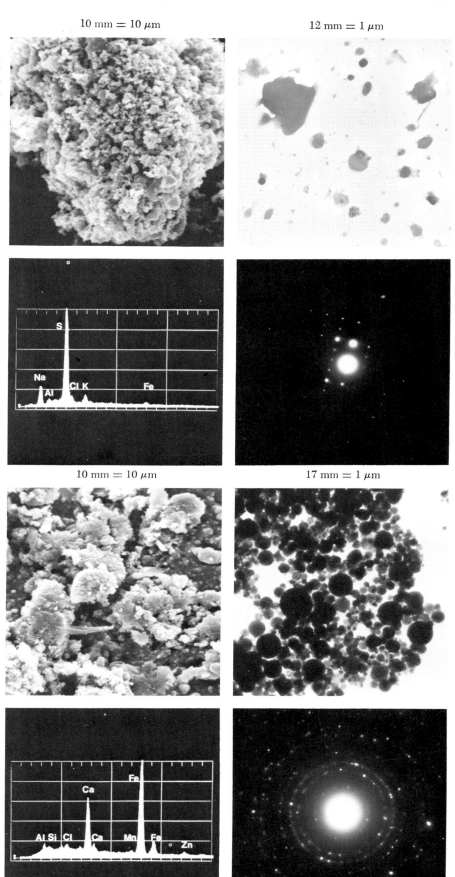

10 mm = 10 μm　　　12 mm = 1 μm

10 mm = 10 μm　　　17 mm = 1 μm

10 mm = 10 μm   15 mm = 1 μm

921   Steel (blast furnace)

The particle in the foreground of the SEM micrograph is iron oxide; the angular particle in the background is calcium carbonate. The EDXRA shows high Fe and smaller amounts of Al, Si, Cl and Ca.

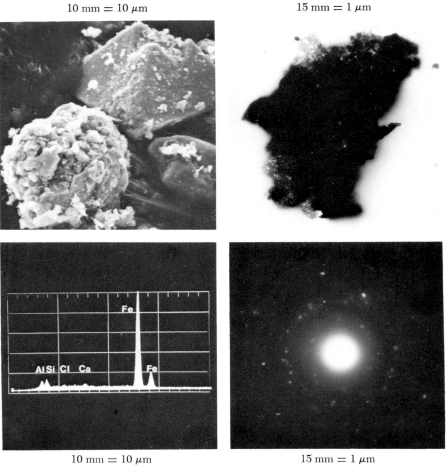

10 mm = 10 μm   15 mm = 1 μm

922   Vanadium Processing

The sample is a residue from a vanadium processing operation. The SEM shows a glosslike slag which is probably a calcium silicate compound. The EDXRA shows high Ca and Si and lesser amounts of Mg, Al and Fe. The Fe may be an instrument artifact.

923 Zinc Concentrate

A particle of zinc oxide (zincite) can be seen in this SEM micrograph. Zincite is the major component in this sample. The EDXRA shows Zn and also S in a high concentration. This may be from another mineral associated with the zinc ore, possibly sphalerite (ZnS).

924 Alizarin Lake, $C_{14}H_8O_4$

Alizarin, 1,2-dihydroxyanthraquinone, is precipitated as a red calcium lake in the presence of aluminum hydroxide. EDXRA indicates that this dyed, amorphous gel is a phosphated type. TEM shows that the submicrometer clusters seen by SEM consist of spheres typically 0.1 μm in diameter. SAED confirms that these are amorphous.

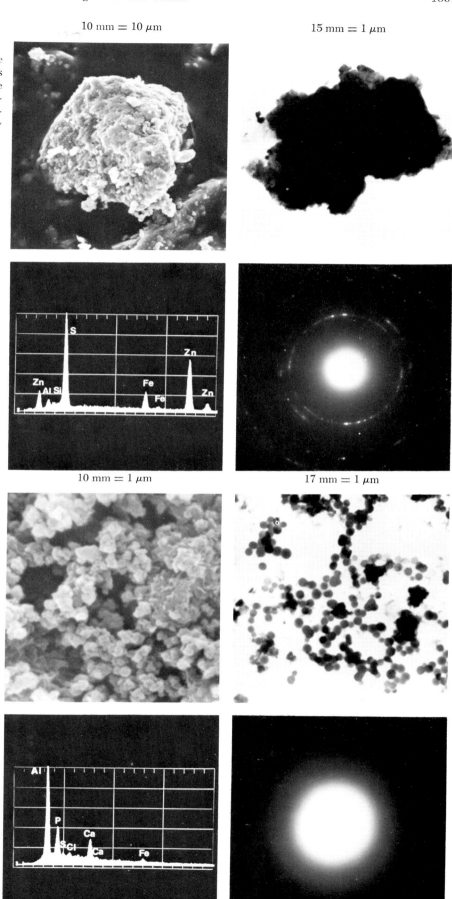

10 mm = 10 μm 15 mm = 1 μm

10 mm = 1 μm 17 mm = 1 μm

925 Anatase, β-TiO$_2$
   JCPDS #21-1272

Pyramid faces are visible on some individual crystals in the TEM micrograph of anatase, one of two tetragonal polymorphs of TiO$_2$. The other, *rutile* (*186, 448*), is also used as a white pigment. The 0.1 μm crystals form clusters averaging 0.3–0.5 μm in diameter. EDXRA shows a trace of aluminum from the sample support. (See also *672*.)

10 mm = 1 μm   17 mm = 1 μm

926 Aureolin, K$_3$Co(NO$_2$)$_6$·1.5H$_2$O

Aureolin, or cobalt yellow, is potassium cobaltinitrite. It has been used as a watercolor pigment since 1861. The TEM micrograph hints that these equant particles are crystals in the cubic system, and the SEM supports this impression, especially with the combination cube-octahedron at the upper center.

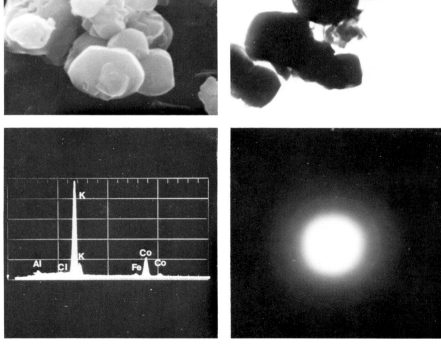

10 mm = 1 μm   15 mm = 1 μm

927 Bitumen (asphaltum)

Bitumen, a solidified tar obtained since ancient times from natural deposits, was formerly used in oil painting. Also derived from petroleum refining, it is soluble in oil and organic solvents. It is brittle, fracturing conchoidally to thin, sharp-edged flakes. In addition to high S, EDXRA indicates traces of silica or silicates, implying a natural origin for this sample, No. 4.04.4 in the Forbes collection. (See also 478.)

10 mm = 10 μm   15 mm = 1 μm

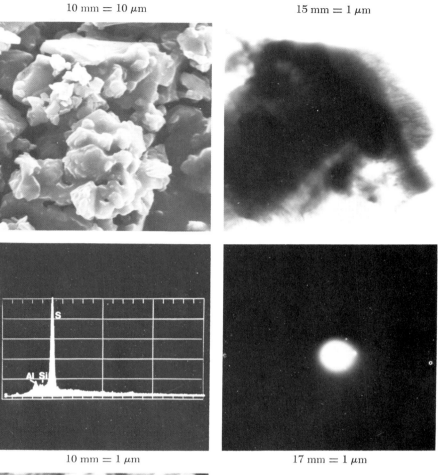

10 mm = 1 μm   17 mm = 1 μm

928 Cadmium Orange, CdS + BaSO₄
   JCPDS #6-314 and 24-1035

Hexagonal cadmium sulfide is coprecipitated with orthorhombic barium sulfate to form this cadmium orange pigment. By SEM the 0.05–0.2 μm CdS crystals are shown adhering to the surfaces of the 0.5–2 μm crystals of $BaSO_4$. Aluminum and iron in the EDXRA pattern are background artifacts.

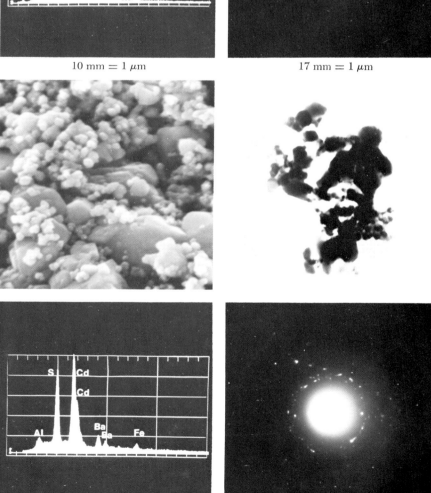

10 mm = 1 μm

15 mm = 1 μm

929 Cadmium Yellow, CdS + BaSO₄
    JCPDS #6-314 and 24-1035

Like *cadmium orange* (*928*), this pigment is made by coprecipitating cadmium sulfide with barium sulfate. Both components occur as larger crystals than in *928*; the CdS is about 0.2 μm in average particle size, and the BaSO₄ sometimes approaches 5 μm, too large to show a crystalline SAED pattern.

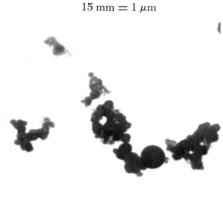

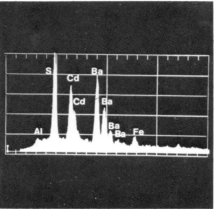

10 mm = 10 μm

15 mm = 1 μm

930 Calcined Bone, Ca₃(PO₄)₂
    JCPDS #9-348

Calcined bone (bone white), made by roasting animal bones, is mainly tricalcium phosphate. The SEM micrograph shows a coarse agglomerate with a spongelike surface to which box-shaped crystals adhere. The rhombohedral crystal habit of Ca₃(PO₄)₂ is not revealed. TEM indicates the porous microstructure.

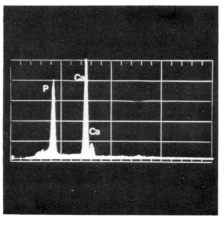

931 Carmine,

$(C_{22}H_{20}O_{13})_2Ca \cdot$
$xAl_2O_3 \cdot yH_2O \cdot zCaSO_4$

Carmine pigment is the aluminum, calcium lake of carminic acid, a natural dyestuff extracted from the dried bodies of female cochineal insects, *Coccus cacti* L. Markedly angular, 0.5–1 μm particles of the lake form porous agglomerates 2–15 μm in diameter. See also *scarlet* (958).

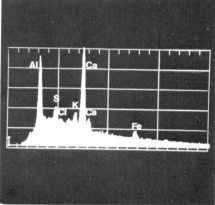

10 mm = 1 μm

17 mm = 1 μm

932 Chalk, CaCO₃

Natural chalk is a marine deposit of microfossil remains composed of calcium carbonate. The fossils, usually ridged and perforated button-shaped plates, are called coccoliths. In this sample from England's Dover cliffs, coccoliths such as the one shown by SEM are 2–9 μm across, with fragments as small as 1–1.5 μm. SAED shows off-axis hexagonal patterns. The sample also contains concretions of coccoliths and fragments as large as 75 μm.

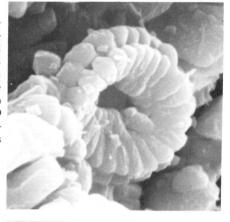

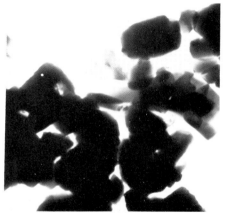

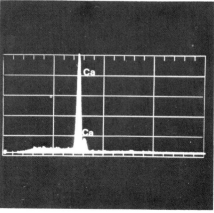

10 mm = 10 μm   15 mm = 1 μm

933 Charcoal Black

Charcoal black pigment contains clay and other minerals as well as wood particles in various stages of carbonization. SAED indicates graphitization of the 3 μm particle shown by TEM. SEM shows a larger particle, clearly recognized as wood by the pitted vessel element. At least some recognizable wood particles must be present to identify wood charcoal black.

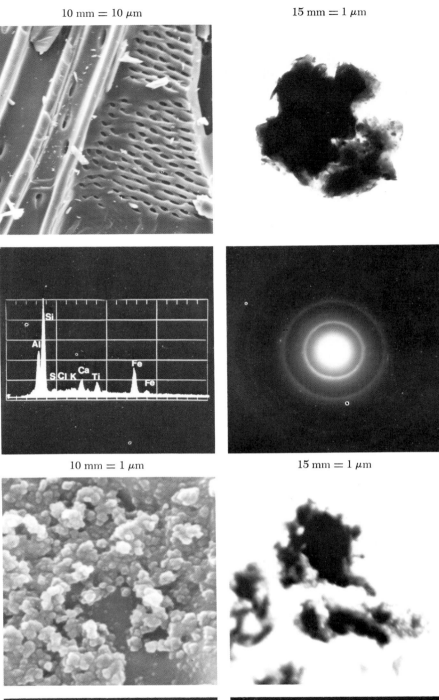

10 mm = 1 μm   15 mm = 1 μm

934 Cobalt Blue, CoO·Al$_2$O$_3$
JCPDS #10-458

Cobalt blue is cobalt aluminate, a blue color made by calcining cobalt oxide or phosphate with aluminum compounds. It became commercially available in 1804. SEM shows that the fine-grained texture observed by light microscopy is due to submicrometer grains fused to the surface of larger (1–50 μm) particles.

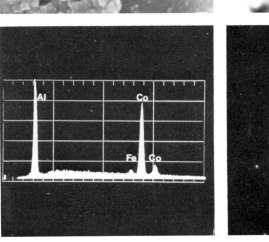

935   Cobalt Green, xCoO·yZnO

Cobalt green, a bluish-green pigment available since 1835, is usually made by calcining a cobalt salt with zinc oxide. The product, of variable composition, is considered a solid solution between CoO and ZnO. Rounded 2–5 μm particles make up irregular, fused agglomerates mostly no larger than 10 μm but sometimes as big as the 50 μm clump in the SEM micrograph.

10 mm = 10 μm   15 mm = 1 μm

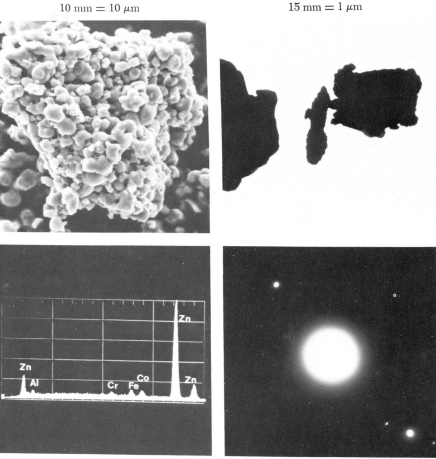

936   Cobalt Violet (dark), Co$_3$(PO$_4$)$_2$
JCPDS #13-503

"Dark" or "deep" cobalt violet is anhydrous cobalt phosphate made by precipitation, washing and heating. The pigment forms as thin, slightly angular, polycrystalline flakes, shown by TEM, which may form agglomerates up to 50 μm in diameter, as shown by SEM. Cobalt violet has been used by artists since about 1860. Cobalt violet "pale" is anhydrous cobalt arsenate, a toxic pigment not present in this sample.

10 mm = 10 μm   17 mm = 1 μm

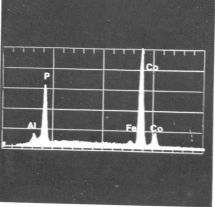

10 mm = 1 μm

15 mm = 1 μm

937 Chrome Orange, PbCrO₄·PbO
JCPDS #8-437

Chrome orange is a basic lead chromate.
This sample, from Winsor and Newton,
also contains a little strontium chromate.
The monoclinic crystals of basic lead chromate are seen by SEM and TEM most often
as rods, 0.1–0.3 × 2–3 μm, sometimes as
raftlike aggregates of these rods. Lead chromate pigments became commercially available about 1818. See also *chrome yellow*
(*439, 938*).

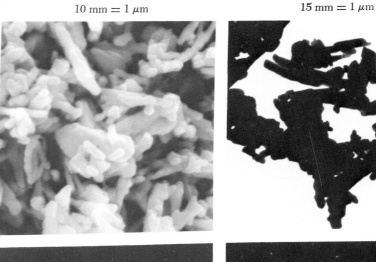

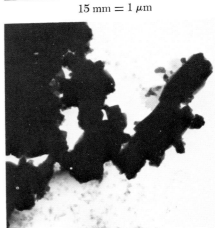

10 mm = 1 μm

15 mm = 1 μm

938 Chrome Yellow (deep), PbCrO₄
JCPDS #8-209

Pale shades of chrome yellow are solid solutions of lead chromate and lead sulfate; the
deeper shades are PbCrO₄ alone, a monoclinic crystalline compound. This sample
also contains a little strontium chromate
and is diluted with *chalk* (*932*). Pigment
particles appear as 1–2 μm tablets and 0.2–
× 1–2 μm rods. Some very small, thin
are visible by TEM. See also *chrome*
(*439*) and *chrome orange* (*937*).

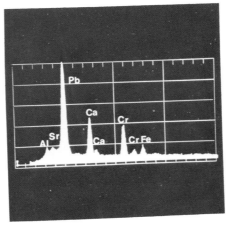

935 Cobalt Green, xCoO·yZnO

Cobalt green, a bluish-green pigment available since 1835, is usually made by calcining a cobalt salt with zinc oxide. The product, of variable composition, is considered a solid solution between CoO and ZnO. Rounded 2–5 μm particles make up irregular, fused agglomerates mostly no larger than 10 μm but sometimes as big as the 50 μm clump in the SEM micrograph.

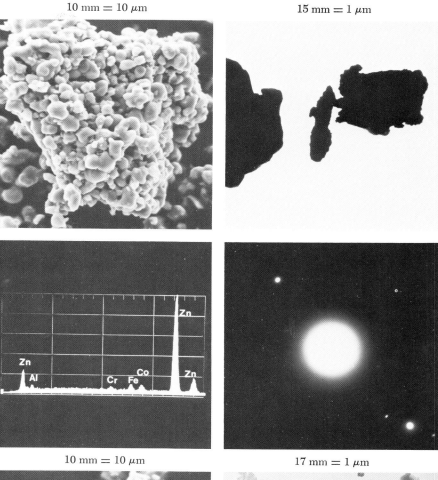

10 mm = 10 μm   15 mm = 1 μm

936 Cobalt Violet (dark), Co₃(PO₄)₂
JCPDS #13-503

"Dark" or "deep" cobalt violet is anhydrous cobalt phosphate made by precipitation, washing and heating. The pigment forms as thin, slightly angular, polycrystalline flakes, shown by TEM, which may form agglomerates up to 50 μm in diameter, as shown by SEM. Cobalt violet has been used by artists since about 1860. Cobalt violet "pale" is anhydrous cobalt arsenate, a toxic pigment not present in this sample.

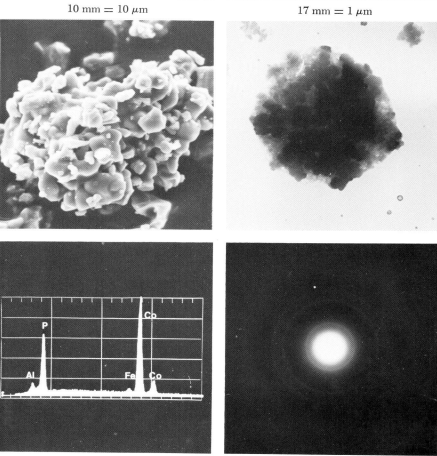

10 mm = 10 μm   17 mm = 1 μm

10 mm = 1 µm   15 mm = 1 µm

937 Chrome Orange, PbCrO₄·PbO
JCPDS #8-437

Chrome orange is a basic lead chromate. This sample, from Winsor and Newton, also contains a little strontium chromate. The monoclinic crystals of basic lead chromate are seen by SEM and TEM most often as rods, 0.1–0.3 × 2–3 µm, sometimes as raftlike aggregates of these rods. Lead chromate pigments became commercially available about 1818. See also *chrome yellow* (*439, 938*).

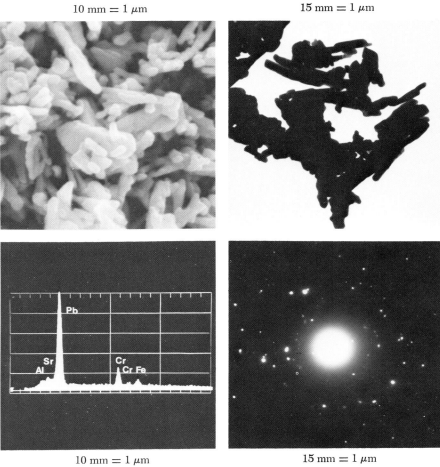

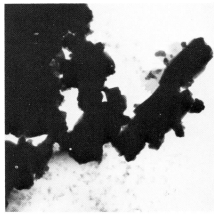

10 mm = 1 µm   15 mm = 1 µm

938 Chrome Yellow (deep), PbCrO₄
JCPDS #8-209

Pale shades of chrome yellow are solid solutions of lead chromate and lead sulfate; the deeper shades are PbCrO₄ alone, a monoclinic crystalline compound. This sample also contains a little strontium chromate and is diluted with *chalk* (*932*). Pigment particles appear as 1–2 µm tablets and 0.2–0.3 × 1–2 µm rods. Some very small, thin flakes are visible by TEM. See also *chrome yellow* (*439*) and *chrome orange* (*937*).

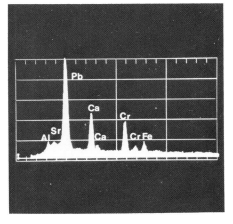

10 mm = 10 μm   10 mm = 1 μm

939 Chromium Oxide Green, Cr$_2$O$_3$
**   JCPDS #6-504**

Chromium oxide green is anhydrous chromium oxide, Cr$_2$O$_3$, not to be confused with Cr$_2$O$_3\cdot$2H$_2$O, usually called *viridian* (965). Cr$_2$O$_3$ crystals are hexagonal scalenohedral basal tablets or equant prisms with rhombohedral cleavage. Hexagonal crystal symmetry is not obvious in the 1–2 μm particles clustered in the SEM micrograph but is suggested by TEM. Cr$_2$O$_3$ was first known as an artist's pigment about 1862.

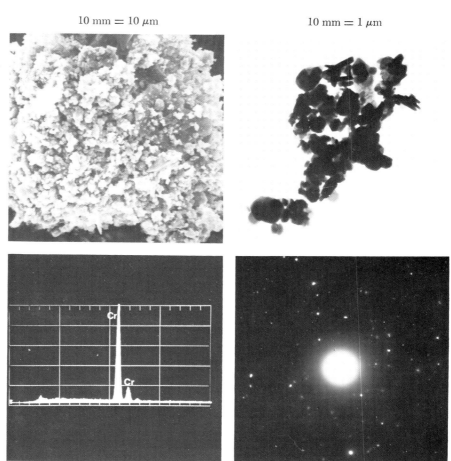

10 mm = 10 μm   10 mm = 1 μm

940 Emerald Green
**   Cu(C$_2$H$_3$O$_2$)$_2\cdot$3Cu(AsO$_2$)$_2$**

Emerald green is copper aceto-arsenite. It is also called Paris green and Schweinfurt green. It is very toxic. It crystallizes most characteristically as the coarse, leafy spherulites shown by SEM. Some samples do not contain such characteristic spherulites and may need chemical data for identification. Emerald green was first made commercially in 1814.

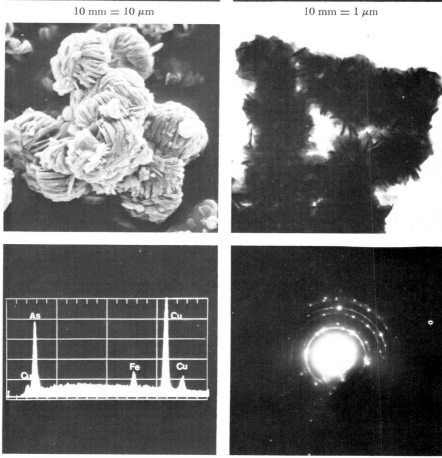

941   Gamboge

Gamboge is a yellow gum resin obtained from Far Eastern trees, especially from the Cambodian *Garcinia hanburii*. The EDXRA pattern is typical of a natural organic product. The rounded, crumbled-looking particles shown by SEM appear bubbly and porous at higher magnification in the TEM. Gamboge, known in China in the 12th Century, was first taken to Europe at the end of the 16th Century.

942   Indian Yellow, $C_{19}H_{16}O_{11}Mg \cdot 5H_2O$

The yellow synthetic magnesium (or calcium) salt of euxanthic acid has now replaced natural Indian yellow, an organic pigment formerly obtained from bovine urine. Prismatic or tabular crystals can be recognized in the SEM micrograph. TEM shows mostly finer particles and a few prisms.

10 mm = 10 μm   15 mm = 1 μm

10 mm = 1 μm   10 mm = 1 μm

943 Ivory Black, C,Ca$_3$(PO$_4$)$_2$
JCPDS #9-169, 9-348

Ivory black, known since classical times, is made by calcining ivory scraps to yield charred, but not ashed, ivory particles. Whether the crystals are regarded as *apatite* (*118*) or tricalcium phosphate (see *930*), they are principally hexagonal calcium phosphate crystals in a matrix of charred organic matter. Large, oval Ca$_3$(PO$_4$)$_2$ particles are seen mixed with thin flakes and numerous small particles 1 μm or less.

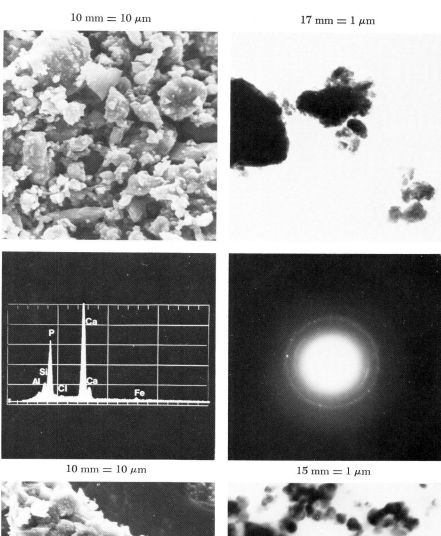

10 mm = 10 μm   17 mm = 1 μm

944 Jasper Green, SiO$_2$

Jasper is a colored variety of *chalcedony* (*135*), a cryptocrystalline form of SiO$_2$. This sample, Forbes No. 9.12.4, contains large particles, up to 100 μm, which by SEM look like quartz grains plastered together. TEM shows agglomerates composed of two or more submicrometer spheroids. SAED shows hexagonal symmetry as well as off-axis crystal orientations.

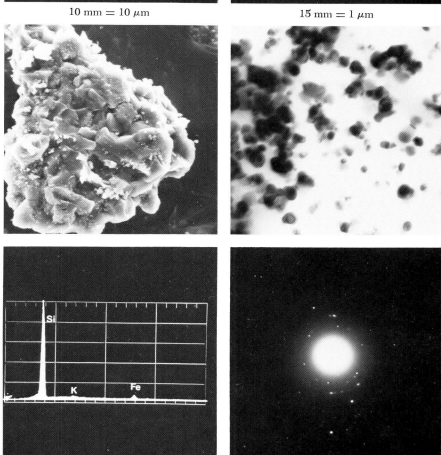

10 mm = 10 μm   15 mm = 1 μm

10 mm = 1 μm   15 mm = 1 μm

945   Lampblack, C

Lampblacks, manufactured since ancient times, have always been made by burning oil or tar in a restricted air supply and collecting the soot. Sulfur from the fuel is found by EDXRA, but the soot itself consists chiefly of 0.05–0.1 μm rounded particles of carbon. Characteristic chains of colloidal carbon particles are seen by TEM. See also *carbon* (370, 371, 372) and *coke* (*gas black*) (494).

10 mm = 1 μm   15 mm = 1 μm

946   Lead Tin Yellow,
Pb$_2$SnO$_4$ and PbSnO$_3$
JCPDS #24-589

Lead tin yellow is made by heating lead and tin oxides together. Depending on the reaction temperature, a tetragonal (Pb$_2$SnO$_4$) or a cubic (PbSnO$_3$) compound crystallizes. Both exhibit glassy fracture. Individual, <1–3 μm particles in this sample are often joined together to make 2–8 μm agglomerates. Many of the agglomerated crystals show distinctly angular profiles, especially by TEM. Lead tin yellow was used in painting from about 1300 to 1750, forgotten and then rediscovered in 1940.

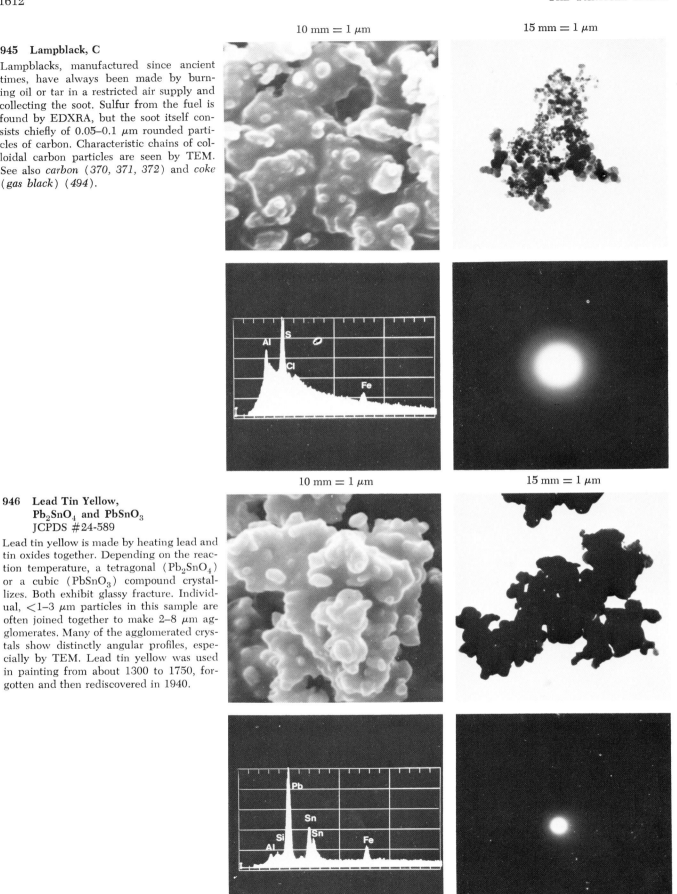

947 White Lead (Cremnitz White), $2PbCO_3 \cdot Pb(OH)_2$
JCPDS #13-131

Cremnitz white is a type of white lead which artists regard as superior to the Dutch process pigment. It is made by reacting litharge (PbO), instead of metallic lead, with acetic acid and CO_2. TEM shows well-crystallized, hexagonal basal plates about 0.5–2 μm across. Some plates, <0.5 μm thick, are seen sticking out from the agglomerate shown by SEM. See also *422*.

948 Lemon Yellow (deep), $BaCrO_4$
JCPDS #15-376

Both barium and strontium chromates are sold as the pigment, lemon yellow. This sample is $BaCrO_4$. It consists of two kinds of 3–10 μm yellow particles: single crystals, as orthorhombic prisms and dipyramids, and polycrystalline rosettes. Both kinds are well represented in the SEM micrograph. $BaCrO_4$ was first made in the laboratory in 1809. No date is recorded for its first use as an artist's pigment.

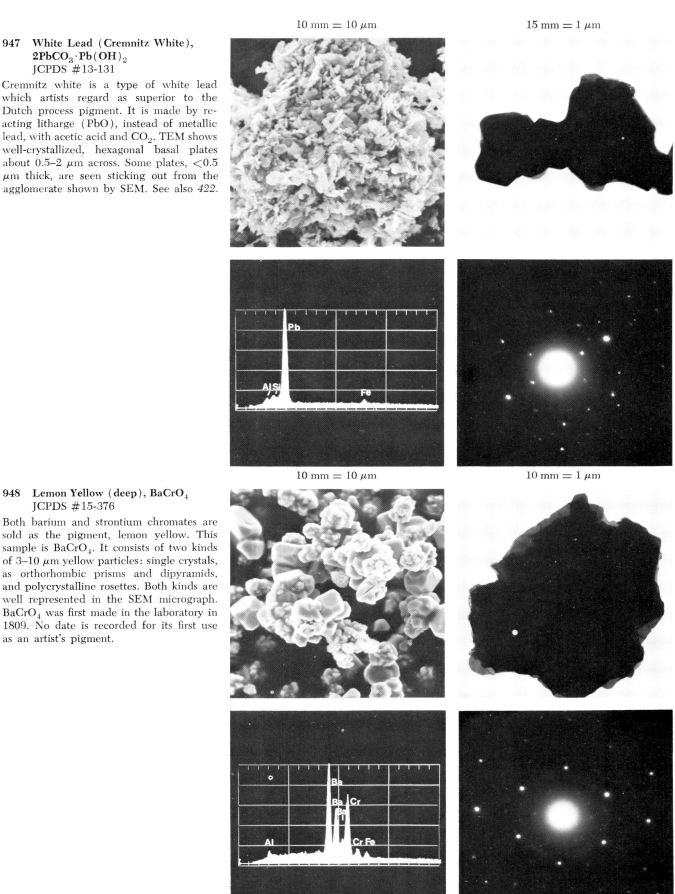

10 mm = 10 μm   15 mm = 1 μm

10 mm = 10 μm   10 mm = 1 μm

10 mm = 10 μm

10 mm = 1 μm

949 Litharge, PbO
JCPDS #5-561

Yellow lead monoxide is known in two forms, tetragonal litharge and orthorhombic *massicot* (*406*). Properties and appearance are so similar that they are best told apart by x-ray diffraction. Tablets and plates with rounded edges seen by SEM and TEM are typical of both these furnace products. This "litharge" sample, from Fezandie and Sperrle, is actually shown to be massicot by diffraction. PbO is now used as a drier, no longer as a pigment.

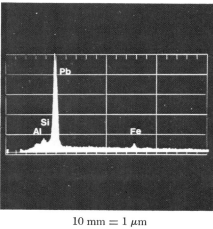

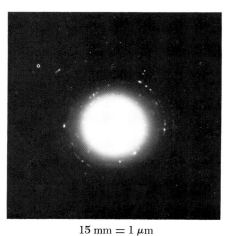

10 mm = 1 μm

15 mm = 1 μm

950 Madder Lake,
$C_{14}H_8O_4 + C_{14}H_8O_5 + Al(OH)_3$

Madder, extracted since Greek antiquity from the root of *Rubia tinctorum* L., contains two red dyes, *alizarin* (*924*) and purpurin. Madder lake is made by adding alum to the extract and precipitating with an alkali. The product consists of fine-grained flakes of dyed aluminum hydroxide up to 18 μm wide. SEM shows the surface with grain size 0.1–0.5 μm. Flakes even smaller than these grains are seen by TEM.

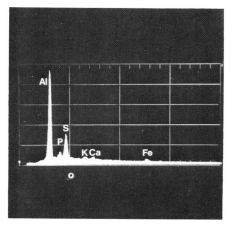

951   Mars Black, Fe_3O_4
      JCPDS #19-629

Mars black is magnetite, the magnetic oxide of iron, Fe_3O_4 or $FeO \cdot Fe_2O_3$. In this sample, 0.1–0.4 μm particles of the pigment are seen as cubic crystals (octahedra and rhombic dodecahedra), especially by TEM. Production of synthetic magnetite pigment did not become common until after about 1910. See also *165*.

952   Mauve, $C_{27}H_{25}N_4(SO_4)_{0.5}$

Mauve, the first artificial dye, was discovered in 1856. It is a mixture of phenazine dyes. This sample contains both magenta and blue dyes supported on flakes and rounded tablets of magnesium aluminum silicates as large as 25 μm. The dye particles themselves are submicrometer. Mauve is a fugitive color formerly used to dye cloth and still sometimes used as an artist's watercolor.

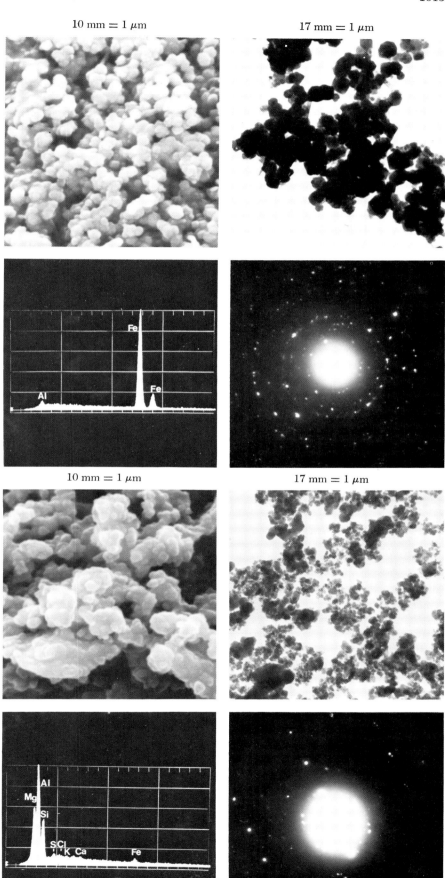

10 mm = 1 μm   17 mm = 1 μm

10 mm = 1 μm   17 mm = 1 μm

10 mm = 10 μm   17 mm = 1 μm

953   Orpiment, As$_2$S$_3$
JCPDS #24-75

Orpiment is an ancient paint pigment now
considered too toxic for use. These yellow,
monoclinic arsenic trisulfide crystals are
large, rectangular tablets with many <1–
10 μm surface particles. The latter are triangular or acute angled; some appear layered. The striated grid pattern observed on
the large crystals by light microscopy is
probably too coarse to be seen at 1000X
by SEM.

10 mm = 10 μm   10 mm = 1 μm

954   Pompeian Blue, CaO·CuO·4SiO$_2$

Pompeian blue, the modern equivalent of
the ancient synthetic pigment, Egyptian
blue, is a calcium copper silicate. Its glassy
fracture is well illustrated by SEM. The tetragonal crystal symmetry hinted at by the
TEM picture is confirmed by the SAED
pattern. This sample is No. 8.01.2 in the
Forbes collection.

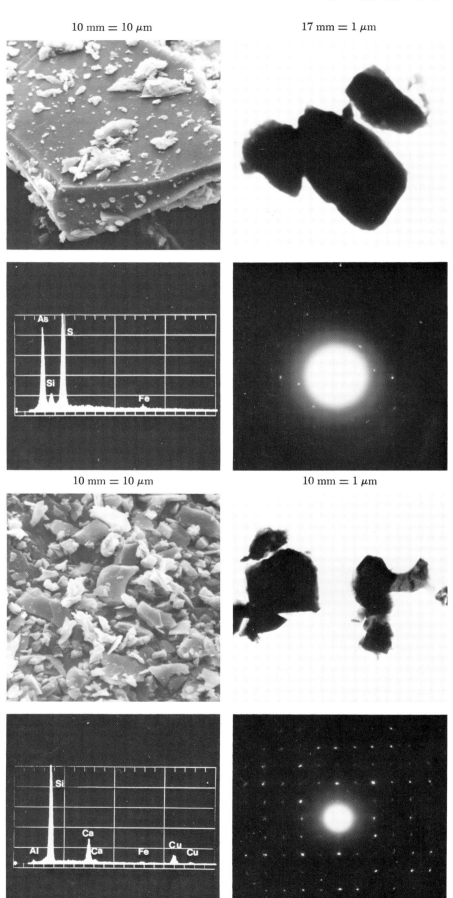

955   Prussian Blue, Fe$_4$[Fe(CN)$_6$]$_3$
       JCPDS #1-239

Prussian blue, discovered about 1704, was quickly adopted as an artist's color. FeNH$_4$ Fe(CN)$_6$ is now substituted for the original Fe$_4$[Fe(CN)$_6$]$_3$. The precipitated pigment is a very finely divided powder with particles of colloidal size, 0.01–0.2 μm, as seen by TEM. EDXRA shows that chromium is present and probably indicates that a dichromate was used as oxidizing agent in manufacturing the pigment.

956   Realgar, As$_2$S$_2$
       JCPDS #9-441

Realgar, the orange-red disulfide of arsenic, is an ancient pigment no longer used because of its toxicity. This sample, No. 5.01.3 of the Forbes collection, consists of coarse particles (up to 60 μm) with deep fissures illustrating the glassy fracture of this monoclinic crystalline compound. Irregular surface ridges are visible on some particles by SEM. Smaller fragments adhere to the large particles.

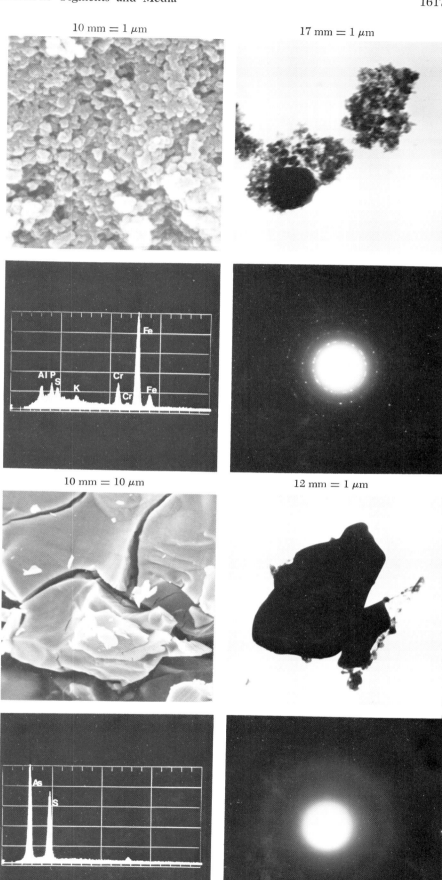

10 mm = 1 μm   17 mm = 1 μm

10 mm = 10 μm   12 mm = 1 μm

10 mm = 100 μm　　　　　　　　　　12 mm = 1 μm

957　Saffron

Saffron is a golden yellow dye extracted from the dried stigmas of *Crocus sativus* flowers. The color, now obsolete in painting, was formerly used in manuscript illumination. The micrographs show dried flower parts and fragments: rounded grains with shriveled surfaces and rectangular forms stacked together. EDXRA indicates natural organic material, perhaps with windborne mineral dusts.

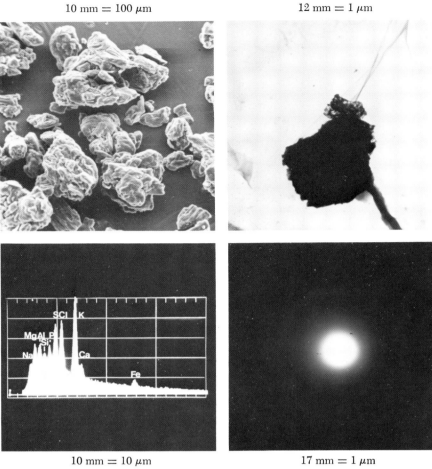

10 mm = 10 μm　　　　　　　　　　17 mm = 1 μm

958　Scarlet Lake

The natural scarlet dye extracted from the kermes insect, *Kermococcus vermilio*, dates back to Mesopotamia. It is now supplanted by synthetic dyes. This lake pigment, the potassium salt of an unspecified red dye, appears by TEM as thin, boat-shaped laths 1–1.5 μm long. Distinct profile angles are visible at the ends of most crystals.

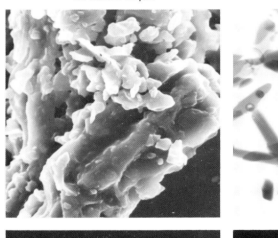

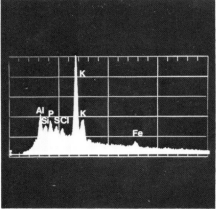

10 mm = 10 μm   15 mm = 1 μm

959   Smalt

Smalt, a ground potassium silicate glass colored blue by CoO addition, dates from 11th Century China. The conchoidally fractured particles are mostly <1–5 μm but include chunks up to 30 μm. Gas bubbles within the chunks are apparent on broken surfaces, *e.g.*, at right center of the SEM picture. Some 2 μm blobs decorate the otherwise smooth, glassy surface.

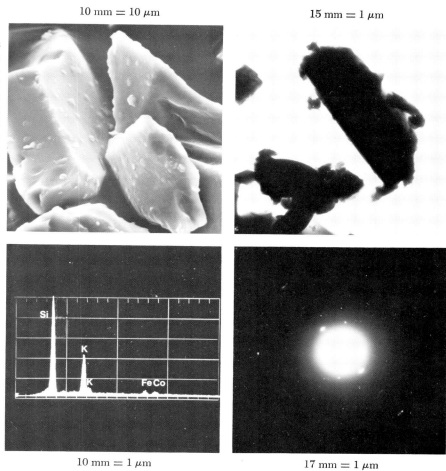

10 mm = 1 μm   17 mm = 1 μm

960   Terre Verte
     JCPDS #9-434 and 17-521

Terre verte, also called green earth, is chiefly glauconite with celadonite, both of which are monoclinic Fe, Mg, Al, K hydrosilicates of the mica group. The pigment is a weathering product of augite and hornblende, used from ancient times. The polycrystalline particles are composed mostly of thin, roughly rectangular plates stacked together. TEM shows flakes with very thin edges.

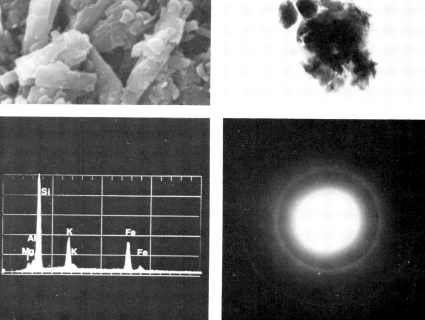

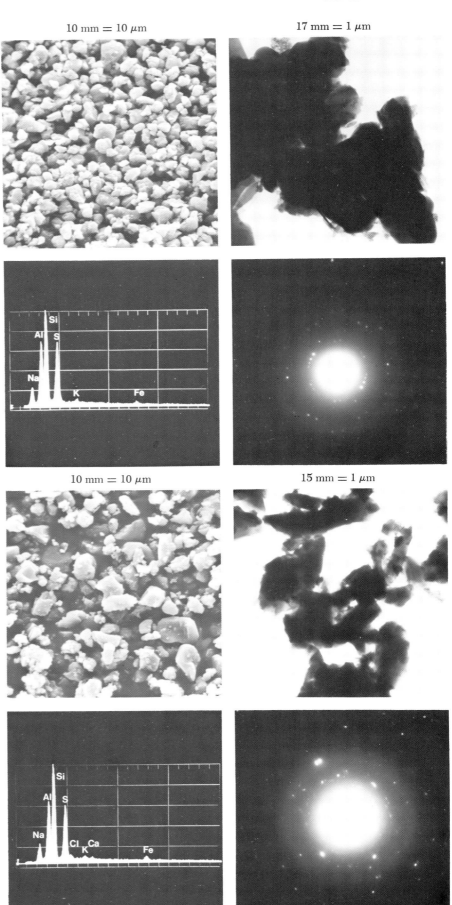

961 **Ultramarine, Synthetic,**
     $Na_{8-10}Al_6Si_6O_{24}S_{2-4}$
     JCPDS #17-749

Ultramarine is a cubic sodium aluminum
silicate made commercially as a furnace
product since 1828, gradually supplanting
the natural *ultramarine* (*962*) pigment
made by grinding the blue mineral, *lazurite* (*709*). The crystal morphology of these
equant particles is unclear by SEM, but
TEM shows faces suggesting rhombic dodecahedra and cubes. See also *449*.

962 **Ultramarine, Natural**
     JCPDS #2-325

Natural ultramarine is made from lapis
lazuli, a semiprecious stone composed
mainly of *lazurite* (*709*). Lazurite is chemically the same as synthetic ultramarine, but
the natural pigment, Forbes No. 8.02.23,
contains calcium and mineral impurities.
The equant ground fragments show the
poor cleavage of these cubic lazurite crystals. EDXRA shows high Al, Si and S, with
Na, Cl, K, Ca, and Fe also present.

963 Burnt Umber

A brown earth pigment available from earliest times, burnt umber was not used in Europe before the late 15th Century. It is made by roasting *raw umber (964)*. The umbers contain manganese oxide as well as iron oxides. The pigment particles are small, polycrystalline aggregates up to about 10 μm in diameter; they are composed of particles down to submicrometer size.

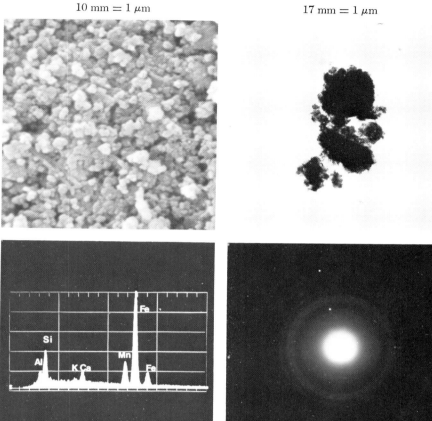

10 mm = 1 μm   17 mm = 1 μm

964 Raw Umber

Raw umber is a brown earth pigment containing manganese dioxide as well as iron oxides. It is widely distributed and therefore varies widely in composition and appearance. It contains other minerals as impurities, especially quartz and calcite. The size range is from <1 to 20–30 μm, greater than in *burnt umber (963)*. Raw umber, known from ancient times, was first used in Europe about 1500.

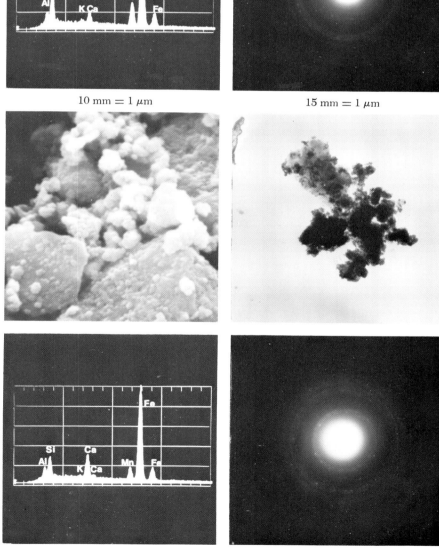

10 mm = 1 μm   15 mm = 1 μm

10 mm = 10 μm   17 mm = 1 μm

965   Viridian, Cr$_2$O$_3$·2H$_2$O

Viridian is also called transparent chromium oxide green to distinguish it from the "opaque" anhydrous pigment (939). The 1–10 μm particles are polycrystalline aggregates. The larger grains are rounded, the smaller are angular. The pigment became available to artists by 1862.

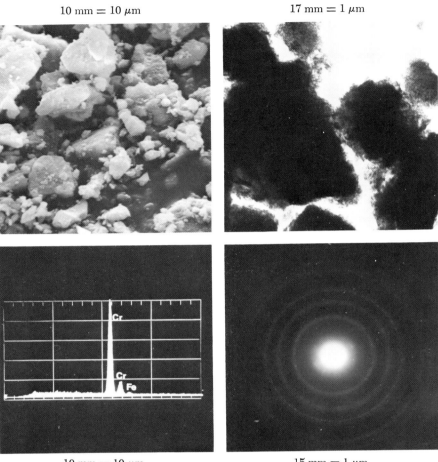

10 mm = 10 μm   15 mm = 1 μm

966   Whiting, CaCO$_3$

"Whiting" originally meant refined, pulverized *chalk* (932) but has come to include all finely divided natural calcium carbonates, whether from *limestone* (161), chalk, marble or *oyster shell* (524). This sample is chiefly ground *calcite* (133). Many of the 1–10 μm particles are rhombs. These hexagonal crystals are recognizable by both SEM and TEM.

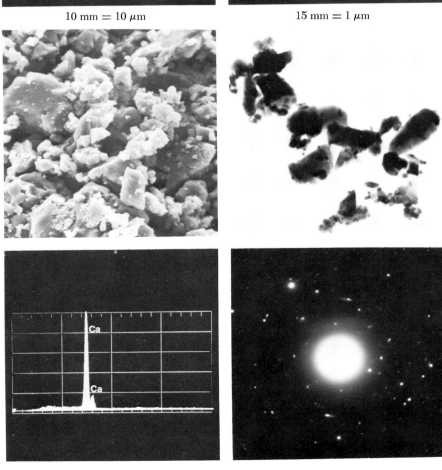

10 mm = 1 μm   15 mm = 1 μm

967   Winsor Blue, $C_{32}H_{16}N_8Cu$

This modern blue pigment, from Winsor and Newton, is copper phthalocyanine. It was discovered in 1928 and offered commercially in 1935. It is diluted with $BaSO_4$ (973). The monoclinic phthalocyanine crystals are <0.5 μm but form larger agglomerates. EDXRA suggests that the pigment in this sample is mixed with aluminum hydroxide.

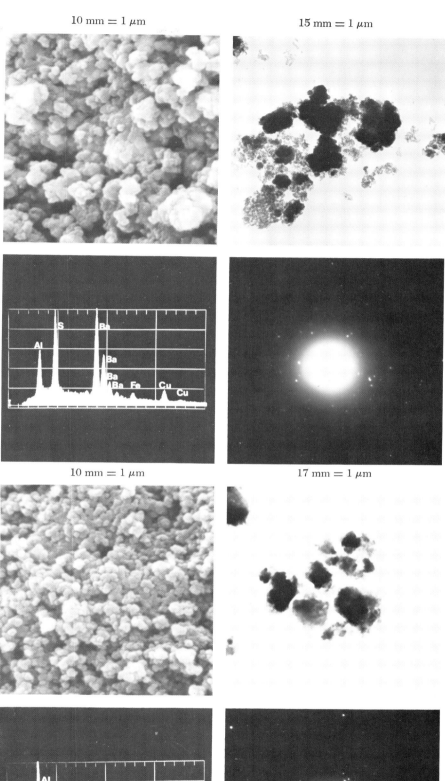

10 mm = 1 μm   17 mm = 1 μm

968   Winsor Violet

This modern artist's color from Winsor and Newton is made by absorbing an organic violet dye (unspecified) on gelatinous aluminum hydroxide. The smallest gel particles, about 0.05 μm across, have formed agglomerates up to 10 μm. Sulfur detected by EDXRA probably represents residual sulfate from gel manufacture. $CaCO_3$ may also be present.

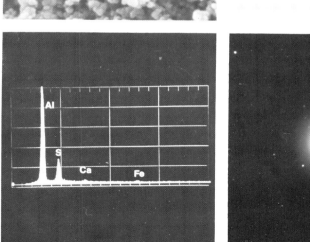

969 Winsor Lemon

This modern artist's color from Winsor and Newton consists of an unspecified yellow organic pigment with barium sulfate as an extender. TEM shows well-formed ortho-rhombic crystals of $BaSO_4$ in clumps; the individual crystals are 0.05–0.5 μm. SEM shows larger crystals covered with these small ones. By XRD the only crystalline component is $BaSO_4$.

970 Yellow Ochre

Ochres are natural earth colors consisting of anhydrous and hydrated iron oxides, silica and clays. Yellow ochre may contain several hydrated iron oxides, especially *goethite (701)*, $Fe_2O_3 \cdot H_2O$. TEM shows the general mixture of minerals. Prisms of goethite, 1–2 μm long, are visible by SEM. Yellow ochre has been used worldwide from antiquity to the present.

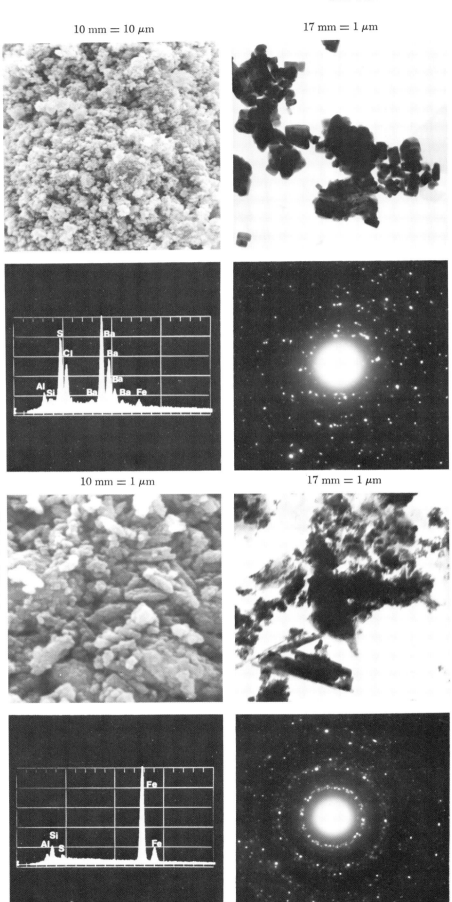

10 mm = 10 μm

17 mm = 1 μm

10 mm = 1 μm

17 mm = 1 μm

971 Zinc White, ZnO
JCPDS #21-1486

Zinc oxide is manufactured by burning zinc ores or metal in an oxidizing atmosphere. The collected fumes consist of stubby hexagonal prisms, mostly 1–2 μm long. A few acicular crystals are also shown by TEM, and occasional skeletal fragments shaped like Y's or boomerangs are seen by SEM. Winsor and Newton introduced ZnO as "Chinese white" for watercolors in 1834. See also *432*.

10 mm = 1 μm   17 mm = 1 μm

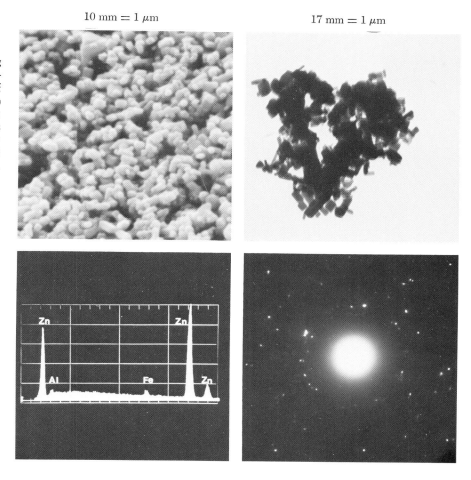

10 mm = 100 μm   10 mm = 10 μm

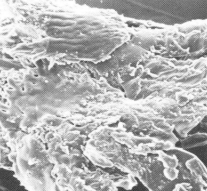  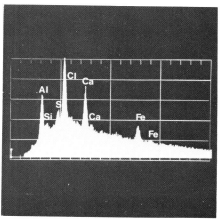

972 Animal Glue—Glue is impure gelatin extracted from animal or fish bones and tissue. It contains other proteins and sometimes inorganics. The dried thin flakes have smooth surfaces drawn into wrinkles. At particle edges the film is often stretched into several tongues, leaving perforations behind the leading edge. A few angular cracks appear.

10 mm = 100 μm   10 mm = 10 μm   10 mm = 1 μm

973 Paint Extender, Barium Sulfate, BaSO₄—JCPDS #24-1035—This sample of barium sulfate was produced as an extender for paint by grinding the orthorhombic mineral, barite. The size of these generally equant, columnar particles varies widely from <1 to 25 μm. Some tendency toward conchoidal fracture is evident in the micrographs. Al and Fe are due to instrument background. See also *barite* (129) and *barium sulfate* (480).

974 Copaiba Balsam—Copaiba balsam is a natural, water-insoluble oleoresin from the South American tree, *Copaifera landsdorfi*. As a painting medium it has serious flaws and is no longer recommended. It forms a thin film which can be cracked into small flakes showing conchoidal fracture with rather soft, occasionally rounded edges.

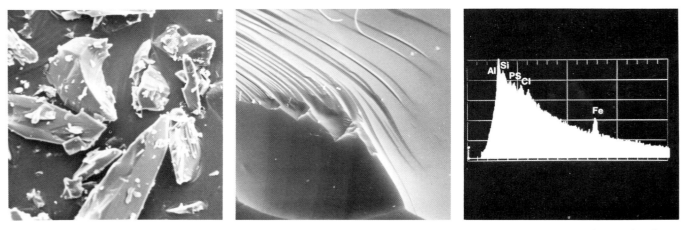

975 Copal Medium—Copals are hard varnish resins from various trees. The chief commercial source is Congo copal, an oil-soluble African fossil resin. The sharp conchoidal fracture of the dry varnish film, seen by SEM, shows the relatively brittle nature of the resin. EDXRA indicates an organic composition with mineral contaminants.

10 mm = 100 μm   10 mm = 10 μm   10 mm = 1 μm

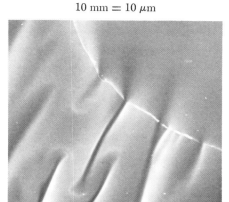
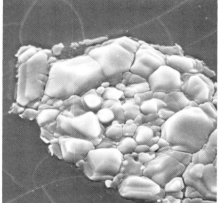

976 Damar—Damar resin, obtained from *Shorea wiesneri* and other East Indian coniferous trees, dissolves in organic solvents such as hydrocarbons and turpentine to form a clear, colorless solution useful as a picture varnish. The soft, draperylike contours of the dry film shown at the highest SEM magnifications characterize the conchoidally fractured edges visible at 100X.

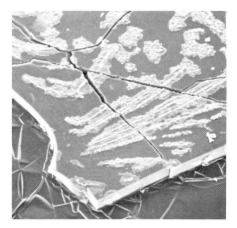
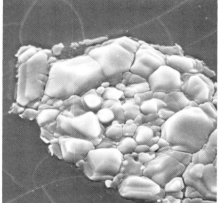
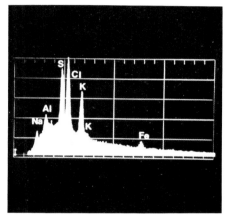

977 Dried Egg White—Egg white (glair) serves as a medium in tempera painting (see also *egg yolk* [978]). It dries, by loss of water, to a thin film composed mainly of albumen. SEM shows the shrinkage cracks and clustered polygonal crystals of NaCl and KCl which form as the film dries.

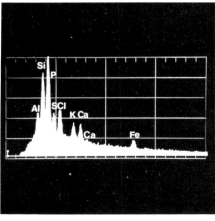
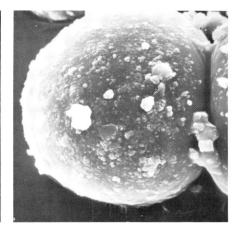
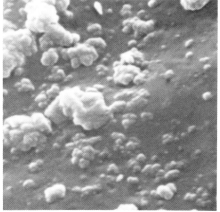

978 Egg Yolk Solids—Egg yolk, the chief egg medium in tempera painting, contains more fats or oils and less albumen than *egg white* (977). The EDXRA phosphorus peak is from lecithin, significantly present in egg yolk but not egg white. Egg yolk solids are droplets, single or coalesced, of oil globules and other constituents encapsulated in albumen.

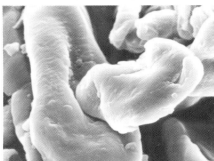

10 mm = 100 μm   10 mm = 10 μm

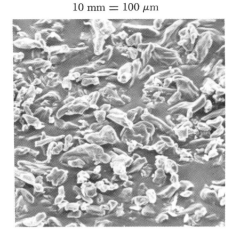
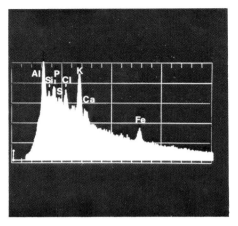

979   Guar Gum—Guar gum is a flour obtained by grinding the endosperm from the seeds of *Cyamopsis tetragonolobus*, a soybeanlike plant. It is a polysaccharide. The particles are irregular in shape but generally elongated and rounded, with hollows or cavities. Guar gum is used as a binder, size or thickening agent in many diverse products including paper, textiles, food and cosmetics.

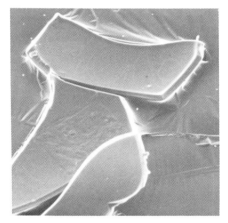
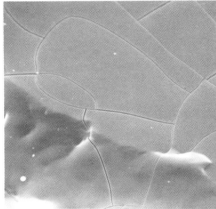
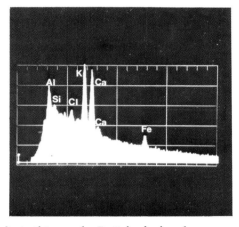

980   Gum Arabic—A natural, water-soluble vegetable gum produced from *Acacia* trees, gum arabic is a complex polysaccharide containing salts of organic acids—the EDXRA indicates K and Ca salts in this sample. Particles broken from a film of gum arabic show a pattern of shallow surface cracks.

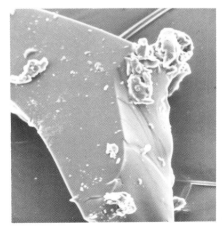

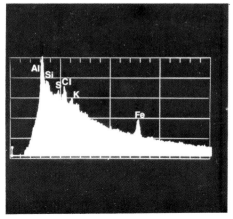

981   Linseed Oil—The chief vegetable drying oil used for oil paints, linseed oil is expressed from the ripe seeds of the flax plant, *Linum usitatissimum*. It is composed of the triglycerides of several fatty acids; the marked peaks in the organic EDXRA pattern represent background. Particles chipped from the dried oil film show smooth surfaces and glassy fracture.

10 mm = 100 μm   10 mm = 10 μm   10 mm = 1 μm

 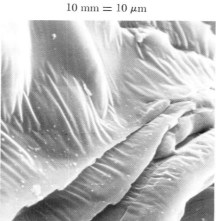 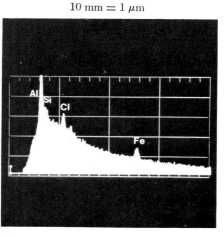

982 Lucite®—Lucite is a synthetic methyl methacrylate polymer. The particles in the micrographs are filings from this smooth, hard, thermoplastic material. The thin flakes are wrinkled and distorted by their treatment with the file. EDXRA shows an organic composition with accentuated peaks which are due to background. See also *methyl methacrylate (460)*.

 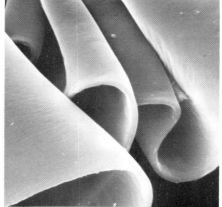 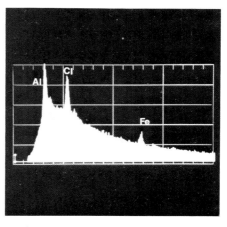

983 Polyvinyl Acetate—The flexible nature of this smooth film of the synthetic polymer, polyvinyl acetate, grade AYAA, is well depicted by SEM. EDXRA shows an organic substance; the aluminum, chlorine and iron peaks represent background. Polyvinyl acetate films are transparent, colorless and non-yellowing. See also *polyvinyl acetate (466)*.

  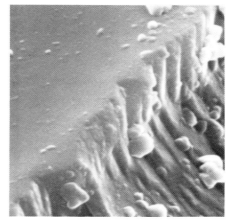

984 Shellac—Shellac is a natural resin secreted by the lac scale insect, *Kerria lacca*. It is composed of aliphatic polyhydric acids mixed with about 6% of wax and forms a tough, hard film which fractures conchoidally. The terraced appearance of the broken edges is related to the degree of brittleness in this film of high-grade "orange shellac."

10 mm = 100 μm   10 mm = 10 μm   10 mm = 1 μm

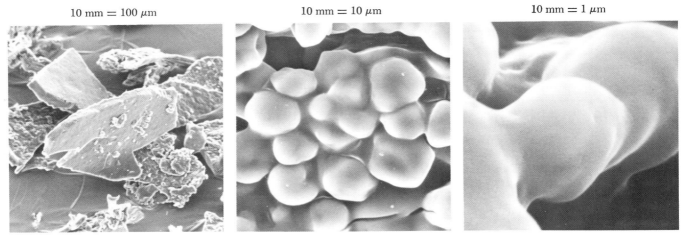

985 Starch Paste—Starch paste is made by mixing dry cereal starch with cold water and pouring the resulting suspension into boiling water. The adhesive paste thus formed dries to a film composed of partially cooked starch. At 1000X and 10,000X uncooked, polygonal grains of *cornstarch (334)* are clearly seen embedded in the matrix of cooked starch.

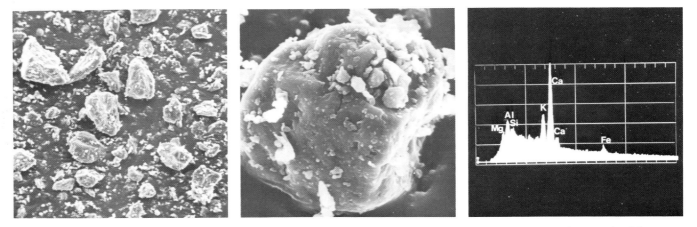

986 Gum Tragacanth—Gum tragacanth, a gum from *Astragalus* shrubs, is a mixture of an organic acid, a neutral polysaccharide, starch and cellulose. It forms the binder for pastel crayons. Upon ashing, 2–3% residue remains—EDXRA shows the elements to be found. Large, somewhat conchoidal particles of gum are cluttered with nondescript small particles which adhere to their surfaces.

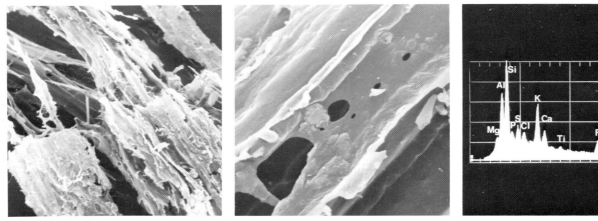

987 Bagasse, TVA—The boiler fuel in this case is bagasse which is the woody remains of sugar cane after the juices have been extracted. The incomplete combustion results in material that still shows woody structure when viewed with the SEM. The equant and elongated particles show pits and veins. The EDXRA shows high Al and Si from soil carried in with the bagasse. The other elements probably came from the plant tissues.

10 mm = 100 μm   10 mm = 10 μm

  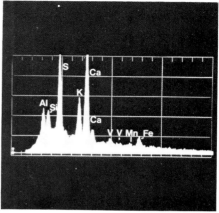

988 Bark Burner—This product is an example of inefficient combustion, as evidenced by the burned bark and wood fragments. These fragments still show woody structures such as veins. There are also spherical soot particles with rough surfaces. The EDXRA shows high calcium which is from calcium carbonate derived from the decomposition of calcium oxalate in the bark. The high sulfur and also some calcium come from calcium sulfate in the oil soot particles. The remaining elements are from soil and plant tissues.

989 Diesel Exhaust

This sample, collected directly from the exhaust pipe of a diesel engine, shows very small, ∼0.1 μm particles of carbon. These particles are the result of incomplete combustion, and the agglomerates are held together by an oily matrix. The EDXRA shows a high background consistent with a predominantly carbon compound.

10 mm = 1 μm   17 mm = 1 μm

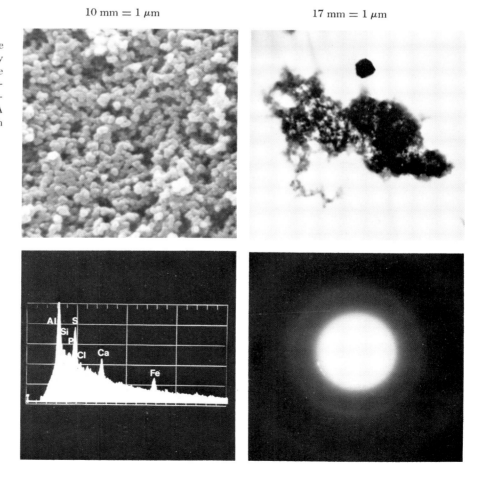

10 mm = 100 μm   10 mm = 10 μm

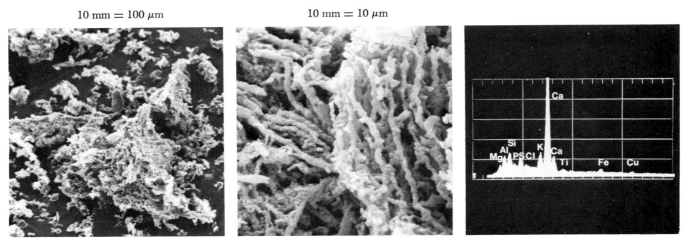

990 Fireplace Ash—Fireplace ash will always present a very variable sample, reflecting the nature of the fuel used. In this instance light microscopy has identified *calcium carbonate* (*485*) as a principal ingredient, and EDXRA supports this. Wood and paper fibers, carbonized to various degrees, are present. Incombustible mineral residues are also to be expected.

991 Gas Furnace

This sample is from a cold air return on a gas furnace. The majority of particles seen in the SEM micrograph are calcium sulfate. The tabular *gypsum* (*151*) crystals come from the plaster in the house. The EDXRA shows high Ca and S. The tabular crystal habit can also be seen in the TEM micrograph.

10 mm = 10 μm   17 mm = 1 μm

992 Heat Pump Dust

Quartz (183) and *gypsum (151)* are the principal constituents of this dust sample collected on a heat pump filter. The SEM micrograph shows fibrous components which include *paper (70–73)*, *seed hairs (77–84)* and spherical droplets of *oil soot (557–558)*. The quartz and gypsum occur as angular particles. The EDXRA shows high Si, S, Cl and Ca.

10 mm = 10 μm

12 mm = 1 μm

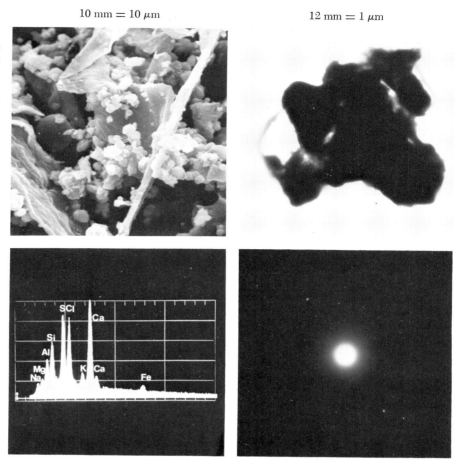

10 mm = 100 μm

10 mm = 10 μm

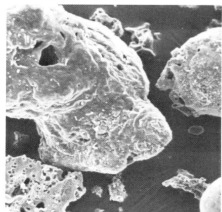

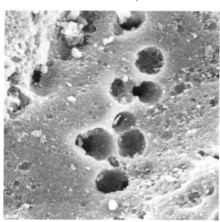

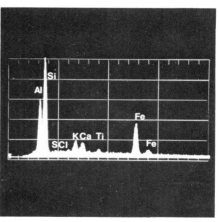

993 Locomotive, Steam—The flyash from a steam locomotive indicates the fuel was coal. The particles have the characteristic sintered appearance of *coal flyash (562–575)* with numerous gas bubble holes in their surfaces. The high Al and Si shown in the EDXRA come from the quartz and clay minerals commonly found in coal.

10 mm = 100 μm   10 mm = 10 μm   10 mm = 1 μm

994 Oil Flyash, Power Plant—The sample shows mostly an ash typical of a high efficiency burner. Power plants rely on high efficiency combustion to produce electrical power at the lowest cost. The round particles indicate that partial melting of the ash has occurred. The presence of V in the flyash is an indicator of its oil origin.

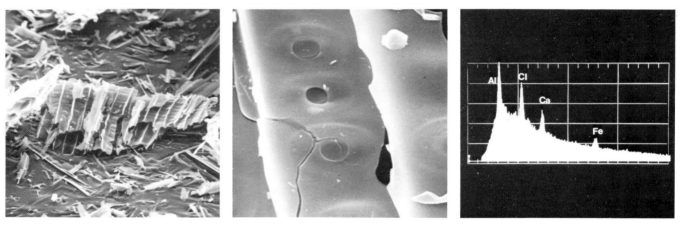

995 Wood, Burned—The structure of the wood can be seen in the SEM micrographs. The wood fragments are flat and elongated and have pits and veins. The pits shown are circular. The EDXRA shows a peak for Ca that is probably from the decomposition of the calcium oxalate in the wood.

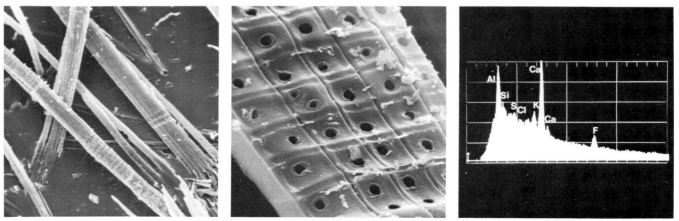

996 Wood Burning Fireplace—The wood used in this case was stored outdoors for several months. During that time, biological decomposition of the lignin occurred that caused the separation of the wood fibers. Circular pits can be seen in the fibers, and the EDXRA shows high Ca that is attributed to the decomposition of calcium oxalate from the bark.

10 mm = 100 μm   10 mm = 10 μm

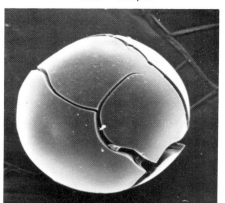  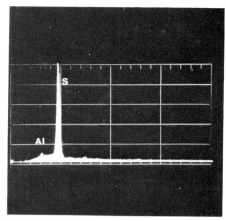

997 Amberlite® (acid)—This high capacity ion-exchange resin, developed commercially by Rohm and Haas, consists of spheres several hundred micrometers in diameter (that shown at 100X is approximately 450 μm). The resin is brittle and the spheres are thus frequently cracked. The conchoidal nature of this fracture is clearly seen at 1000X. EDXRA shows only S with Al as an artifact from the instrument.

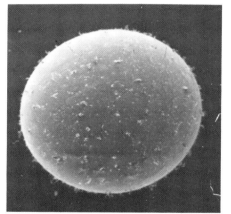 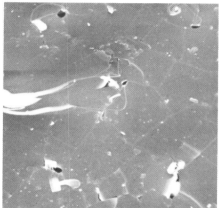 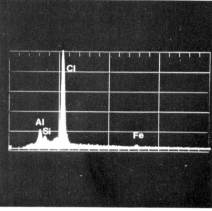

998 Amberlite® (base)—This ion-exchange resin is the base version of *Amberlite (acid)* (997). Again, the resin consists of spheres several hundred micrometers in diameter, but these show less tendency to crack than do the acid spheres. EDXRA shows Cl as the major peak with contaminant traces of Al, Si and Fe.

 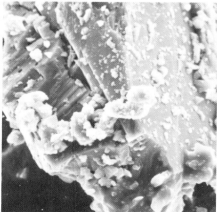 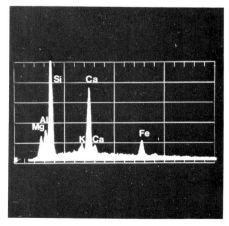

999 Asphalt Road Pavement—Little or no positive identification can be made of the components of this sample on the basis of SEM. Both *asphalt* (*478*) and *quartz* (*183*) fracture conchoidally, thus the large angular fragments might be either, although the fracture steps of asphalt are less sharply defined than those of quartz. EDXRA differentiates the two, provided there are no interfering silicates embedded in the asphalt. Other phases identified by light microscopy and contributing to the EDXRA pattern are *calcite* (*133*) and *iron oxide* (*391*). The presence of Mg, Al and a trace of K suggests that clays, micas, feldspars or other silicates are also present. It should be noted that, in some regions, up to 3% asbestos may be added to asphalt road surfacing.

10 mm = 100 μm   10 mm = 10 μm   10 mm = 1 μm

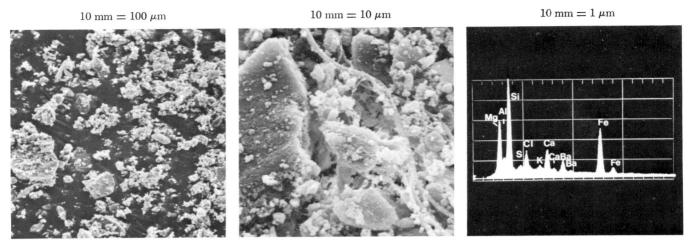

1000 Auto Brake Lining—Auto brake linings show a wide range of compositions depending on whether they are for disc or drum brakes and the severity of usage for which they are designed. Chrysotile asbestos is the major constituent, chosen for its thermal stability, relatively high friction level and rein- forcing properties. Phenolics and modified phenolics are used as binders; friction modifiers may include nonabrasive materials such as cured resins, carbon black, graphite and ground rub- ber, and abrasive materials such as alumina, silica, ground limestone, barites and some metal or metal oxides.

1001 Christmas Tree Flock—This flock for decorating Christ- mas trees consists entirely of coniferous *chemical wood fibers* (*73*). Pits, some of them visible at 100X, aid in the assignment of a coniferous origin. The clean separation and absence of mechanical damage indicate a chemical separation process.

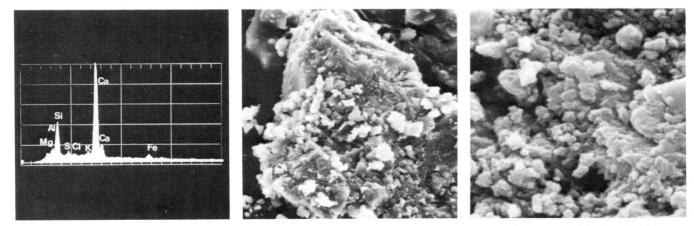

1002 Concrete Pavement—Concrete is a mixture of Portland cement, sand and aggregate or "ballast." The latter component may range from crushed rock of quite large size (several inches) down to gravels of ¼ to ½ inch diameter. The major constituents in this sample are shown by light microscopy to be *limestone* (*133*), *iron oxide* (*391*) and hydrated calcium silicates. For a more detailed description of cement and its constituents, see *246–258*. EDXRA shows high Ca and Si with Mg, Al, S, Cl, K and Fe also present.

10 mm = 100 μm   10 mm = 10 μm   10 mm = 1 μm

1003 Eraser, Ink—The most prominent features in this eraser dust are the large, angular fragments of *quartz* (*183*). The matrix is seen as a porous structure with some evidence of a particulate filler. EDXRA shows principally Ca (from the *limestone* (*133*) observed by light microscopy), Si (from the quartz), Ti from *titanium dioxide* (*448*) observed by light microscopy and probably the particulate filler noted above. Also present are K, Fe and Zn together with significant S and Cl from the *rubber* (*469*).

1004 Eraser, Pencil—Somewhat similar in appearance to the *ink eraser dust* (*1003*), this sample differs in that the matrix appears somewhat less porous and contains fewer abrasives. There are fewer large quartz fragments, and EDXRA shows a diminished Si peak with no Ti or Zn present.

1005 Soil, Garden—The composition of garden soil will vary considerably both on a large scale geographically and within any one individual yard. The principal components visible here by SEM are *quartz* (*183*) and clay. EDXRA shows Al, Si, K, Fe and a trace of Ba. Other constituents that should normally be expected would be feldspars, micas, amphiboles, plant debris and fallout from local industries.

10 mm = 100 μm   10 mm = 10 μm   10 mm = 1 μm

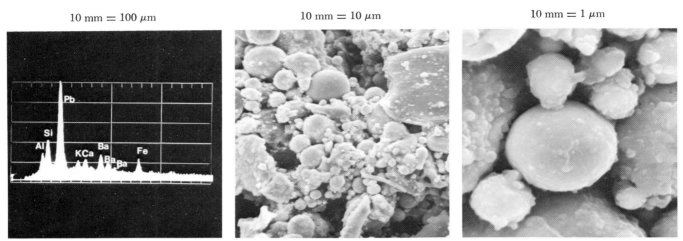

1006 Gunshot Residue—These spherical and granular particles are seen by EDXRA to consist primarily of lead compounds. Al, Si, Ba and Fe are also prominent, with significant K and Ca present. The particle sizes range from about 0.1 μm up to 10 or 20 μm in diameter. Many of the spheres are quite smooth; others have a distinct granularity and appear to be aggregates or agglomerates of smaller particles.

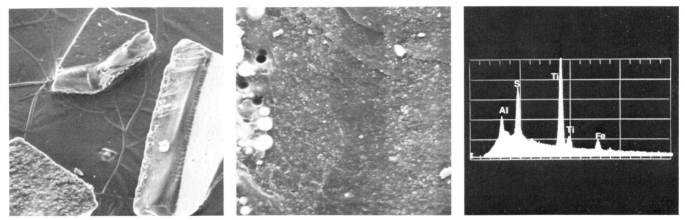

1007 Micro Taggants—These small fragments or flakes are incorporated in explosive products to enable the origin of the product to be determined. Formulated to survive the blast, they are readily located by a combination of their magnetic and fluorescent characteristics. The flakes are layered in a color sequence which encodes such data as product type, manufacturer and date of production. Some evidence of this layering is seen at 1000X, and element data from these layers might help in reading the code. The flakes, however, are best "read" by light microscopy.

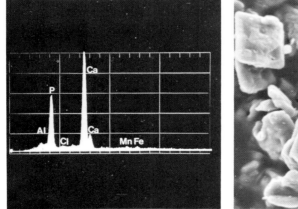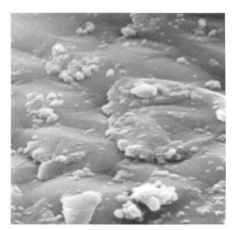

1008 Phosphor, Fluorescent light—These diamond-shaped tablets, about 5–20 μm across, fluoresce intensely in the visible spectrum when excited by the high energy electron beam and thus are readily detected by a cathodoluminescence detector. EDXRA shows Ca and P as the principal elements present. Mn, although present only as a trace element, is a key element in developing the emission characteristics of the phosphor.

10 mm = 100 μm   10 mm = 10 μm

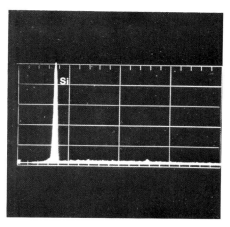

1009   Silica Gel, SiO₂—These large, angular fragments fracture conchoidally and thus resemble glass and the silica minerals, *chalcedony* (*135*), *opal* (*175*) and *quartz* (*183*). Opal tends to show a less well-developed conchoidal fracture and therefore might possibly be differentiated from silica gel by SEM. The other minerals and boro-silicate glass, however, could not be distinguished without a knowledge of their optical properties as all contain only Si in their EDXRA spectrum.

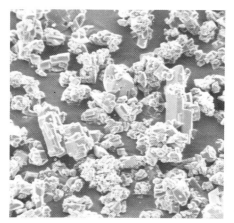

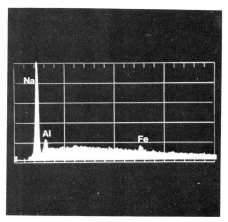

1010   Sodium Oxalate, Na₂C₂O₄—Well-formed crystals, ranging in size from about 1 μm to over 200 μm, characterize this sample. The crystals range from near equant forms to prisms and truncated prisms. Multiple growths, both as parallel growths and as twins, are frequent. EDXRA shows only Na as a significant peak, the Al and Fe being instrumental artifacts.

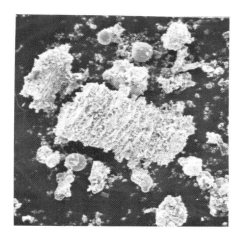
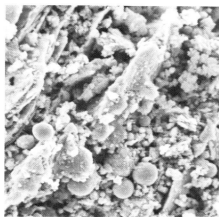
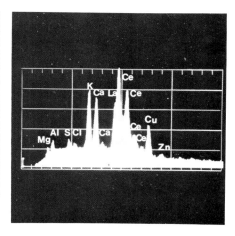

1011   Sparks from Lighter Flint—EDXRA conclusively separates lighter flint residues from gunshot residues, which they closely resemble morphologically. The presence of rare earth elements, in this case La and Ce, together with high K and Ca is diagnostic of the flint.

10 mm = 100 μm   10 mm = 10 μm

1012 Teakettle Scale—These granular aggregates are composed of myriads of small, angular, frequently flaky particles ranging in size from submicrometer to several micrometers across. Light microscopy has indicated that they are *calcium carbonate* (*limestone*) (*131, 161, 485*). This identification is verified by the EDXRA spectrum, which shows only Ca.

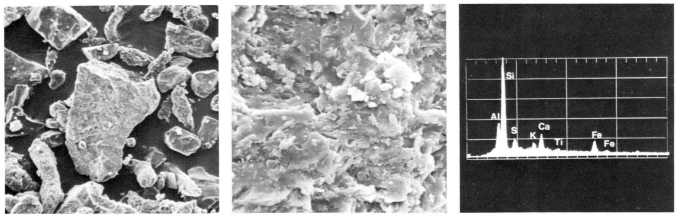

1013 Street Dust—This sample is a mixture of particle types as would be expected. Prominent in the center of the 100X photograph is a large grain of *quartz* (*183*), and just to the right of the bottom tip of this grain is a scroll of abraded *rubber dust* (*468, 469*). EDXRA indicates Al, Si, S, K, Ca, Ti and Fe, suggesting the presence of other minerals such as clays and feldspars.

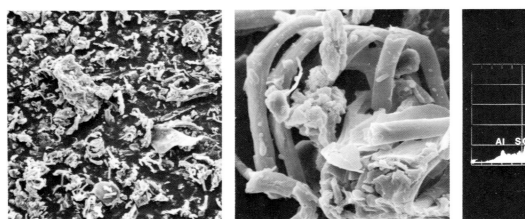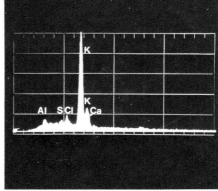

1014 Tobacco Stem Grindings—This sample consists principally of the broken-up spiral vessels of the leaf with only minute traces of leaf tissues. The fragments consist of short segments of curved fibers, about 50 μm long. EDXRA shows principally K with traces of Al, S, Cl and Ca. See also *tobacco dust* (*541, 542*).

10 mm = 100 μm 10 mm = 10 μm 10 mm = 1 μm

1015 Transite® Dust—Transite is the trade name of an asbestos sheet product manufactured by Johns-Manville. The individual components are *Portland cement (246–258)* and asbestos, in this case *chrysotile (122)*. The fibers are readily seen at all magnifications, whereas the cement particles show their morphology most clearly at 10,000X. EDXRA shows high Ca, Si and Mg with Al, Cl, Fe and traces of S and Zn.

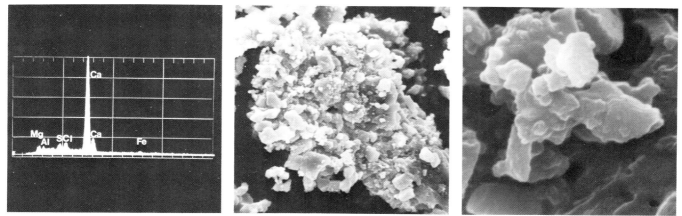

1016 Water Spot Deposits—Water spotting, (for example, of glassware and other utensils) is generally due to small particles of calcium carbonate *(133, 1012)* precipitating out of lime-rich water as its dries. EDXRA thus shows principally Ca with traces of Mg, Al, S, Cl (probably from chlorination of the water) and Fe. The individual particles in the deposit are typically in the micrometer to submicrometer size range.

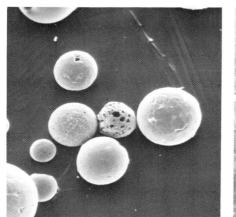
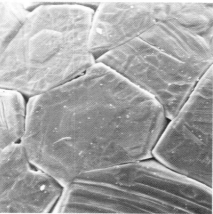
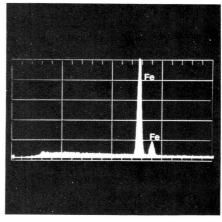

1017 Welding Spheres—These 50–200 μm spheres result from the solidification of metal spattered during a welding operation. Gas blowholes, as seen in the center sphere of the 100X micrograph, are common. The spheres frequently show well-developed crystal outlines on their surfaces. The metal in this sample was steel (the C does not show in the EDXRA), and the welding process was an oxyacetylene one.

10 mm = 100 μm   10 mm = 10 μm   10 mm = 1 μm

1018 Wine Bottle Sediment—The flat, irregularly shaped fragments or flakes from a wine bottle consists of aggregates of very small, 0.2 μm, equant to spherical particles. EDXRA shows S as the principal element with traces of Al, Si, Ca and Fe with a moderately high background suggesting a strong organic component.

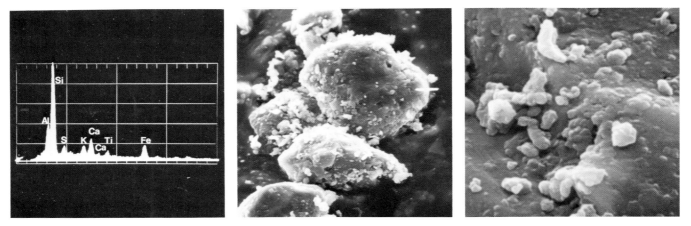

1019 Desert Sand—Quartz and feldspar grains, well rounded by a combination of wind action, solution and reprecipitation, generally characterize desert sands. EDXRA thus shows high Si with K, Ca and Al also prominent. The Fe peak is most likely associated with the iron oxide observed by light microsopy.

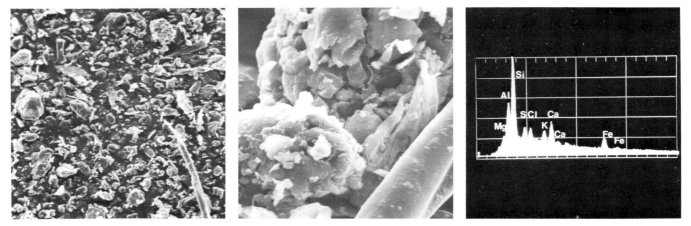

1020 House Dust—House dust is typically composed of the "debris" from the materials of which the house is constructed, from the occupants, from the surrounding neighborhood and from normal household operations. One should expect, therefore, to find a variety of mineral species, plant fibers and pollens, epithelial cells, human and animal (pet) hairs, fabric fibers and food dusts. This diversity is reflected in the EDXRA spectrum which shows Mg, Al, Si, S, Cl, K, Ca and Fe.

10 mm = 10 μm

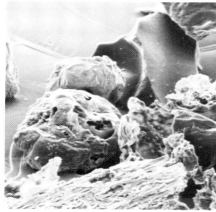 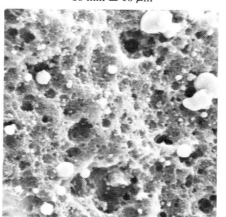 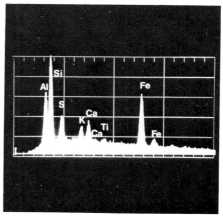

1021   Railroad Right-of-Way—Combustion products are the principal ingredient of this dust sample. *Coal flyash* (*562–575*) is the main component, but some oil soot and charred wood fragments were also observed. Metallic (mostly iron) wear particles, many observed by light microscopy to be oxide coated, are present. EDXRA shows Al, Si, S, K, Ca, Ti and Fe.

 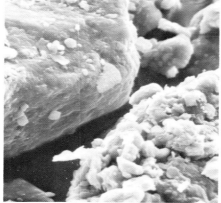 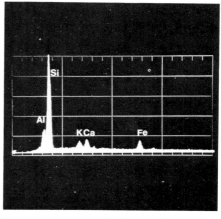

1022   Road Dust—A varied mineral assemblage can be expected from a road dust sample and will, at least in part, reflect the environment of the road, its composition and its usage. This sample, taken in a metropolitan area, shows a high proportion of *quartz* (*407*) as evident by the high Si peak in the EDXRA spectrum. The K, Ca and Al observed are most probably from feldspars; the Fe may be from either the mineral content or from mechanical apparatus.

V. Asbestos Identification by Electron Microscopy

Ian M. Stewart

A. Introduction

For regulatory purposes, asbestos has been defined as one of six mineral types: the serpentine, chrysotile. and the amphiboles: amosite, crocidolite, anthophyllite, tremolite and actinolite.[8] Although the assignment of a mineral name may imply some stoichiometry and a definite chemical formula, it should be borne in mind that such formulae are only approximate and that the complex isomorphous substitutions which occur in real minerals can cause quite considerable variations in the composition of any amphibole mineral. Similarities in chemical composition to other mineral species, such as the pyroxenes and the layer lattice minerals (micas, chlorites, talcs), experimental error in energy-dispersive x-ray analyses, and the possibility of interference from neighboring particles may lead to incorrect identification if chemistry alone is the sole criterion for the identification of the asbestos minerals. Even the combination of morphology and chemical composition is unsatisfactory in terms of an unambiguous identification of asbestos fibers.

Positive identification of a fiber as asbestos also requires a determination that the crystal structure of the fiber is one of the six potentially asbestiform minerals listed. It is assumed here that the fibers are too fine for polarized light microscopy (PLM) since the optical properties of fibers resolvable by PLM are nearly always adequate, along with morphology, for the identification of the asbestos minerals.

Despite the above-mentioned microanalytical difficulties, some workers[9] consider the scanning electron microscope (SEM) to be a possible analytical tool for the determination of asbestos fibers. We believe, as do most other active workers[10,11] in this field, that the SEM, *in the absence of other data to indicate that observed fibers are asbestos and only asbestos,* is an unsatisfactory tool for the identification of asbestos fibers even when combined with energy-dispersive x-ray analysis (EDXRA). Due to the limitations of the SEM with respect to crystallographic determinations and the uncertainties in chemical characterization referred to above, its role in asbestos analysis must be restricted to the analysis of fibers in those cases where asbestos is a known component of the sample. Therefore, this section will be confined to the analysis of asbestos by transmission electron microscopy (TEM).

The TEM, in conjunction with selected area electron diffraction (SAED), does give the combination of morphology and crystal structural information which is sufficiently definitive for the identification of chrysotile asbestos, the asbestos type most likely to be encountered in environmental, food and drug samples. It should be stressed, however, that the SAED data are necessary for the identification of chrysotile. Although morphology alone has been suggested as a sufficient criterion for the identification of chrysotile, Grieger[12] has pointed out several of the "look-alikes" that might be found in environmental samples. Figures 17–19 are based on his work and should require no textual amplification here.

The amphibole asbesiforms present a more difficult problem, although it is frequently possible to identify a fiber as an amphibole by visual examination of the

[8] Occupational Safety and Health Administration, "Standard for exposure to asbestos dust," *Federal Register* 37 (10), 11318–11322 (1972).

[9] Wehrung, J. M., and J. M. McAlear, "Surveying for asbestos and the SEM," *Symposium on Electron Microscopy of Microfibers, Proceedings of the First FDA Office of Science Summer Symposium* (1976), pp. 151–157.

[10] Tuesday Evening Open Discussion, *ibid.*, pp. 115–121.

[11] Ruud, C. O., "Characteristics of silicate mineral fibers as seen by TEM-SAED and SEM-EDXRA," *ibid.*, pp. 106–107; also *Micron* 7, 115 (1976).

[12] Grieger, G. R., "Differentiation of asbestos from other minerals by SAED," *Proceedings of the Electron Microscopical Society of America*, 30th Annual Meeting (1972), p. 546.

Figure 17. Attapulgite clay particles. Although readily differentiated by electron diffraction, this clay bears a close morphological similarity to some chrysotiles. 27,000X.

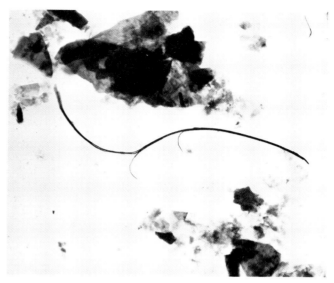

Figure 19. This splayed fiber is actually a thin, flexible ribbon of talc. 6300X.

diffraction pattern. A more critical examination may even suggest the basic amphibole type; *e.g.*, comparison of Figures 20 and 21 shows significant differences in the layer lines which, in ideal patterns such as these, are sufficient to enable one to say, by inspection and comparison with standards, that Figure 20 is the diffraction pattern of an actinolite-tremolite and Figure 21 that of a cummingtonite-grunerite. In general, however, the diffraction patterns will be less perfect than these, and in the absence of chemical information it is possible to say only that the fiber is an amphibole. The present trend toward the addition to the TEM of EDXRA or even WDXRA (see Section I of this volume), together with means for reducing the spot size at the specimen, has now added a very desirable third dimension to the TEM: elemental composition. With this further characterization it is possible to suggest what the amphibole type may be. When fitted to the TEM, however, these detectors are still subject to the same limitations mentioned above for the SEM.

We have, therefore, proposed the following criteria for the positive identification of submicrometer fibers as asbestos:

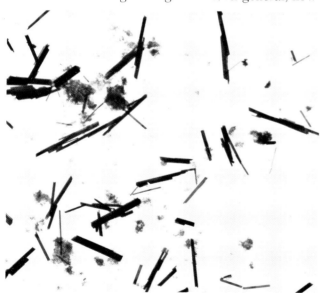

Figure 18. Lead chromate pigment. These needles bear a striking resemblance to amphibole fibers. Traces of $PbCrO_4$ have been found in air samples from a ceramics plant. The $PbCrO_4$ was part of a glaze formulation. An industrial talc, containing the amphiboles tremolite and anthophyllite, was in use at the same plant.

1. The particle should be a fiber—present federal definition, aspect ratio $\geqslant 3:1$.
2. Crystallographically, it should be either the serpentine chrysotile or an amphibole as determined by SAED.
3. If an amphibole, a tentative identification of type should be made on the basis of its EDXRA or WDXRA results, where possible.

It should be noted that the application of these criteria will in all cases lead to a low count for the number of asbestos fibers present, as some fibers will not be unambiguously identified. For example, fibers will not give clear diffraction patterns when over- or underlaid by other crystalline material.

A computerized diffraction pattern interpretation as described by Lee, Lally and Fisher[13] is a promising

Figure 20.   SAED pattern of tremolite. Note the groupings of intense spots on the first layer line. Compare with Figure 21.

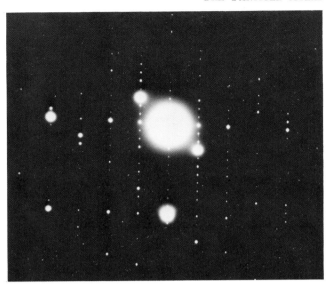

Figure 21.   SAED pattern of "amosite" (fibrous cummingtonite-grunerite). Compare the relative intensities of the intense spots on the first layer line with those of tremolite in Figure 20.

approach to the asbestos problem, but the computer facilities necessary are unlikely to be available to the majority of analysts working in this field. Of course, a logical extension of such programs would integrate in real time morphological information derived, for example, in the scanning mode of a STEM using currently available image analysis technology with diffraction data acquired electronically by the technique of scanning electron diffraction, and elemental data obtained from an EDXRA or electron energy loss spectroscopy (EELS). The hardware for such an integrated system is already available (see Section I of this volume). Software development and the computer capabilities required, however, are still beyond the reach of most electron microscopy laboratories.

The successful determination of asbestos in a sample is directly related to the ability of the analyst to prepare a sample in which the fibers are clearly separated and undamaged in order that they may yield clear and undistorted crystallographic and chemical data. The following section outlines procedures for preparing samples for the electron microscopical determination of asbestos.

B. Bulk and Powder Samples

Bulk and powder samples can be treated as de-

scribed in *The Particle Atlas*, Volume I, with precautions taken to prevent possible cross-contamination, since the friability and small size of the asbestos minerals render them readily airborne.

C. Fluid Samples

Liquid samples can be examined directly by placing a microdrop of the suspension on a TEM grid bearing a carbon support film. To quantitate the amount of asbestos present a calibrated micropipette may be used. Other workers have suggested measuring the diameter of the dried drop on the grid to derive the volume of the originally deposited microdrop. A more reliable method, also applicable to gas samples, is the so-called "direct transfer," method in which a portion of a membrane filter is dissolved *in situ* on the microscope grid. There are two main methods by which this may be accomplished: a condensation washing method and a "wicking" method.

1. Condensation Washing Method

Condensation washing consists of dissolving the filter medium *in situ* on the electron microscope support grid by the controlled evaporation of a solvent and slow recondensation on the filter material. This usually consists of a Soxhlet extractor flask into which is introduced a cold finger side arm carrying a support mesh on which the sample grids are placed. The arrangement is shown in Figure 22; this shows a washer

¹³ Lee, R. J., J. S. Lally and R. M. Fisher, "Identification and counting of mineral fragments," *Proceedings of Workshop on Asbestos*, N.B.S., U.S. Department of Commerce (1978), pp. 387–402.

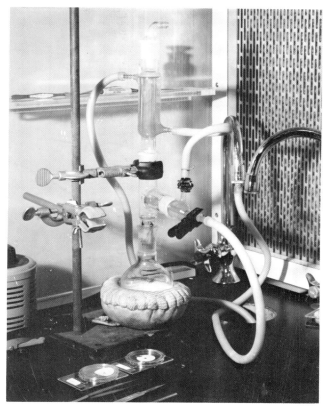

Figure 22. Condensation washing apparatus setup in laminar flow hood.

Figure 23. Typical appearance of water sample prepared by condensation washing. The fiber in the center of the field (grunerite) is approximately 5.5 μm long.

night, provided fluctuations in heating or cooling rates can be avoided. Figure 23 shows a typical water sample prepared using the condensation washing method.

2. Wicking Method

Several wicking methods have been developed for the dissolution of filter material. All depend on capillary action to bring the solvent from a reservoir to the filter to be dissolved and differ only slightly in detail; e.g., one method uses a polyurethane foam, another a filter paper stack, and another a filter paper draped over a "saddle." The method most commonly used at present is known as the "modified Jaffé wick," a combination of the last two methods, using several filter papers draped over a "saddle" of glass slides (Figure 24). This method works best for thin membranes such as small pore size Nuclepore. Nuclepore membranes with larger pore sizes and cellulose membranes in all pore sizes are generally too thick to dissolve satisfactorily.

In practice, a portion of the membrane is placed particle-side down on a previously carbon-coated grid.° A solvent is then added to the dish to a level just below the grids. To minimize curling or distortion of the filter membrane during the early stages of solution, some workers recommend placing a microdrop of solvent on the back of the portion of the filter immediately after placing it on the electron

set-up on a laminar-flow clean bench. A filtered solvent (acetone for membrane filters of the mixed ester type or chloroform for the polycarbonate Nuclepore®) is warmed in the flask by a heating mantle to temperature just able to maintain a condensing vapor-front falling about 1 cm short of the cold finger. The resulting vapors slowly condense on the cold finger and cause slow dissolution of the filter material. A careful balance is maintained between the heating rate and the cooling water flow through the cold finger by observing both the position of the condensation front on the walls of the vessel and the rate of drop formation on the end of the finger (which should be no more than 2–3 drops per second). If the top surface of the support mesh appears wet, the condensation rate is too high.

With proper refluxing conditions, dissolution of the filter will require approximately 4–8 hours. A higher dissolution rate indicates too high a condensation rate, leading to excessive solvent present at the filter and thus possible wash-off of particles from the grid. Too slow a dissolution rate is preferable to too high á rate, and the washing time can safely be extended to over-

---

° If Nuclepore® is used, the filter itself may be carbon-coated prior to dissolution, which results in better retention of particles.

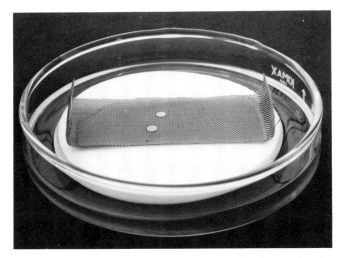

Figure 24. Modified Jaffé wick appartus for dissolution of polycarbonate filters.

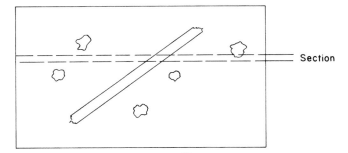

Figure 25. Schematic of the plane of sectioning.

microscope grid. The dish is then covered and the filter is allowed to dissolve over a period of about 24 hours with replenishing of the solvent if required. It is important that the solvent not be allowed to evaporate completely. The grids are removed from the dish by lifting the support screen and then setting this aside to allow evaporation of any adhering solvent.

The wicking methods are currently more popular than condensation washing because the latter requires special apparatus and closely controlled heating and cooling conditions. The wicking methods, on the other hand, require no special apparatus, other than normal laboratory glassware; they are simpler to perform and can be left to run unattended for as long as is necessary with only occasional addition of solvent.

D. *Tissue Samples*

Methods for the examination of the asbestos content of tissue by electron microscopy can be split into two classes: (1) direct methods of sectioning and extraction replication for samples where the existing "*in vivo*" relationship between the asbestos fiber and the tissue (whether normal or abnormal) is important; and (2) indirect concentration methods, which include tissue digestion, normal ashing (high-temperature) and oxygen plasma ashing (low-temperature), where the bulk tissue mineral burden is determined.

1. Direct Methods

Direct methods such as sectioning and/or replication are the only methods suitable for studying the interaction of individual asbestos particles with tissue

cell structures. The technique of ultramicrotomy is well established in biomedical electron microscopy, and the skilled operator will produce sections of high quality with little or no distortion of the tissue structure. The presence of mineral particles in the tissue, however, may lead to sectioning artifacts. These artifacts may be developed, for example, as a result of chattering of the knife upon hitting a hard particle; or, frequently, the fiber may pluck out of the embedding tissue and tear the remainder of the section. The resulting damage may distort either the tissue, the fiber, or both. Additionally, as illustrated schematically in Figure 25, the plane of sectioning may entirely miss some fibers and may lead to an erroneous apparent morphology of others; thus it is necessary to examine a large number of serial sections to obtain a true picture of the foreign mineral distribution in the bulk tissue. Nevertheless, microtoming remains the best way in which the interaction between particle and tissue can be studied directly.

An alternative method which gives almost as good a picture of the particle/tissue interrelationship is that of extraction replication. Variations of this technique are well known to material scientists, but it has been less extensively applied to biological samples. The steps in replication are shown schematically in Figure 26. For tissue samples, a plastic primary replicating medium is used. This medium may be cast directly onto the tissue surface, flowed on as a solution, or pressed onto the surface after softening the polymer with a solvent. When the polymer has hardened, by polymerization or by loss of solvent, the replica may be removed from the surface. In some cases it can be removed by gently pulling with tweezers, and in others it can be removed after first backing the replica with a more substantial film, such as transparent Scotch® tape. When it is removed in this way, the asbestos fibers exposed at the section surface are retained by the replica in their original positions relative to the tissue structure. At the same time, a replica of this

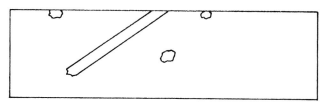

Tissue containing particulate material

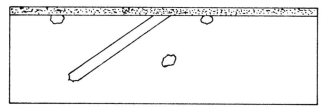

Primary replica (black) cast on tissue surface

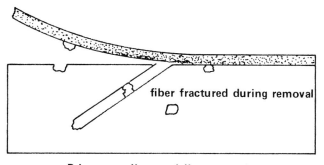

fiber fractured during removal

Primary replica partially removed, extracting particles from surface

Secondary carbon replica after dissolution of primary replica

Figure 26.   The steps in replication which give a good picture of the particle/tissue interrelationship.

tissue structure is imprinted in the plastic matrix. Such replicas may be sufficiently thin for direct examination in the TEM, but a more stable secondary replica is generally prepared by the vacuum evaporation of carbon onto the primary plastic replica, which is then dissolved away. The contrast of the tissue structure may be enhanced by shadowing with a heavy metal.

2. Indirect Methods

Both the sectioning and the replication techniques require that the asbestos fibers be exposed in the plane of sectioning. As a result, tedious serial sectioning is generally necessary to find the material of interest. However, if the information sought is not the specific interaction between the fiber and the cell, then bulk methods may be applied which concentrate the minerals by rendering down a comparatively large mass of tissue, thus yielding the total mineral burden of the tissue sample. Three such methods are recognized:

a. tissue digestion
b. normal ashing (high-temperature)
c. plasma ashing (low-temperature)

a. Tissue digestion

Tissue digestion has long been used in conventional bioassays. The tissue is immersed in an oxidizing medium which destroys the tissue structure, thereby liberating the unattacked asbestos fibers which may then be concentrated by centrifuging and/or filtering the suspension. Subsequent dispersal of the asbestos fibers for TEM enables their identification, size measurement and counting, hence the determination of their content per unit mass or volume of original tissue. While several digestants have been suggested, care has to be exercised to ensure that the digestant does not attack the asbestos fibers. Additionally, it is essential to establish that the reagents used are not contaminated, as they cannot readily be filtered without attacking the filter medium. Soluene®, for example, which has previously been used for asbestos determination in tissue,[14] at least until recently has itself been contaminated with asbestos from asbestos filters used to separate metal salts precipitated during manufacture. Because the reagent is viscous, centrifuging removes very little of this asbestos and, because of its reactivity with most organic fiber media, filtration is impracticable.

---

[14] Cunningham, H. M., and F. D. Pontefract, "Penetration of asbestos through the digestive tract of rats," *Nature* **243**, 352–353 (1973).

Thus this solvent cannot be used for asbestos studies without first being checked for asbestos. With caution, it could be used for other mineral studies. Similarly, some caustic solutions may also have been in contact with asbestos filters during manufacture, while levels of asbestos contamination as high as 3×10^7 fibers per liter have even been encountered in a reagent-grade isopropanol.[15] It is important, therefore, to verify by blanks the cleanliness of all reagents and solvents used. At McCrone Associates, all solvents used for particle isolation or fractionation are pre-filtered several times through 0.22-μm pore size membrane filters before use.

Table I outlines typical steps in the preparation of a tissue sample by the digestion process.

Table I

Preparation of tissue by digestion

Step 1. An aliquot of the tissue sample is placed in a glass vial.
Step 2. Digestant is added to the vial in a quantity sufficient to effect total digestion of the tissue mass present.
Step 3. Hold vial in an oven at 50–80°C for 1.5–3 days.
Step 4. Remove vial from oven and add particle-free° methanol to the digesting solution.
Step 5. The diluted digesting solution is filtered through a 0.22-μm pore size membrane filter.
Step 6. Prepare filters for TEM by direct transfer method.

° "Particle-free" is triple filtered with last filtration through 0.22-μm pore size membrane filter.

b. High-temperature ashing

This method of tissue preparation, as its name implies, consists simply of incinerating the tissue sample in oxygen at an elevated temperature, generally in the range 400–550°C, sufficiently high to result in combustion of the organic material but not high enough to cause degradation or phase transformation of the asbestos fibers present. The resulting ash is suspended in water, lightly ultrasonerated to break up aggregates, and then concentrated by ultracentrifuge or filtration. If the ash is centrifuged down, drops of known volume can be pipetted onto carbon-coated TEM grids. If filtered, the filtered ash can be prepared for examination by a direct transfer method such as condensation washing or Jaffé wicking. A typical sequence in high-temperature ashing is given in Table II.

High-temperature ashing works well for many tissue types. While some of the more massive tissue specimens, such as muscle and liver, exhibit a tendency to form "coke" particles which resist break up by ultra-

---

15 Giles, P., Private communication.

Table II

Preparation of tissue by high-temperature ashing

Step 1. An aliquot of the tissue sample is placed on a glass slide or in a small test tube.
Step 2. The slide or test tube with the sample is placed in the range of 450–550°C and is maintained at this temperature for 5–8 hours.
Step 3. The ashed sample is resuspended in particle-free water which is then lightly ultrasonerated prior to filtration through a 0.22-μm pore size membrane filter.
Step 4. Prepare filter for TEM by direct transfer method.

soneration, much of this coking can be overcome by longer combustion times.

c. Low-temperature ashing

In low-temperature ashing the tissue is consumed more slowly at lower temperatures (usually <100°C). As a result, the formation of coke is minimized. The sample is incinerated in an oxygen plasma generated by applying a radio frequency signal to a chamber containing oxygen at a reduced pressure, typically 1 torr, and the resulting ionization of the gas produces a highly active oxygen cloud at the specimen surface, oxidizing the organic material with minimal increase in sample temperature. The ashed material is resuspended, filtered and prepared for examination by a direct transfer method as described for high-temperature ashing. Although tissue samples prepared by this technique are generally free from coke lumps, the more dense tissues can still pose some problems due to low diffusivity of the oxygen into the interior of the sample. These problems may be reduced by homogenization or maceration of the tissue prior to ashing, but such techniques can result in changes in the morphology or size distribution of the asbestos fibers. Steps in the low-temperature ashing procedure are outlined in Table III.

E. Beverages and Foodstuffs

Beverages and foodstuffs can be treated quite straightforwardly using one or the other of the methods given above. Solid foods are generally amenable to low-temperature ashing. Some solid foods which may have had surface contact with asbestos can be studied by careful washing with subsequent filtration of the washings or by extraction replication of the surface. In some instances, however, pretreatment may be necessary before the conventional methods are used; for example, vegetable oils may be solvent extracted, and starch and carbohydrates may be digested by

Table III

Preparation of tissue by low-temperature (oxygen plasma) ashing (LTA)

Step 1. An aliquot of the tissue sample is placed on a glass slide.
Step 2. The slide is placed in the LTA chamber which is then evacuated.
Step 3. Oxygen is bled into the chamber to give a pressure of approximately 1 torr.
Step 4. RF power is applied to the chamber and tuned. It is then adjusted to approximately 10–25 watts. The resulting plasma is maintained for sufficient time to oxidize all organic matter (usually several hours for small samples).
Step 5. The ashed sample is removed and 1–2 drops of 1 N HCl are added to the ash. After not more than 1–1.5 minutes, this suspension is diluted with particle-free water.
Step 6. The diluted suspension is lightly ultrasonerated.
Step 7. Filter the ultrasonerated suspension through a 0.22-μm pore size membrane filter.
Step 8. Prepare filter for TEM by direct transfer method.

alkalis or by enzymes, although in the latter case a complex product might require an equally complex digestant. Acid treatments should generally be avoided, as even dilute hydrochloric acid at room temperature will result in the degradation of chrysotile.[16]

F. Conclusion

In establishing a procedure for any individual sample type, consideration must be given at all times to the preservation of the integrity of the asbestos fibers in the sample. The importance of choosing the proper preparation method and the proper analytical tools, and of having a well-trained operator, should be emphasized in application of asbestos preparation and identification.

---

[16] Chen, J. T., "Infrared studies of the effects of acid, base, heat and pressure on asbestos and structurally related substances," J. AOAC **60** (6), 1266–1276 (1977).

VI. Use of Automation in Laboratory Instrumentation

Charles H. Bowen and Donald A. Brooks

A. Introduction

What Can Automation Do for a Research Laboratory?

Automation of ultramicroanalytical instrumentation will allow the automatic performance of routine analyses on a continuous basis with a significant increase in speed and accuracy. For example, automation of the electron microprobe has allowed analysis of samples 10 to 100 times faster than by manual operation, and without an operator. Collection and processing of data which previously required 2 to 3 hours can now be performed in 2 to 10 minutes using the automated system. Automation also allows reduction and/or interpretation of the data 100 to 200 times faster than before. Thus, automation of most analytical techniques will free the operator, allowing more than one operation at a time, significantly increasing the sample throughput and providing statistically better and more accurate data.

The role of the computer in automation systems has been well established in the past 10 to 15 years. The computer has actually evolved from the large, bulky main frame computer system occupying a specially designed room to a miniaturized circuit on a single silicon chip less than 1 cm² in area. Along with this significant decrease in size, a significant cost reduction has also been achieved. Therefore, justification for automation and control of various equipment has been made considerably easier. Previously, due to the physical size and cost of computers, a large number of instruments were required to share one computer. But now with the significantly reduced cost of microcircuits it is possible to decentralize and equip each individual analytical instrument with its own dedicated computer. Thus, with the advent of the microprocessor, dedicated computer systems have found their way into many applications, e.g., word processing, programmable calculators, machine controls and, of prime concern to particle analysts, analytical instrumentation. Again, due to the evolution of the microcomputer, computer systems are ideally suited for the automation of not only high volume complicated analytical techniques, but those applications that require repetitive or routine techniques as well. The microprocessor now allows the speed and accuracy of automated control on a dedicated basis.

Exactly what are microcomputers and microprocessors? A microcomputer consists of a microprocessor and the associated peripheral devices for input and output to the computer as well as the necessary control devices to coordinate the automation of, say, an EMA. The microprocessor is the main portion of the microcomputer; it is a monolithic large-scale integrated circuit containing the central processing unit and logic system of the computer. With the recent advances in microminiaturization it would not be uncommon to find a complete microcomputer (exclusive of input/output devices) contained on a single printed circuit board. The microprocessor was originally developed by, and for, the space program, its first applications being to computerized machine tools, aircraft and spacecraft navigation systems, operational controls, guidance and other similar highly sophisticated devices. The microcomputer's usefulness has significantly increased, due not only to its small size and relatively low cost, but also to its building block design concept. Now, a manufacturer can easily design an automation system to fit a specific application by providing not only the necessary memory, but the necessary ancillary equipment as well. This does not necessarily mean that the mainframe concepts of yesteryear are obsolete and phasing out, although computers have been growing smaller and their capacity increasing significantly. The larger service bureaus still require new giant computers to process increasing workloads, maintain the necessary memory banks and, at the same time, lower operating costs. Such systems are required for business information systems by insurance companies, banking facilities and auto rental or airline reservation firms requiring large in-house computer installations to maintain all of their business operations and daily records.

B. McCrone Associates' Automation Advances

Since publication of the first four volumes of *The Particle Atlas, Edition Two,* several major additions and improvements to laboratory automation have been incorporated within the systems at McCrone Associates. Based on twelve years of operational experience with the automated electron microprobe system, refinements and modifications have been made to advance the state-of-the-art in the ultramicroanalysis area. The specific advances made to the computer probe system (CPS) described in Volume I (pp. 183–195) are summarized in a following paragraph. Automation of the ion microprobe mass analyzer and the gas chromatograph/mass spectrometer system have also been completed and are discussed in another paragraph.

Automation of the electron microprobes has changed considerably since the publication of Volume I. In fact, at McCrone Associates, automation of the newest of the two electron microprobes, the EMX-SM, was modified and upgraded by changing from a time-sharing system using a PDP-15® to a dedicated system utilizing a PDP-8E® computer and the same basic principles outlined in Volume I. To advance the state-of-the-art in this area a change was also made to incorporate updated and improved electronics within the interface system as well as more sophisticated programming techniques. These changes now make the CPS more applicable to the wide diversity of problems encountered in particle analyses. The PDP-8E is, in turn, buffered to the PDP-15 computer and can, therefore, exchange data with the system for use in the data reduction phase of our analyses. Figure 27 details in block diagram form our present automation systems and those of the near future. Use of the PDP-15 computer in analyzing data obtained from other various instruments, which are also either connected directly or buffered through a smaller system, has proven invaluable. Data can also be directly input from remote terminals which are available for use with any of the equipment within our laboratory. For example, data observed while using an optical microscope, the EMMA and/or the TEM can be directly read into the main computer system and used in particle size distribution and/or statistical calculations via the portable remote terminals.

C. Dedicated versus Time-Sharing Computer Systems

In the past two years the fastest growing area in the computer industry has been the small dedicated computer which, in turn, has led to the decentralized processing of data. Work efforts are now performed within the respective departments or technical areas. That is, small dedicated computers now perform many of the tasks that had been previously performed on a time-sharing basis, both in-house and through external service bureaus. In fact, the concept of producing a smaller and lower cost system has pushed the state-of-the-art into the microprocessor area and, with further miniaturization, advances will continue to be made in this area.

With the significant changes being made in the computer area, changes have also occurred in terminology. A distinction is now made between decentralized processing and distributed data processing. The main difference is that in a distributed data processing system all of the computations are still performed at a single central processing unit through the use of remote input terminals and output devices. That is, the remote input and output terminals are actually part of a time-sharing service of the central processing unit at a company's main computer facility, whereas in a decentralized processing system each operation is provided with its own dedicated computer specifically adapted to its respective needs. For example, dedicated systems are often used in the control and automation of highly sophisticated electronic equipment, in word processing systems and in finance and accounting departments. Each of these areas would have its own computer facility rather than being required to tie into a larger central processing unit within the facility. A combined system concept can also exist, wherein a specific area performs on a decentralized basis but in turn is buffered to the larger central processing system. In fact, in several instances this concept is utilized within our laboratory.

Whether one chooses to use a dedicated or a time-sharing system today depends upon the actual application. For example, instrument control and data reduction can be done directly and more efficiently with a small dedicated computer than by tying into a larger facility programmed to handle many instruments at one time. The prime disadvantage in time sharing is that when the main system goes down, anything tied

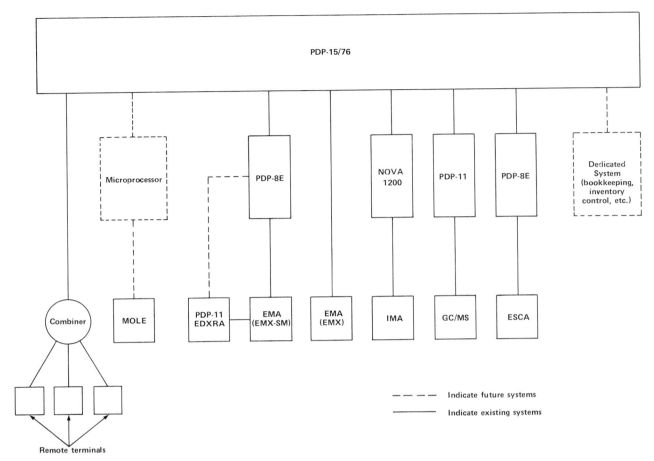

Figure 27.   Block diagram of automation systems at McCrone Associates.

to it goes down as well. This includes any instrumentation control systems which then either have to be left down or operated on a manual basis. As McCrone Associates is an ultramicroanalytical service laboratory with its livelihood dependent on the use of its unique and sophisticated equipment, instrument downtime and availability are critical. It is for these reasons that we have converted our automation systems to small decentralized or dedicated data processing systems. Although these dedicated computers are buffered or directly accessed to the large central computer system within our facility, their operation is otherwise independent of the large system.

Other applications within the laboratory such as x-ray diffraction data interpretation through the use of the ASTM data bank can be handled only through the capacity of an extremely large computer facility. Therefore, an external time-sharing system is required by most users. Our PDP-15 is connected directly to one of the electron microprobes, indirectly to the other electron microprobe through a dedicated PDP-8E, and indirectly to the ion microprobe through a dedicated

Data General Nova computer. For the last five years our photoelectron spectrometer unit, ESCA, has been controlled through a PDP-8E, and, just in the past year, a PDP-11® has been interfaced for control and data interpretation on our gas chromatograph/mass spectroscopy system. Each of these computers, in turn, will be buffered to the main computer. Within MA, smaller computers are now being used to maintain the control of the analytical instrumentation and to collect the data generated. While the specific instrument is being controlled, the data can be transferred to the larger computer for data reduction or interpretation. Thus, the choice of computers and automation systems and the respective methods of use are directly dependent upon the functions they perform and the criteria established by their users.

D. Automation of the Electron Microprobe Analyzer

As mentioned earlier, the computer probe system (CPS) automation of one of our electron microprobes, the EMX-SM, was upgraded using a dedicated 24K memory, 12 bit PDP-8E computer. Thus, we changed from a time-sharing system to a dedicated on-line system. The intent was to use the computer for short-term analyses wherein rapid changes in software could easily be made on-line to conform with the analysis being performed.* This was accomplished using FOCAL® as the compiler and assembly level subroutines as in the PDP-15 to drive the various hardware components within the system. Since publication of the first four volumes of *The Particle Atlas, Edition Two*, significant improvements have been made in the CPS hardware by replacing the reed relays with solid state switching devices in 98% of the control applications. These new devices have significantly increased spectrometer control efficiency and data acquisition accuracy.

With the use of FOCAL software it is possible to change a program on-line, as the FOCAL compiler is core resident at all times. Therefore, the control programs can be changed and tailored in a very brief time to modify the respective spectrometer elemental stopping points for data collection, background and interference corrections. The CPS, now using a dedicated PDP-8E computer system, is used on a routine basis; in 95% of the analyses performed it has replaced the manual sequencing of spectrometers as provided by the microprobe manufacturer.

E. Use of the CPS System for Mass Scanning Analyses

Although the CPS system has been used routinely for mass scanning analyses on a variety of samples, its applications to a specific NIOSH project are summarized.

The project required the analyses of a large number of dust particles from five different smelters to correlate the size and composition of different compounds with tumorous growths in laboratory animals. At least 1000 particles from each sample were to be located, identified and analyzed quantitatively for 25 elements, using all three of the microprobe's wavelength spectrometers. In total, approximately 5800 particles were analyzed.

After experimenting with several different sample preparation methods, it was determined that the best results could be obtained by dispersing the total sam-

* A large portion of the software used in our CPS system was developed by the General Electric Corporation, Pleasanton, California, with Mr. Lee Reed as Manager. Credit is acknowledged for the efforts of Mr. Fred Halliday, Gordon Cleaver, Conrad Peterson and Dr. Mitch Gregory.

ple on a highly polished beryllium substrate from a droplet suspension of particles. Evaporation of the solvent leaves well-dispersed individual particles ranging from less than 0.8 μm to 10 μm in size.

Although it was intended to use existing software (as described in Volume I), it became necessary to modify the programs for this specific project. The capability of producing a hard copy of the data obtained during the analyses was retained in order to verify the quality of the output data. It was also decided to save analysis time by reducing the data in bulk after a batch of runs had been completed. This, in turn, allowed continuous mass scanning analyses to be rapidly performed. Additional software was written in order to present the data in a concise form to conform with the client's needs. These data were presented in tables as follows:

1. *Individual particle analysis sheet:* One sheet was prepared for each individual particle analysis showing the count rates for each element observed and the normalized percentages calculated after subtracting background (Table IV).
2. *Particle size distribution data summary:* A particle size distribution summary by percent was prepared over the range from 0 to 10 μm. This table summarizes the number and the percentage of particles in each category (Table V).
3. *Number of particles bearing various percentages I:* A summary of the normalized elemental concentration found within each sample was prepared. Specifically, this includes the number of particles containing percentages of specific elements in two categories: 5–10% and greater than 10% (Table VI).
4. *Number of particles bearing various percentages II:* The same data presented in Table VI were prepared with a finer breakdown. The number of particles bearing percentages of specific elements between 5 and 10%, 10 and 30%, 30 and 50%, 50 and 75%, and 75 and 100% are detailed (Table VII).
5. *Occurrence of elements with major quantity:* This is a summary of the number of particles bearing >5% of each major element tabulated in descending order of occurrence (Table VIII).
6. *Average size of particle with major elements:* A summary showing the average size for particles containing each element (Table IX).

When this project was initiated, quantitative analyses obtained by the WDXRA system within the CPS

Table IV

Individual particle analysis data

```
SAMPLE  NO : ATLAS VI/77208        DATE DATA ACQUIRED: 5-22-78
PARTICLE NO: 301                   DATE  OF  REPORT  : 6-01-78

PARTICLE SIZE(UM):  1.01
```

TOTAL COUNTS FOR REQD ELEMENTS & RESPECTIVE BACKGROUND POSITIONS

ELEMENT	COUNTS		ELEMENT	COUNTS
BG*	27		AS	29
K	25		SE	12
SB	33		BR	8
CA	27		AL	11
TE	23		SI	26
BG	17		BG	18
I	20		HG	29
TI	22		TL	25
V	33		S	30
BG	23		PB	93
BG	24		BG	25
CR	20		CD	112
BG	20		O	2
FE	43		BG	5
CU	135		F	3
BG	178		BG	3
ZN	255		NA	6
BG	15		BG	8
			MG	38

NORMALIZED DATA

ELEMENT	MEASURED VALUE	MEASURED PERCENT	STD DEV
MAJOR**			
PB	1.101	65.50	7.70
AS	0.502	31.30	16.80
MINOR**			
S	0.003	1.40	0.40

```
NOTE:
 * BG=BACKGROUND
** NORMALIZED PERCENTAGES >5% ARE MAJOR, FROM 1-5% MINOR;
   ELEMENTS WITH NORMALIZED VALUES <1% NOT PRINTED OUT
```

Table V

Particle size distribution summary

```
SAMPLE  NO : ATLAS VI/77208        DATE DATA ACQUIRED: 5-22-78
                                   DATE  OF  REPORT:   6-01-78
```

PARTICLE * SIZE RANGE(UM)	NO. OF PARTICLES WITHIN RANGE	PERCENTAGE BY RANGE(%)
0-1	34	10.86
1-2	123	39.30
2-3	50	15.97
3-4	28	8.95
4-5	25	7.99
5-6	15	4.79
6-7	16	5.11
7-8	7	2.24
8-9	8	2.55
9-10	7	2.24
>10	0	0.00
TOTAL	313	100.00%

```
NOTE:
*SIZE RANGE OF 0-1 REPRESENTS THE RANGE OF > ZERO BUT LESS THAN OR
 EQUAL TO ONE; SIMILARLY FOR THE OTHER SIZE RANGES.
```

Table VI

Summary I—number of particles bearing various elemental percentages

```
SAMPLE  NO : ATLAS VI/77208        DATE DATA ACQUIRED: 5-22-78
PARTICLE NOS: 1-313                DATE  OF  REPORT  : 6-01-78
```

NO. OF PARTICLES WITH RESPECTIVE ELEMENTS

ELEMENTS	>10%	5-10%	TOTAL
K	4	0	4
SB	1	1	2
CA	2	18	20
TE	0	0	0
I	21	1	22
TI	1	0	1
V	0	0	0
CR	16	11	27
FE	32	10	42
CU	6	10	16
ZN	14	4	18
AS	9	0	9
SE	0	0	0
BR	0	0	0
AL	3	0	3
SI	19	19	38
HG	0	0	0
TL	0	0	0
S	50	152	202
PB	293	4	297
CD	4	1	5
O	26	0	26
F	15	5	20
NA	0	0	0
MG	0	0	0

and the EDXRA were compared; the data for major and minor elements from the two systems were in good agreement. Because trace elements are usually not detected with the EDXRA, the trace concentrations measured by WDXRA (CPS) could not be compared.

Although the software and hardware utilized on this project were optimized during the course of the project, various delays were encountered due to the EMA

Table VII

Summary II—number of particles bearing various elemental percentages

```
SAMPLE  NO : ATLAS VI/77208        DATE DATA ACQUIRED: 5-22-78
PARTICLE NOS: 1-313                DATE  OF  REPORT  : 6-01-78
```

PARTICLES CONTAINING ELEMENTS IN QUANTITIES INDICATED

ELEMENT	75-100%	50-75%	30-50%	10-30%	5-10%	TOTAL
K	1	0	2	1	0	4
SB	0	0	0	1	1	2
CA	0	0	0	2	18	20
TE	0	0	0	0	0	0
I	0	0	4	17	1	22
TI	0	0	0	1	0	1
V	0	0	0	0	0	0
CR	3	0	1	12	11	27
FE	1	0	11	19	10	42
CU	0	0	0	6	10	16
ZN	0	0	8	6	4	18
AS	0	1	4	4	0	9
SE	0	0	0	0	0	0
BR	0	0	0	0	0	0
AL	0	1	0	2	0	3
SI	0	1	0	18	19	38
HG	0	0	0	0	0	0
TL	0	0	0	0	0	0
S	7	7	3	33	152	202
PB	180	59	33	21	4	297
CD	0	0	0	4	1	5
O	2	11	10	3	0	26
F	2	1	2	10	5	20
NA	0	0	0	0	0	0
MG	0	0	0	0	0	0

Table VIII

Occurrence of elements with major quantities

```
SAMPLE  NO : ATLAS VI/77208          DATE DATA ACQUIRED: 5-22-78
PARTICLE NOS: 1-313                  DATE  OF  REPORT  : 6-01-78
```

```
        NUMBER OF PARTICLES WITH MAJOR ELEMENTAL QUANTITIES
        -----------------------------------------------------
```

ELEMENT	NO OF PARTICLES
PB	297
S	202
FE	42
SI	38
CR	27
O	26
I	22
CA	20
F	20
ZN	18
CU	16
AS	9
CD	5
K	4
AL	3
SB	2
TI	1
TE	0
V	0
SE	0
BR	0
HG	0
TL	0
NA	0
MG	0

spectrometer failures. Most of these breakdowns were due to equipment-wear problems. Since the necessary repairs were made by in-house personnel, our downtime was relatively short. Although the CPS system is completely automated and operates on an unattended basis, trained personnel looked in on the system from time to time to check that everything was functioning and responding properly.

Even with the minor delays encountered, it was

Table IX

Average size of particles with major elements

```
SAMPLE  NO : ATLAS VI/77208          DATE DATA ACQUIRED: 5-22-78
PARTICLE NOS: 1-313                  DATE  OF  REPORT  : 6-01-78
```

ELEMENT	AVERAGE SIZE(UM)	FREQ. OF OCCURRENCE
TI	6.44	1
K	4.04	4
O	3.70	26
I	3.62	22
F	3.24	20
AL	2.99	3
S	2.99	202
ZN	2.94	18
PB	2.90	297
FE	2.85	42
CD	2.81	5
CU	2.48	16
SI	2.44	38
CR	2.24	27
SB	2.14	2
AS	1.72	9
CA	1.67	20
TE	0.00	0
V	0.00	0
SE	0.00	0
BR	0.00	0
HG	0.00	0
TL	0.00	0
NA	0.00	0
MG	0.00	0

possible, barring any major delay, to perform complete analyses for 25 elements on as many as 65 particles in one day of continuous operation. In an earlier study[17] while searching airborne particles for lead compounds and limiting the search to only three elements, approximately 12,000 particles were scanned within a two-week period (approximately 720 particles/day). Thus, one can easily see that, although a computerized system enables the analyses of considerably more particles than do manual operations, the analytical time involved is dependent upon the specific analyses required and the accuracy desired. The operational experience gained in performing these and other similar projects has enabled us to better define the criteria needed for the design of future CPS systems—they must be rugged and built with better spectrometers and spectrometer drives, improved stage drive systems and a highly stable power supply system.

F. Automation of the Ion Microprobe

Implementation of the automation system for our ion microprobe mass analyzer (IMA) has been completed. As a result, the IMA has gained considerable speed and accuracy not only for single particle analyses but for elemental mass ratio measurements as well. That is, statistically better data are now obtainable since the computer enables us to make considerably more measurements in the same time period required by the manual system.

The automation system as shown in the block diagram of Figure 28 consists of a Data General Nova 1200 computer with 32K words of 16 bit core memory, two moving head disk drives with a total capacity of 1.2 megawords of 16 bits each, a high-speed paper tape reader, a Tektronic 4010 video terminal with a 4610 hard copier, a Teletype KSR33 teletype with a reader punch, a Systron Donner 6151 megahertz counter/timer, a Datel System 256 analog input-output system and a digital input-output board. In addition, a new Hall probe was installed for field strength monitoring, a Keithley 427 current amplifier for aperture control and two Kepco magnetic field power supplies for primary and secondary field strength control. The respective controls and switches for switching from manual to automatic operation or vice versa were built into a specially designed instrument panel. System software presently allows continuous mass scanning, peak stepping, isotope ratioing and depth profil-

---

[17] Ter Haar, G. L., and M. A. Bayard, "Composition of airborne lead particles," *Nature* **232**, 553–554 (1971).

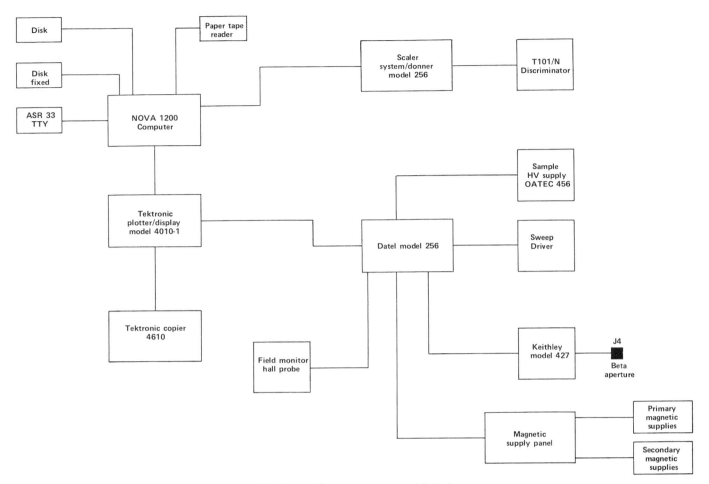

Figure 28.   Ion probe computer system block diagram.

ing with these four basic programs performed under Data General's real-time operating system RDOS.®

As originally delivered by Applied Research Laboratories, the mass scan analyses performed on the IMA required approximately 15 minutes each, with the majority of the time being required by the data output device, an X/Y plotter. Implementation of the automated control system allows these same mass scan analyses to be done in 2–4 minutes and with better accuracy. Rather than outputting the data as they are generated, the computer collects all the data and then generates the mass spectrum on the video display at the end of a scan, giving the same or higher sensitivity than the original X/Y plotter system. Its operation is controlled entirely by the Nova 1200, and the secondary magnet voltage is automatically increased using a variable scan rate proportional to either the magnetic field or mass number. Counts from the secondary ion detector are acquired by the scaler and stored within the computer and, through the use of

step scanning, up to 30 preselected masses are scanned a number of times. For each mass position the magnet voltage is adjusted to select the approximate mass position and then the ratio plates sweep about a small portion of that position in the mass spectrum. The counts collected at each position are then integrated, yielding an average intensity for each specific mass number.

For isotope ratioing the magnet is automatically set to a fixed value in the center of the preselected mass range to be evaluated. The secondary beam is then rapidly swept a number of times over the desired mass range and the respective data collected. Interpretation of the data is then accomplished by identifying the peaks of interest and integrating the counts at each of these peaks. The isotope ratios are, in turn, automatically calculated by the computer. Automation enables us to provide statistically better data since we can now make 20 measurements automatically in the same time that it previously took to make one measurement.

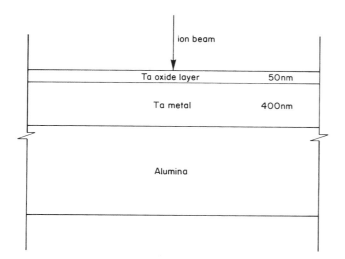

Figure 29.   Illustration of a tantalum thin film resistor.

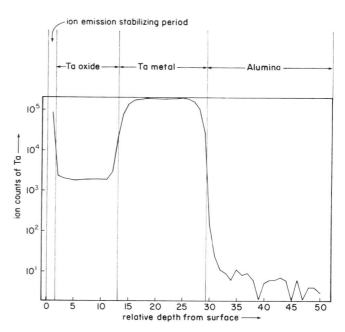

Figure 30.   Depth profile of a tantalum thin film resistor.

Depth profiling is accomplished by directing the primary beam in a rectangular spiral starting from the center of the raster and moving outward. The system is capable of reading counts for up to eight elements during a single run by changing the secondary magnet current while the ion beam is boring into the sample. This information is then displayed on the Tektronix scope after data reduction is performed, and a hard copy output can then be obtained for permanent retention if desired. The time required for depth profiling is dependent upon (1) the sputter rate, which can be varied from approximately 0.1 to 10 Angstroms/ sec, and (2) the desired depth. For example, Figures 29 and 30 illustrate the depth profile of a tantalum thin film resistor. The device consists of a thin layer of tantalum oxide on a thin layer of tantalum metal on an alumina substrate. As the electrical resistance of the device is directly proportional to the oxide layer thickness, the prime emphasis was to determine this thickness. Thus, by being able to measure and control the insulator thickness, the electrical resistance of the device can be adjusted easily for various applications. From Figure 30, the thickness of the tantalum oxide and the tantalum metal layer can easily be calculated once the sputter rate has been determined by microinterferometry. In this particular device the thickness of the tantalum oxide was found to be approximately 50 nm while the tantalum metal was determined to be 400 nm.

The software concepts used within this system are the same as those associated with the CPS system on the EMA, i.e., Fortran programs with assembly language drivers for hardware sequencing. The ion microprobe automation system was designed by the General Electric Corporation, Pleasanton, California, with the principal contributors being J. D. Stein, H. A. Storms and M. C. Gregory under the direction of L. L. Reed, Manager of the Advanced Nuclear Applications Division.

G. Gas Chromatography/Mass Spectrometry Automation

Although the gas chromatograph/mass spectrometer (GC/MS) is not a particle analysis system, its automation is a good example of the extension of the techniques and methods used in automating the electron microprobe and ion microprobe. The technology and experience gained are directly applicable to the automation of any mass spectrometer system. McCrone Associates is in the final stages of automating its GC/ MS system. The basic mass spectrometer, a Bell and Howell Model 21-490, has been continuously updated, but prior to initiating its automation a Tekmar liquid sample concentrator Model LSC-1 was added to the system for the analysis of water samples. The automation system consists of a Digital Equipment Corporation PDP-11/VO3 LSI-11® microcomputer utilizing 32K words of 16 bit memory, two floppy disks having a capacity of 256K 16 bit words each, and a LA 36 Decwriter® for control and mass spectra printout. The respective data are collected by an analog to digital converter Model ARV11. Control functions are provided through a DRV11 data device which is capable of outputting 2 to 3 volts of pulse height under program control in order to initiate data collection by the GC/MS system. A real-time clock has also been included within the system to increase the data acquisition rate by the A/D converter to a maximum rate of one piece of data every 27 microseconds. As a further addition, a floating point chip (FIS) has been installed within the system to enhance the sample throughput by speeding up the mathematical calculations.

It was initially thought at the beginning of the GC/MS automation program that most of the programming could be written as in the EMA and IMA automation systems; however, it was later determined that this method was too slow. Thus, it was necessary to write the final data acquisition program in assembly language and run it under DEC's RT11® real-time executive. Software for data output could still be written in Fortran with both mass spectra bar graphs being output on the Decwriter or the GC graphics system. Analysis run time of a particular scan is variable and controlled by the complexity of the corrections being made and the operator input to the main data acquisition program. Determination of the respective background levels can be performed either manually or automatically and directly input to the correction programs.

By the time this volume is published, automation of the system will be complete. Data output is presently reproducible, but incorporation of calibration methods as well as certain hardware modifications will be made in order to reduce extraneous system noise and increase the system stability.

Automation of the GC/MS system will enable us to perform analyses on a variety of samples automatically with an extremely fast turn-around time. The speed, accuracy and sensitivity are critical in analyses of this nature.

H. Future Automation Possibilities

With automation technology rapidly changing from the large bulky systems of 10 years ago to the mini- and microcomputers of today, the automation possibilities for any facility performing routine or complicated functions are limitless. At McCrone Associates the following automation possibilities exist for the near future.

1. The tandem computerization of the energy-dispersive x-ray analysis and the wavelength crystal spectrometers on the electron microprobe systems will be performed to enhance the speed and accuracy with which the data collection and interpretation are performed.

2. The automation of the MOLE system will be performed to significantly increase the data collection function and, in turn, the data reduction requirement. Since the MOLE system has essentially no moving parts, the data collection area would be relatively easy to automate. However, the data reduction area is significantly more complicated in that at the present time a data base with which to compare and interpret the results does not exist. Thus, the computer would enable us to more quickly and accurately generate a data base for comparison with many varied and different samples.

3. Computerization of the scanning electron microscope has been considered so that a particle or sample can be directly identified by recognition of a pattern based on both morphological characteristics and energy-dispersive x-ray data.

I. Conclusion

Particle analysis laboratories should take full advantage of computerized analytical instrumentation to handle increasingly complex microanalytical problems. By maintaining a leading position in the automation of our particle analysis facilities, McCrone Associates has been able to avoid increases in the cost of services during the past five years. Furthermore, the data are now better, and problems previously impossible to solve are now routine. An interesting comparison of costs shows that whereas complete characterization and chemical identification of a single particle sample may cost several hundred dollars, the cost per particle in a mass scan of several thousand particles is less than one dollar.

Once automated particle analysis instrumentation is available, a wide variety of new microanalytical applications becomes immediately possible. For example, a new procedure for the detection of gunshot residue on the hand of a person who has recently fired a gun has been developed by the Aerospace Corporation.[18] The method involves the detection of three elements (Pb, Sb and Ba) in rounded opaque particles found on a firing hand. The automated mass scanning of particles from a suspect can be quickly and routinely performed in much less time than manually, with better accuracy and hard-copy readout of test results. Obviously, computers have already revolutionized, and will continue to revolutionize, particle analysis problems.

---

18 The Aerospace Corporation, *Gunshot Residue Detection Using Inorganic Luminescence*, September 1975.

VII. Literature Survey

Listed here are references to books and articles which are representative of the literature in this volume.

Electron Microscopy—General

2407. Abstracts: *Electron Microscopy*, Vol. 1, quarterly, P.R.M. Science and Technology Agency Ltd., London, 1973.

2408. Alderson, R. H., *Design of the Electron Microscope Laboratory*, Vol. 4 of *Practical Methods in Electron Microscopy*, A. M. Glauert, Ed., North-Holland/American Elsevier, Amsterdam-New York, 1975.

2409. Baker, R. T. K., P. S. Harris and R. B. Thomas, "Controlled atmosphere electron microscopy," *Res. Dev.* 24, No. 1, 22–24 (1973).

2410. Barrett, C. S., and T. B. Massalski, *Structure of Metals*, 3rd ed., McGraw-Hill, New York, 1966.

2411. Beer, M., "Electron microscopy," Review, *Anal. Chem.* 46, 428R–430R (1974).

2412. Beer, M., "Electron microscopy," Review, *Anal. Chem.* 48, No. 5, 93R–95R (April 1976).

2413. Bernhard, W., and H. Koops, "Kompensation der farbabhaengigkeit der vergroesserung und der farbabhaengigkeit der bilddrehung eines elektronenmikroskops," *Optik* 47, No. 1, 55–64 (1977).

2414. Bowen, D. K., and C. R. Hall, *Microscopy of Materials*, John Wiley & Sons, New York, 1975.

2415. Brodeur, P., *Asbestos and Enzymes*, Ballantine Books, New York, 1972.

2416. Corvin, I., "Preparing biological specimens for electron microscopy," *Res. Dev.* 23, No. 8, 28–31 (1972).

2417. Cosslett, V. E., "Current developments in high voltage microscopy," *J. Microsc.* 100, 233–246 (1974).

2418. Cowley, J. M., "Electron microscopy," Review, *Anal. Chem.* 50, No. 5, 76R–80R (April 1978).

2419. Dawes, C. J., *Biological Techniques in Electron Microscopy*, Barnes and Noble, New York, 1971.

2420. Dietrich, I., F. Fox, E. Knapek, G. Lefranc, K. Nachtrieb, R. Weyl and H. Zerbst, "Improvements in electron microscopy by application of superconductivity," *Ultramicrosc.* 2, No. 2–3, 241–249 (1977).

2421. Diggle, J. W., Ed., *Oxides and Oxide Films*, Vol. 1, Marcel Dekker, Inc., New York, 1972.

2422. Dorignac, D., M. E. C. Maclachlan and B. Jouffrey, "Quantitative approach to molecular resolution electron microscopy," *Nature* 264, No. 5586, 533–534 (1976).

2423. Easterling, K. E., "Recent developments in quantitative electron microscopy," *Int. Met. Rev.* 22, 1–24 (March 1977).

2424. Fertig, J., and H. Rose, "Reflection on partial coherence in electron microscopy," *Ultramicrosc.* 2, No. 2–3, 269–279 (1977).

2425. Ferwerda, H. A., B. J. Hoenders, A. M. J. Huiser and P. van Toorn, "On the phase reconstruction problem in light and electron microscopy," *Photogr. Sci. Eng.* 21, No. 5, 282–289 (1977).

2426. Fisher, R. M., "Electron microscopy—1 million volts and beyond," *Res. Dev.* 23, No. 1, 18–22 (1972).

2427. Fisher, R. M., "Electron microscopy," Review, *Anal. Chem.* 42, 362R–366R (1970).

2428. Glasgow, "Electron microscopy and analysis group conference on developments in electron microscopy," *Rev. Sci. Instr.* 10, 1208–1209 (1977).

2429. Glauert, A. M., *Practical Methods in Electron Microscopy*, Vols. 1–4, The Netherlands and American Elsevier Publishing Co., New York, 1972–1975.

2430. Goodhew, P. J., and L. E. Cartwright, *Electron Microscopy and Analysis*, Wykeham Publication, London, 1975.

2431. Greaves, R. H., and H. Wrighton, *Practical Microscopical Metallography*, Chapman and Hall, London, 1967.

2432. Griver, P., *Electron Optics*, 2nd ed., Pergamon Press, New York, 1972.

2433. Hayat, M. A., *Principles and Techniques for Electron Microscopy: Biological Applications*, Vol. I (1970)–Vol. VI (1976), Van Nostrand Reinhold Company, New York.

2434. Hayat, M. A., *Positive Staining for Electron Microscopy*, Van Nostrand Reinhold Company, New York, 1975.

2435. Heydenreich, J., "Possibilities and limits of electron microscopy," *Microscopica Acta* 79, No. 4, 301–326 (1977).

2436. Hirsch, P. B., A. Howie *et al.*, *Electron Microscopy of Thin Crystals*, Butterworths, London, 1965.

2437. Hoppe, W., "Prospects of three-dimensional high resolution electron microscopy of non-periodic structures," (Max-Planck-Inst. fuer Biochem, Martinsried, Ger.), B. Grill, *Ultramicrosc.* 2, Nos. 2–3, 153–168 (April 1977).

2438. Lee, L., Ed., *Metal Surfaces*, Vol. 1 of *Characterization of Metal and Polymer Surfaces*, Academic Press, Inc., New York, 1977.

2439. Loretto, M. H., and R. E. Smallman, *Defect Analysis in Electron Microscopy*, Chapman and Hall, London, 1975.

2440. McAlear, J. H., "Electron microscopy," Review, *Anal. Chem.* 44, 97R–100R (1972).

2441. McCall, J. L., and W. M. Mueller, Eds., *Microstructural Analysis, Tools and Techniques*, Plenum Press, New York, 1973.

2442. McCrone, W. C., "Choice of analytical tool," *Am. Lab.* (1971).

2443. Meek, G. A., *Practical Electron Microscopy for Biologists*, Wiley-Interscience, New York, 1970.

2444. Meek, G. A., and H. Y. Eder, *Analytical and Quantitative Methods in Microscopy*, Cambridge University Press, New York, 1977.

2445. Misell, D. L., Ed., *Developments in Electron Microscopy and Analysis*, Proceedings of the Institute of Physics Electron Microscopy and Analysis Group Conference, The Institute of Physics, Bristol, London, 1977.

2446. Modin, H., and S. Modin, *Metallurgical Microscopy*, John Wiley & Sons, New York, 1973.

2447. Mokotoff, G. F., *Electron Microscopy Laboratory Technique*, Library Research Associates, Monroe, NY, 1973.

2448. Morton, L., Ed., *Advances in Electronics and Electron Physics*, Vol. 21, Chapter by Oatley, Nixon and Pease, Academic Press, New York, pp. 181–247, 1965.

2449. Parsons, D. F., *Some Biological Techniques in Electron Microscopy*, Academic Press, New York, 1970.

2450. Pinta, M., *Modern Methods for Trace Element Analysis*, Ann Arbor Science Publishers, Ann Arbor, MI, 1978.

2451. Proto, G. R., and K. R. Lawless, "Lorentz electron microscopy of domain walls in single-crystal evaporated iron films," *J. Appl. Phys.* 46, No. 1, 416–421 (1975).

2452. Rackham, G. M., and J. A. Eades, "Specimen contamination in the electron microscope when small probes are used," *Optik* 47, No. 2, 226–232 (1977).

2453. Rose, H., "Nonstandard imaging methods in electron microscopy," *Ultramicrosc.* 2, No. 251–267 (1977).

2454. Russell, P. A., and A. E. Hutchings, *Electron Microscopy and X-Ray Applications*, Ann Arbor Science Publishers, Ann Arbor, MI, 1978.

2455. Ruud, C. O., "Characteristics of silicate mineral fibers as seen by TEM-SAED and SEM-EDXRA," *Micron* 7, 115 (1976).

2456. Skvarla, J. J., and D. A. Larson, "An electron microscopic study of pollen morphology in the Compositae with special reference to the Ambrosiinae," *Grana Palynologica* 6, 210–269 (1965).

2457. Swift, J. A., *Electron Microscopes*, Barnes and Noble, New York, 1970.

2458. Thomas, G., *Electron Microscopy and Structure of Materials*, University of California Press, Berkeley, 1972.

2459. Valdre, U., *Electron Microscopy in Material Science*, Academic Press, New York, 1971.

2460. van Toorn, P., and H. A. Ferwerda, "On the problem of phase retrieval in electron microscopy from image and diffraction pattern—4. Checking of algorithm by means of simulated objects," *Optik* 47, No. 2, 123–134 (1977).

2461. Wealkey, B. S., *A Beginner's Handbook in Biological Electron Microscopy*, Churchill Livingstone, Edinburgh–London, 1972.

2462. Wisse, E., W. T. Daems, I. Molendar and P. Van

Duijin, *Electron Microscopy and Cytochemistry,* North–Holland Publishing Company, Amsterdam, 1974.

Transmission Electron Microscope—Applications

2463. Baker, R. T. K., P. S. Harris, R. B. Thomas and R. J. Waire, "Applications of controlled atmosphere electron microscopy," *JEOL News* **10e,** 18 (1972).

2464. Bradac, M., "Untersuchung der inneren struktur von anstrifilmen," *Plaste u. Kautschuk* (Teil Anstriehstoffe) **20,** 458–460 (1973).

2465. Cunningham, H. M., and F. D. Pontefract, "Penetration of asbestos through the digestive tract of rats," *Nature* **243,** 352–353 (1973).

2466. Dickson, M. R., "Electron microscopy in enzyme analysis," *Lab. Prac.* **23,** No. 7, 392–395 (1974).

2467. Foster, R. H., and J. S. Evans, "The measurement of soil microstructure," *Microscope* **22,** 323–339 (1974).

2468. Gard, J. A., *The Electron Optical Investigation of Clays,* Mineralogical Society, London, 1971.

2469. Hayat, M., *Electron Microscopy of Enzymes,* Vols. I and II, Van Nostrand Reinhold Company, New York, 1973 and 1974.

2470. Hearle, J. W. S., and S. C. Simmens, "Electron microscope studies of textile fibers and materials," *Polymer* **14,** No. 6, 273–285 (1973).

2471. Henderson, B., "Electron microscope microanalyses applied to pathological conditions for identification and quantitation of fine particulates" (Abstract), *Microscope* **23,** No. 4, 263 (1975).

2472. Horne, R. W., "The development of the electron microscope and its application to biology in the past decade," *Proc. Roy. Micros. Soc.* **11,** No. 3, 117–130 (1976).

2473. Humphreys, C. J., "Recent applications of high voltage electron microscopy in various branches of science," *Microscope* **22,** 129–140 (1974).

2474. James, P. F., and P. W. McMillan, "Transmission electron microscopy of partially crystallized glasses," *J. Mater. Sci.* **6,** 1345 (1971).

2475. Lee, R. J., J. S. Lally and R. M. Fisher, "Identification and Counting of Mineral Fragments," *Proceedings of Workshop on Asbestos,* C. C. Gravatt, P. D. LaFleur and Kurt F. J. Heinrich, Eds., NBS, U.S. Dept. of Commerce, pp. 387–402, 1978.

2476. Murr, L. E., *Electron Optical Applications in Materials Science,* McGraw-Hill Book Co., New York, 1970.

2477. Occupational Safety and Health Administration, "Standard for exposure to asbestos dust," *Federal Register* **37,** No. 110, 11318–11322 (1972).

2478. Pande, A., "Electron microscope studies of the fine structure of cellulose and modified cellulose," *Lab. Prac.* **21,** No. 7, 479-482 (1972).

2479. Parsons, D. F., I. Uydess and V. R. Matricardi, "High voltage electron microscopy of wet whole cells," *J. Microsc.* **100,** 153–167 (1974).

2480. Pelzbauer, Z., "Ionenatzung in der elektronenmikroskopie der polymeren," *Plaste u. Kautschuk* (Teil Ansteichstoffe) **20,** 382-384 (1973).

2481. Rossouw, C. J., *et al.,* "Applications of energy analysis in a transmission electron microscope," *Vacuum* **26,** 427–432 (1976).

2482. Schoon, T. G. F., "Eine präparationstechnik zur untersuchung makromolekularer substanzen in Elektronenmikroskop," *Mikroskopie* **25,** 343–345 (1969).

2483. Stanka, P., "Zur interpretation der elektronenmikroskopischen abbildung von zytemembranen im dunnschwitt II. Experimentelle prufung," *Mikroskopie* **30,** 91–94 (1974).

2484. Tanaka, Y., and J. R. Gordman, *Electron Microscopy of Human Blood Cells,* Medical Dept., Harper and Row, New York, 1972.

2485. Wiesenberger, E., "Eine elektronenmikroskopisch answertbare goldreaktion," *Mikrochimica Acta,* 908–924 (1972).

2486. Zeedijk, H. B., "Elektronenmikroskopische untersuchung von asbestkorperchen und asbestfasern in der lunge eines mesotheliom-patienten," *Mikrochimica Acta,* 977–984 (1973).

Transmission Electron Microscope—Instrumentation

2487. Ast, D. G., "Sensitivity and detective quantum efficiency of electron microscope plates at high voltages," *J. Appl. Phys.* **45,** No. 10, 4638–4643 (1974).

2488. Chapman, S. K., *Understanding and Optimising Electron Microscope Performance,* Perkin-Elmer EM Publications, Beaconsfield, Buckinghamshire, 1976.

2489. Dumont, R., D. Rossier, P. Bonhomme, A. Beorchia and B. Meunier, "Phototius: Image intensifier and converter for an electron microscope," *J. Phys. E.* **10,** No. 5, 520–524 (1977).

2490. Hibbert, G., D. R. West and J. W. Edington, "An improved energy analysing electron microscope," *J. Phys. E.* **4,** 1086 (1971).

2491. Knowles, F., and F. Lockett, "Electron microscopy plates or sheet film," *Brit. J. Photog.* **122**, No. 5998, 492–593 (July, 1975).

2492. Marcus, R. B., R. R. Sheng and C. J. Calbick, "A high vacuum large volume specimen chamber for an electron microscope," *J. Phys. E* **5**, 234 (1972).

2493. Moore, V. E., and R. H. Packwood, "A novel rate meter eyepiece for the electron microscope," *Rev. Sci. Instr.* **42**, 533–534 (1971).

2494. Murray, R. T., "An energy dispersing x-ray detector, coupled to a Philips EM 300 electron microscope," *J. Phys. E* **6**, 19 (1973).

2495. Parsons, D. F., and H. M. Johnson, "Possibility of a phase contrast electron microscope," *Appl. Opt.* **11**, 2840 (1972).

2496. Sprys, J. W., "Specimen holder for energy dispersive x-ray analysis in the transmission electron microscope," *Rev. Sci. Instr.* **46**, No. 6, 773–774 (1975).

2497. Thomas, E. L., and D. G. Ast, "Operation of a Channeltron image intensifier in the electron microscope," *J. Phys. E.* **6**, 273 (1973).

2498. Ward, P. R., and R. F. Mitchell, "A facility for electron microscopy of specimens in controlled environments," *J. Phys. E.* **5**, 160 (1972).

2499. Wohlenberg, T., and L. Henriksen, "Defocusing distances, magnifications and high resolution in Lorentz electron microscopy," *J. Phys. E.* **4**, 1079 (1971).

Transmission Electron Microscope—Techniques

2500. Abrahams, M. S., and C. J. Buiocchi, "Cross-sectional specimens for transmission electron microscopy," *J. Appl. Phys.* **45**, No. 8, 3315–3316 (1974).

2501. Abrahams, M. S., and C. J. Buiocchi, "Addendum: Cross-sectional specimens for transmission electron microscopy," *J. Appl. Phys.* **46**, No. 1, 471 (1975).

2502. Agar, A. W., R. H. Alderson and D. Chescoe, *Principles and Practice of Electron Microscope Operation*, American Elsevier Publishing Co., Inc., New York, 1974.

2503. Anaskin, I. F., E. V. Ageev, P. A. Stoganov and V. V. Moseev, "Correction of electron-microscope images by means of holographic filters," *Instru. Exp. Tech.* **19**, No. 1, Part 2, 228–230 (January–February, 1976).

2504. ANSI/ASTM E20-68, "Standard Recommended Practice for Analysis by Microscopical Methods for Particle-Size Distribution of Particulate Substances of Subsieve Sizes," *1977 Annual Book of ASTM Standards*, Part 41, 27–36, 1977.

2505. Baumeister, W., and M. H. Hahn, "Suppression of lattice periods in vermiculite single crystal specimen supports for high resolution electron microscopy," *J. Microsc.* **101**, 111–120 (1974).

2506. Codling, B. W., and J. C. Mitchell, "A method of embedding tissue culture preparations in situ for transmission electron microscopy," *J. Microsc.* **106**, Part 1, 103–106 (January 1976).

2507. Courtoy, R., and L. J. Simar, "Importance of controls for the demonstration of carbohydrates in electron microscopy with the silver methenamine or the thiocarbyhydrazide-silver proteinate methods," *J. Microsc.* **100**, 199–211 (1974).

2508. Gannon, J. R., and R. J. D. Tilley, "A technique for preparing holey carbon films for high resolution electron microscopy," *J. Microsc.* **106**, Part 1, 59–61 (January 1976).

2509. Geissinger, H. D., "A precise stage arrangement for correlative microscopy for specimens mounted on glass slides, stubs or EM grids," *J. Microsc.* **100**, 113–117 (1974).

2510. Ghosh, Sanjib, K., "Photogrammetric calibration of electron microscopes," *Microscopica Acta* **79**, No. 5, 419–426 (1977).

2511. Hayat, M. A., *Basic Electron Microscopy Techniques*, Van Nostrand Reinhold Company, New York, 1972.

2512. Hoch, H., "Dunkelfeldabbildung von schwachen phasenobjekten im elektronenmikroskop," *Optik* **47**, No. 1, 65–85 (1977).

2513. Horne, R. W., *Techniques for Electron Microscopy*, D. H. Kay, Ed., F. A. Davis Company, Philadelphia, 1967.

2514. Huiser, A. M. J., A. J. J. Drenth and H. A. Ferwerda, "On phase retrieval in electron microscopy from image and diffraction pattern," *Optik* **45**, No. 4, 303–316 (July 1976).

2515. Kanig, G., "Ein neues kontrastierverfahren fur die elektronenmikroskopische untersuchung von polyathylen," *Kolloid-Z. W. Z. Polymere* **251**, 782–783 (1973).

2516. Knobler, R. L., "A simple technique to improve contrast of low-contrast electron micrographs," *J. Biol. Photog. Assoc.* **42**, No. 2, 54 (1974).

2517. Knowles, F., and H. Addie, "Printing calibrated micrographs for publication," *Brit. J. Photog.* **121**, 1008–1009 (1974).

2518. Köehler, J. K., *Advanced Techniques in Biologi-*

cal Electron Microscopy, Springer–Verlag, New York, 1973.

2519. Kolbel, H. K., "Partially carbon-coated support films—qualities and application," *Mikroskopie* 30, 208–214 (1974).

2520. Konitz, H., "Das babinet'sche prinzip in der elektronenoptik," *Microscopica Acta* 73, 25–28 (1972).

2521. Martin, C. J., and J. D. Boyd, "A method for calibrating a specimen-heating stage in the electron microscope," *J. Phys. E.* 6, 21 (1973).

2522. Ortiz, L. W., and B. L. Isom, "Transfer technique for electron microscopy of membrane filter samples," *Amer. Ind. Hyg. Assoc. J.*, 55, No. 7, 423–425 (1974).

2523. Pfefferkorn, G., *Beitrage zur elektronenmikroskopischen direktabbildung von oberflachen*, R. A. Remy, Münster, Germany, 1973.

2524. Podbrdsky, J., "High resolution in-focus Lorentz electron microscopy," *J. Microsc.* 101, 231–243 (1974).

2525. Porter, D. A., and J. W. Edington, "Improvement in the accuracy of microanalysis with the combined electron microscope and energy analyzer," *Rev. Sci. Instr.* 10, 1179–1182 (1977).

2526. Reimer, L., and P. Hagemann, "Anwendung eines rasterzusatzes zu einem transmission-selektron-mikroskop-2. Abbildung kristalliner objekte," *Optik* 47, No. 3, 325–336 (1977).

2527. Reunhack, E. H., "Preparation of electron microscope disk specimens by ultrasonic impact grinding," *Rev. Sci. Instr.* 44, 655 (1973).

2528. Robards, A. W., *Ultrastruktur der pflanzlichen zelle—einfuhrung in grundlagen methoden und ergebnisse der elektronenmikroskopie*, Georg Thieme Verlag, Stuttgart, Germany, 1974.

2529. Rostgaard, J., "A defect produced in low power electron micrographs by thin-foil objective apertures," *J. Microsc.* 101, 291–297 (1974).

2530. Schabtach, E., "A method for the fabrication of thin-foil apertures for electron microscopy," *J. Microsc.* 101, 121–126 (1974).

2531. Sinclair, R., "High resolution TEM," *Ind. Res.* 15, 62–65 (1973).

2532. Stewart, I. M., and D. M. Rowe, "A method for examining optically selected areas in the electron microscope," *J. Phys. E.* 4, 1089 (1971).

2533. Strauss, B. M., "Techniques for correlating areas in the SEM and TEM," *Metallogr.* 6, No. 4, 323–335 (1973).

2534. Thomas, G., *Transmission Electron Microscopy of Metals*, J. Wiley and Sons, New York, 1962.

2535. Treiblmayr, K. and K. Pohlhammer, "The use of a microfilter apparatus for fixation and dehydration of small biological specimens in electron microscopy" (in German), *Mikroskopie* 30, 229–233 (1974).

2536. Uyeda, R., "Bright and shadow images of an atom in the transmission electron microscope," *Ultramicrosc.* 2, No. 2–3, 205–206 (1977).

2537. Uyeda, N., T. Kobayashi, E. Suito, Y. Harada and M. Watanabe, "Molecular image resolution in electron microscopy," *J. Appl. Phys.* 43, 5181 (1972).

2538. Veres, I. W., H. Krug, H. Baumbach and A. Ocsenyi., "Physikalische und photochemische methoden zur bessern ausschopfung des informationsgehaltes elektronenmikroskopischer aufnahmen," *Mikroskopie* 30, 257–261 (1974).

2539. Von Harreveld, A., J. Trubatch and J. Steiner, "Rapid freezing and electron microscopy for the arrest of physiological processes," *J. Microsc.* 100, 189–198. (1974).

2540. Williams, J. C., and N. Paton, "Transmission Electron Microscopy," Chapter 40 in Vol. IV of *Systematic Materials Analysis*, J. H. Richardson and R. V. Peterson, Eds., Academic Press, New York, 1974.

Scanning Electron Microscope—Applications

2541. Anon., "Electron beam in textiles," *Chemistry* 47, 22–23 (1974).

2542. Anon., "Textured yards and fabrics as seen by the scanning electron microscope," *Textile Ind.* 138, 60–63 (1974).

2543. Armstrong P. B., "A scanning electron microscope technique for study of the internal microanatomy of embryos," *Microscope* 19, 218 (1971).

2544. Bradley, S. A., and E. P. Dahlberg, "Scanning electron microscopy as an integral technique in failure analysis," *Materials Eval.* 35, 43–48 (1977).

2545. Brownlee, D. E., "Elemental abundances in interplanetary dust," *Nature* 252, No. 5485, 667–669 (1974).

2546. Carroll, D. F., "Scanning electron micrographs of plasma–sprayed Al_2O_3," *J. Amer. Ceram. Soc.* 54, 587 (1971).

2547. Cecil, L. M., G. Eglinton and J. N. M. Firth, "Coatings of organic compounds on metals: detection by scanning electron microscopy," *Lab. Prac.* 23, 120–121 (1974).

2548. Chatfield, E. J., and H. Pullan, "Real time 3-D scanning electron microscopy: its potential and applications," *Can. Res. and Dev.* 1, No. 3, 17–19 (1974).

2549. Cochran, J. K., Jr., "Ceramic microscopy using Al₂O₃," *Bull. Am. Ceram. Soc.* 50, 295–297 (1971).

2550. De Nee, P. B., "Mine dust characterization using the scanning electron microscope," *Am. Ind. Hyg. Assoc. J.* 33, No. 10, 654–660 (1972).

2551. Eyre, T. S., and K. Dutta, "Some applications of the scanning electron microscope in wear studies," *Lub. Eng.* 31, 521–528 (1975).

2552. Gaines, A. M., and J. M. Handy, "Mineralogical alteration of Chinese tomb jades," *Nature* 253, No. 5491, 433–434 (1975).

2553. Green, L., and J. R. Moon, "A microscopical examination of an alleged 1933 penny," *J. Microsc.* 96, 381–384 (1972).

2554. Griffin, N. S., "Focal length modulation of electromagnetic lenses with particular application to scanning electron microscopes," *J. Phys. E.* 9, No. 11, 935–936 (1976).

2555. Hall, J. P., Jr., "SEM study of nucleation sites in pool boiling from 304 stainless steel," *J. Heat Transfer* 96, 132–137 (1974).

2556. Hayat, M. A., *Principles and Techniques for Scanning Electron Microscopy: Biological Applications*, Vol. I (1970)–Vol. IV (1975), Van Nostrand Reinhold Company, New York.

2557. Hayes, L., "Scanning the image," *Ind. Res.* 14, 44 (1972).

2558. James, J., W. L. Jongebloed and I. Molenaar, "The role of hair structure in sound production of bowed instruments," *Mikroskopie* 28, 298–304 (1972).

2559. Johari, O., "Characterizing materials with the SEM today," *Res. Dev.* 25, 16 (August 1974).

2560. Jutte, S. M., and J. F. Levy, "Scanning reflection electron microscopy in studies of wood structure and its degradation," *IAWA Bull.* 1, 3–13 (1971).

2561. Kessel, R. G., and C. Y. Shih, *Scanning Electron Microscopy in Biology: A Student's Atlas on Biological Organization*, Springer–Verlag, New York, 1974.

2562. MacDonald, N. C., C. T. Hovland and R. L. Gerlach, "Scanning Auger microscopy for microelectronic device characterization and quality control," *Scanning Electron Microsc.*, (March 1977).

2563. MacQueen, H. R., G. Judd and S. Ferriss, "The application of scanning electron microscopy to the forensic evaluation of vehicular paint samples," *J. For. Sci.* 17, No. 4, 659–667 (1972).

2564. Martin, P. S., and C. M. Drew, "Scanning electron photomicrographs of southwestern pollen grains," *J. Ariz. Acad. Sci.* 5, 147–176 (1969).

2565. Martin, P. S., and C. M. Drew, "Additional scanning electron photomicrographs of southwestern pollen grains," *J. Ariz. Acad. Sci.* 6, 140–161, (1970).

2566. Midgley, H. G., and K. Pettifer, "Electron optical study of hydrated high-alumina cement pastes," *Trans. Brit. Ceram. Soc.* 71, 55–59 (1972).

2567. Murat, M., and Y. Arnaud, "Morphologie und kristallgefage von naturlichen und synthetischen calciumsulfaten I. Untersuchung von faserartigen gipssteinen," *Tonind. Ztg.* 97, 160–164 (1973).

2568. Reumuth, H., "Faserlegung der natur und der technik, ein mikro-biotechnischer vergleich," *Mikroskopie* 25, 297–312 (1969).

2569. Sakaguchi, H., "Application of scanning electron microscopy to biology," *Japan Analyst* 22, 1113-1120 (1973).

2570. Segnit, E. R., and C. A. Anderson, "Scanning electron microscopy of fired illite," *Trans. Brit. Ceram. Soc.* 71, 85-88 (1972).

2571. Semlitsch, M., and H. G. Willert, "Gewebsveränderungen im bereiche metallischer hüftgelenke: mikroanalytische untersuchungen mittels spektralphotometrie, elektronenmikroskopie und elektronenstrahl-mikrosonde," *Mikrochimica Acta*, 21–37 (1971).

2572. Seoweroff, B. A., and G. C. Padgett, "The structure and thermal behaviour of ceramic fibre blankets," *Trans. Brit. Ceram. Soc.* 72, 11–14 (1973).

2573. Troutman, S., G. G. Johnson, Jr., E. W. White and J. Lebiedzik, "Automated quantitative SEM characterization of complex particulate samples," *Am. Lab.* 16, No. 2, 31 (1974).

2574. Wehrung, J. M., and J. H. McAlear, "Surveying for asbestos and the SEM," *Symposium on Electron Microscopy of Microfibers*, Proceedings of the First FDA Office Science Summer Symposium, 151–157, 1976.

2575. Zulliger, H. R., and W. D. Stewart, "Bulk mode analyses in scanning electron microscopes," *Am. Lab.* 9, No. 4, 75 (1977).

Scanning Electron Microscope—Instrumentation

2576. Anon., "Better resolution in scanning micrographs," *Microstructures* 2, (1), 27–28 (1971).

2577. Beck, V., "Slow scan display system for a scanning electron microscope," *Rev. Sci. Instr.* **44**, 1064 (1973).

2578. Bowers, F. M., and G. S. Ellis, "Simple multisample stage for the scanning electron microscope," *Rev. Sci. Instr.* **48**, 1107–1108 (August 1977).

2579. Christow, A., "Comparison of electron sources for high-resolution Auger spectroscopy in an SEM," *J. Appl. Phys.* **47**, No. 12, 5464–5466 (1976).

2580. Dao, J., "An automated scanning electron microscope/electron microprobe for chemical and biological research," *Am. Lab.* **6**, No. 9, 19 (1974).

2581. Desjardins, P. R., and M. B. Barkley, "Mica disk supports for particulate specimens for scanning electron microscopy," *J. Microsc.* **97**, 389 (1973).

2582. Gibson, E. D., and J. D. Verhoeven, "Device for precise alignment of electron beam and sample in the scanning electron microscope," *Rev. Sci. Instr.* **10**, 1076 (October 1977).

2583. Goldstein, J., and H. Yakowitz, *Practical Scanning Electron Microscopy: Electron and Ion Microprobe*, Plenum Press, New York, 1975.

2584. Gopinath, A., and W. J. Tee, "New electron energy analyzer for voltage measurement in the SEM," *J. Phys. E.* **10**, No. 6, 660–663 (1977).

2585. Grove, C. A., G. Judd and R. Horn, "Evaluation of SEM potential in the examination of shotgun and rifle firing pin impressions," *J. For. Sci.* **19**, No. 3, 441–447 (1974).

2586. Guldberg, J., "Scanning electron microscopy using beam induced currents," *Scand. J. Metallogr.* **6**, No. 1, p. 9 (1977).

2587. Hill, M. S., and A. Gopinath, "Channel plate multiplier as an emissive mode detector in the SEM," *Rev. Sci. Instr.* **48**, No. 7, 806–808 (1977).

2588. Lawvik, M. K., and S. D. Liu, "A new specimen mounting system for scanning electron microscopy," *J. Microsc.* **101**, 329–331 (1974).

2589. Marshall, D. C., "Dual camera attachment for a scanning electron microscope," *J. Phys. E.* **6**, 30 (1973).

2590. Martin, F. W., "Is a scanning ion microscope feasible?" *Science* **179**, 173–175 (1973).

2591. Norville, L. R., T. Nagatani and T. Komoda, "Ultra high resolution SEM," *Ind. Res.* **16**, 44–47 (1974).

2592. Oatley, C., "Scanning electron microscope and other electron probe instruments," *Inst. EE Proc.* **122**, 924–946 (September 1975).

2593. Pawley, J. B., and J. T. Norton, "A chamber attached to the SEM for fracturing and coating frozen biological samples," *J. Microsc.* **112**, 169–182 (March 1978).

2594. Peat, C. J., "A modified specimen stub for the scanning electron microscope," *J. Microsc.* **101**, 323–327 (1974).

2595. Phelan, R. J., Jr., and N. L. DeMeo, Jr., "Rapid scanning microscope for light probing and infrared mapping," *Appl. Opt.* **10**, 856–861 (1971).

2596. Ramalingam, S., and A. C. Bell, "A scanning electron microscope stage for the observation of chip formation," *Rev. Sci. Instr.* **44**, 573 (1973).

2597. Schulson, E. M., "Electron channelling patterns in scanning electron microscopy," *J. Mater. Sci.* **12**, No. 6, 1071–1087 (1977).

2598. Servant, J. M., L. Meny and M. Champigny, *Energy Dispersion Quantitative X-Ray Microanalysis on a Scanning Electron Microscope*, CEA Centre d'Etudes Nucleaires de Saclay, (France), CEA-CONF-2781.

2599. Smith, K. C. A., "On line digital image processing for the SEM" (Abstract), *Microscope* **23**, No. 4, 263–264 (1975).

2600. Waldrop, J. R., and J. S. Harris, "Potential profiling across semiconductor junctions by Auger electron spectroscopy in the scanning electron microscope," *J. Appl. Phys.* **46**, No. 12, 5214–5217 (1975).

2601. Wells, O. C., "XY table and tilting stage for scanning electron microscope (SEM)," *Rev. Sci. Instr.* **46**, No. 1, 77–79 (1975).

2602. Woolf, R. J., D. C. Joy and D. W. Tansley, "A transmission stage for the scanning electron microscope," *J. Phys. E.* **5**, 230 (1972).

2603. Yeger, H., and P. J. Lea, "A specimen carrier, storage disc system for scanning electron microscopy (SEM): evaluation of stainless steel as a substratum for cell culture in vitro," *J. Microsc.* **110**, Part 2, 143–148 (July 1977).

Scanning Electron Microscope—Techniques

2604. Anderson, R. M., "Optimizing detail in electron microscopy," *Ind. Photog.* **19** (April 1970).

2605. Bluhm, W. J., and M. N. Haller, "Particle size analysis using differential interference contrast verified by the SEM," *Am. Lab.* **8**, No. 4, 22 (1976).

2606. Booker, G. R., and R. Stickler, "Scanning electron microscope selected-area channelling patterns: dependence of area on rocking angle and working distance," *J. Mater. Sci.* **7**, 712 (1972).

2607. Breton, J. P., "Optimizing the SEM," *Res. Dev.* **25**, No. 5, 28–30 (1974).

2608. Briatry, L. G., "A method for preparing living plant cell walls for scanning electron microscopy," *J. Microsc.* **94**, 181–183 (1971).

2609. Brown, J. A., and A. Teetsov, "Some techniques for handling particles in SEM studies," *Scanning Electron Microscopy/1976*, Vol. III, IIT Research Institute, Chicago, pp. 385–391.

2610. Chatterji, S., N. Moore and J. S. Jeffery, "Preparation of nonconducting samples for the scanning electron microscope," *J. Phys. E.* **5**, 118 (1972).

2611. Clanton, U. S., and G. H. Ladle, "Polyvinyl acetate—methyl alcohol solution as a scanning electron microscope particle mounting medium," *Am. Mineral.* **60**, 327 (1975).

2612. Coates, V. J., and N. Brenner, "Resolution in scanning electron microscopes," *Res. Dev.* **24**, No. 6, 32–34 (1973).

2613. Devaney, J. R., K. O. Leedy, and W. J. Keery, *Notes on SEM Examination of Microelectronic Devices*, NBS Special Publication, Nos. 400–435, April 1977.

2614. Eletti, V., M. Sarracino, F. Rossi and R. L. Colombo, "Energy dispersion x-ray analysis using a scanning electron microscope," *Metallogr.* **5**, 557–561 (1972).

2615. Goldman, M. A., and R. C. Leif, "A wet chemical method for rendering scanning electron microscopy samples conductive and observations on the surface morphology of human erythrocytes and Ehrlich ascites cells," *Proc. Nat. Acad. Sci.* **70**, 3599–3603 (1973).

2616. Grove, C. A., G. Judd and R. Horn, "Examination of firing pin impressions by scanning electron microscopy," *J. For. Sci.* **17**, No. 4, 645–658 (1972).

2617. Hausmann, K., "Preparation methods of unicellular objects for scanning electron microscopy," *Microscopica Acta* **76**, 113–121 (1974).

2618. Hautsche, H., "Die energiedispersive rontgenmikroanalyse am rasterelektronen mikroskop," *Microscopica Acta* **75**, 409–418 (1974); **76**, 11–27 (1974).

2619. Heinzmann, U., "Refined preparation of biological specimens for the scanning electron microscope" (In German), *Microscopica Acta* **76**, 145–146 (1974).

2620. Hoder, D., "Holographic synthesized scanning electron microscope pictures," *Appl. Opt.* **11**, 2372 (1972).

2621. Hodges, G. M., and M. D. Muir, "Autoradiography of biological tissue in the scanning electron microscope," *Nature* **247**, 383–385 (1974).

2622. Holt, D. B., *Quantitative Scanning Electron Microscopy*, Academic Press, New York, 1974.

2623. Ishiba, T., and S. Iida, "A new replica technique using polyvinyl pyrolidone polymer for the transmission and scanning electron microscope," *J. Electron Microsc.* **23**, 197–198 (1974).

2624. JEOL Staff Report, "Preparation of biological specimens for scanning electron microscopy," *JEOL News* 10e, 42 (1972).

2625. Johari, O., "Total materials characterization with the scanning electron microscope," *Res. Dev.* **22**, No. 7, 12–20 (1971).

2626. Joy, D. C., and D. E. Newbury, "Scanning electron microscope selected–area channelling pattern from 1 micron specimen areas," *J. Mater. Sci.* **7**, 741 (1972).

2627. Judd, G., J. Sabo, W. Hamilton, S. Ferriss and R. Horn, "SEM microstriation characterization of bullets and contaminants particle identification," *J. For. Sci.* **19**, No. 4, 798–811 (1974).

2628. Ladle, G. H., and D. S. McKay, "The use of Millipore filters in the preparation of scanning electron microscope mounts of particles less than 20 micrometers," *Am. Mineral.* **58**, 1082–1083 (1973).

2629. Matricardi, V. R., M. S. Clark and F. S. DeRonja, "The comparison of broken surfaces: A scanning electron microscope study," *J. For. Sci.* **20**, No. 3, 507–523 (1975).

2630. Maurata, K., "Spatial distribution of backscattered electrons in the scanning electron microscope and electron microprobe," *J. Appl. Phys.* **45**, No. 9, 4110–4117 (1974).

2631. Maurin, J. K., and R. E. Allred, "Height measurements of surface features with the scanning electron microscope," *Metallogr.* **10**, No. 2, 161–169 (1977).

2632. Osborn, J. S., "A scanning electron microscope test procedure," *J. Phys. E.* **4**, 958 (1971).

2633. Parsons, E., B. Bole, D. S. Hall and W. D. E. Thomas, "Photographic recording of scanning electron microscope images," *Micron* **4**, 291–293 (1973).

2634. Peat, C. J., and B. J. Lloyd, "Direct observation of rock macerates," *Nature* **251**, 294–295 (1974).

2635. Piercy, R. C., "Improving x-ray imaging in the SEM," *Can. Res.* **8**, No. 6, 19 (1975).

2636. Reimer, L., and P. Hagemann, "Recording of mass thickness in scanning electron microscopy," *Ultramicrosc.* **2**, No. 2–3, 297–301 (1977).

2637. Sarracino, M., "A new technique for the examination of fatigue striations with the scanning electron microscope," *Metallogr.* **6**, No. 2, 176–182 (1973).

2638. Soli, G., "A method of 'staining' bacterial cells for the scanning electron microscope," *Microscopica Acta* **72**, 150–153 (1972).

2639. Thurley, K. W., and W. C. Mouel, "The etching of thick Araldite-embedded sections for scanning electron microscopy," *J. Microsc.* **101**, 215–218 (1974).

2640. Wallace, A., "A new approach to the scanning electron microscope," *Microscope* **22**, 255–266 (1974).

Scanning Electron Microscope— General and Miscellaneous

2641. Beers, W. A., "Surface characterization; the total approach," *Res. Dev.* **26**, 18 (November 1975).

2642. Gilmore, C. P., *The Scanning Electron Microscope: World of the Infinitely Small*, New York Graphic Soc., Greenwich, 1972.

2643. Hayes, T. L., "Trends and prospects in scanning electron microscopy," *J. Microsc.* **100**, 133–142 (1974).

2644. Hearle, J. W. S., J. T. Sparrow and P. M. Cross, *The Use of the Scanning Electron Microscope*, Pergamon Press, New York, 1972.

2645. Holt, D. B., M. D. Muir, P. R. Grant and I. M. Boswarva, Eds., *Quantitative Scanning Electron Microscopy*, Academic Press, New York, 1974.

2646. Johari, O., and I. Corvin, "Scanning electron microscopy and the law," Review, *Can. Res.* **9**, No. 2, 24–30 (1976).

2647. Johari, O., and P. B. DeNee, Eds., *Scanning Electron Microscopy/1972*, IIT Research Institute, Chicago, pp. 249–255.

2648. Johari, O. and I. Corvin, Eds., *Scanning Electron Microscopy/1973; 1974; 1975; 1976; 1977; 1978*, IIT Research Institute, Chicago.

2649. Kimoto, S., "The scanning microscope as a system," *JEOL News* **10**e, 2 (1972).

2650. Oatley, C. W., *The Scanning Electron Microscope*, Cambridge University Press, London, 1972.

2651. Ohnsorge, J., and R. Holm, *Scanning Electron Microscopy. An Introduction for Physicians and Biologists,* Georg Thieme Verlag, Stuttgart, 1973.

2652. Phillips, V. A., *Modern Metallographic Techniques and Their Applications*, Wiley-Interscience, New York, 1971.

2653. Reimer, L., and G. Pfefferkorn, *Raster-Elektronenmikroskopie*, Springer-Verlag, New York, 1973.

2654. Reimschuessel, A. C., "Scanning electron microscopy—Part I," *J. Chem. Educ.* **49**, No. 8, A413–A419 (1972).

2655. Reimschuessel, A. C., "Scanning electron microscopy—Part II," *J. Chem. Educ.* **49**, No. 9, A449–A459 (1972).

2656. Russ, J. C., "Use of the scanning electron microscope in the materials science," *AMST, Spec. Tech. Publ.* STP 480, 214–248 (1970).

2657. Russ, J. C., "Scanning electron miscroscopy," Chapter 16 of *Systematic Materials Analysis*, Vol. 2, J. H. Richardson and R. V. Peterson, Eds., Academic Press, New York, 1974.

2658. *Science Year, The World Book Science Annual/1976*, Chapter by E. J. Chatfield on stereo anaglyphs: "A new dimension in the microscope," Field Enterprises Educational Corp., pp. 128–137, 1975.

2659. Thornton, P. R., *Scanning Electron Microscopy*, Chapman and Hall, London, 1968.

2660. Troughton, J. H., and F. B. Sampson, *Plants: A Scanning Electron Microscope Survey*, J. Wiley and Sons, New York, 1973.

2661. Wells, O., *Scanning Electron Microscopy*, McGraw-Hill, New York, 1974.

Electron Microprobe Analyzer—Applications

2662. Armstrong, J. T., and P. R. Buseck, "Quantitative chemical analysis of individual microparticles using the electron microprobe: Theoretical," *Anal. Chem.* **47**, No. 13, 2178–2192 (1975).

2663. Bloch, R., and A. Krilmburg, "Elekronenstrahlmikroanalyse von komplex-carbiden," *Mikrochimica Acta*, 1240–1246 (1970).

2664. Buckmelter, J. R., and J. K. Kennedy, *Electron Microprobe Characterization of Vapor Grown INAS (1-X) p (X) Layers,* Air Force Cambridge Laboratories, Massachusetts, Report No. AD758 592, August 1972.

2665. Hall, T., P. Echlin and R. Kaufmann, *Microprobe Analysis as Applied to Cells and Tissues*, Academic Press, New York, 1974.

2666. Jedwar, J., "Isolement et étude intégree d'une microparticale minérale par microscopie photonique micro-diffraction. X. microscopie et microsonde électroniques," *Bull. Soc. Belge Geol. Paleont. Hydrol.* **80**, 177–182 (1971).

2667. Karagianne, M. I., "Application of physical and nuclear methods to the examination of archaeological finds and works of art" (in Greek), *Chem. Chron. Genike Ekdosis* **37**, 144–152 (1972).

2668. Laboratory Staff, "Computer controlled JXA-50A electron probe microanalyzer system," *JEOL News* 10e, 27 (1972).

2669. Leute, V., "Die electronenstrahl-mikrosonde als analytisches instrument zur aufklarung von feststoffreaktionen," *Mikrochimica Acta*, 107–115 (1971).

2670. Malissa, H., F. Hermann, F. Kluger and W. Kiesl, "Chemical and microprobe investigations of the Allende meteorite," *Mikrochimica Acta* **3**, 434 (1972).

2671. Malissa, H., and M. Grasserbauer, "Uber die moglichkeiten des einsatzes eines rontgenstrahlanalysators mit primaranregung in der analytischen chemie," *Mikrochimica Acta*, 914–927 (1970).

2672. Meier, H., "Zur anwendung der elektronenstrahlrontgenmikroanalyse in der spurenanalyse," *Mikrochimica Acta*, 61–70 (1970).

2673. Namae, T., and H. Yotsumoto, "Application of electron probe microanalyzer to biology," *JEOL News* 10e, 24 (1972).

2674. Shibuya, M., "Application of electron probe x-ray microanalyzer to agricultural and zoological studies," *JEOL News* 10e, 36 (1972).

2675. Ter Haar, G. L., and M. A. Bayard, "Composition of airborne lead particles," *Nature* **232**, 553–554 (1971).

Electron Microprobe Analyzer—Instrumentation

2676. Evans, H. R., and R. P. Christian, "Adaptation of the x-ray milliprobe for the examination of small single crystals obtained from lunar samples," *Appl. Spect.* **26**, 313 (1972).

2677. Griffin, N. S., "Simple stereoscan stage modification to allow the mounting of large specimens," *J. Phys. E.* **6**, 207 (1973).

2678. Haas, M., and O. Meijer, "Simple back-reflection Kossel camera as an attachment on an electron probe microanalyzer," *J. Phys. E.* **5**, 312 (1972).

2679. Lebiedzik, Jr., E. W. White and R. J. R. S. B. Bhalla, "Simple instrumentation for rise and decay time measurement of cathodoluminescence in an electron microprobe," *Rev. Sci. Instr.* **45**, No. 3, 451–452 (1974).

2680. Oertel, A. C., *Computer Program for Use in Electron-Probe Microanalysis When Some Concentrations are Known*, Commonwealth Scientific and Industrial Research Organization, Glen Osmona, Australia, Report No. PB221 896/4, 1973.

Electron Microprobe Analyzer—Techniques

2681. Andruschenko, N. S., and Y. P. Kostikov, "A new method for measuring the chemical shifts of x-ray emission lines and its application in electron microprobe analysis," *Mikrochimica Acta*, 783–790 (1974).

2682. Bastin, G. F., C. P. Heijwegen, F. J. J. Van Loo and G. D. Rieck, "The use of standards in the quantitative electron probe microanalysis of binary metal systems," *Mikrochimica Acta*, 617–625 (1974).

2683. Baun, W. L., "Electron microbeam probe diagnostics on ion scattering craters," *Appl. Spect.* **30**, No. 2, 233–234 (1976).

2684. Black, W. M., and J. H. Robinson, "Measuring rotationally symmetric potential profiles with an electron-beam probe," *J. Appl. Phys.* **45**, No. 6, 2497–2501 (1974).

2685. Feges, J., K. Swoboda and H. Malissa, "Beitrag zur werwendung der mikrosonde fuer stereochemische analyse," *Mikrochimica Acta*, 173–180 (1971).

2686. Hall, T. A. and B. L. Gupta, "Beam–induced loss of organic mass under electron microprobe conditions," *J. Microsc.* **100**, 177–188 (1974).

2687. Heinrich, K. F. J., *Errors in Electron-Probe Microanalysis*, NBS Report No. COM73-50687/5, 1973.

2688. Heinrich, K. F. J., and H. Yakowitz, "Quantitative electron probe microanalysis: Uncertainty in atomic number correction," *Mikrochimica Acta*, 123–124 (1970).

2689. Heinrich, K. T. J., *The Application of Monte Carlo Calculations in Electron-Probe Microanalysis*, NBS, Washington, D.C., Report No. COM-73-50664/4, March 1973.

2690. Heidel, R. H., "Precision and detection limits of certain minor and trace elements in silicates by electron microprobe analysis," *Anal. Chem.* **43**, 1907–1908 (1971).

2691. Henoc, J., "A rigorous correction procedure for quantitative electron probe microanalysis," *NBS Technical Note* **769**, (1973).

2692. Laguitton, D., and R. Rousseau, "Computed alpha coefficients for electron microprobe analysis," *Anal. Chem.* **47**, No. 13, 2174–2178 (1975).

2693. Malissa, H., and I. L. Morr, "Quantitative separation of traces of copper by electrodeposition and determination by electron probe microanalysis," *Mikrochimica Acta*, 241–249 (1971).

2694. McCoy, D. D., and R. G. Gutmacher, "Improved electron microprobe scanning images," *Rev. Sci. Instr.* **46**, No. 4, 460–463 (1973).

2695. Preuss, E., *Quantitative Analysis with Electron Microprobes and Secondary Ion Mass Spectrometry*, Julich, West Germany, 1972.

2696. Reed, S. J. B., *Electron Microprobe Analysis*, Cambridge Monograph on Physics, Cambridge University, London 1975.

2697. Waldl, E., H. Wolfermann, N. Rusovic and H. Warlimont, "High-accuracy, empirical method of quantitative electron microprobe analysis using an energy dispersive system," *Anal. Chem.* **47**, No. 7, 1017–1019 (1975).

2698. Yakowitz, H., "An on-line correction procedure for quantitative electron probe microanalysis," *NBS Technical Note* **796**, 1973.

Electron Microprobe Analyzer— General and Miscellaneous

2699. Anderson, C. A., *Microprobe Analysis*, John Wiley and Sons., Inc., New York, 1973.

2700. Heinrich, K. F. J., *Bibliography on Electron Probe Microanalysis and Related Subjects*, U.S. GPO, Washington, D.C., 1968.

2701. Luttge, U., *Microautoradiography and Electron Probe Analysis*, Springer-Verlag, New York, 1972.

2702. Ogren, J. R., "Electron Microprobe," Chapter 6 of *Systematic Materials Analysis*, Vol. 1, J. H. Richardson and R. V. Peterson, Eds., Academic Press, New York, 143–192, 1974.

2703. Reed, S. J. B., *Electron Microprobe Analysis*, Cambridge Monographs on Physics, Cambridge University Press, Cambridge, London, 1975.

Ion Microprobe Analyzer—Applications

2704. Bayard, M. A., "Applications of the ion probe microanalyzer," (Abstract), *Microscope*, **23**, No. 4, 269 (1975).

2705. Gavrilovic, J., and E. Majewski, "Use of ion and electron microprobes for full characterization of particulate matter," *Am. Lab.* **9**, No. 4, 19 (1977).

2706. Hinthorne, J. R., and C. A. Anderson, "Microanalysis for fluorine and hydrogen in silicates with the ion microprobe mass analyzer," *Am. Mineral.* **60**, 143–147 (1975).

2707. Shimizu, R., T. Ishitani, T. Kondo and H. Tamura, "Practicality of the thermodynamic model for quantitative ion probe microanalysis of low alloy steels," *Anal. Chem.* **47**, No. 7, 1020–1024 (1975).

Ion Microprobe Analyzer—Techniques

2708. Bakale, D. K., B. N. Colby and C. A. Evans, Jr., "High mass resolution ion microprobe mass spectrometry of complex matrices," *Anal. Chem.* **47**, No. 9, 1532–1537 (1975).

2709. Ishitani, T., H. Tamura and T. Kondo, "Quantitative analysis with an ion microanalyzer," *Anal. Chem.* **47**, No. 8, 1294–1296 (1975).

2710. McLaughlin, J. F., and S. S. Cristy, "A vacuum sample holder for an ion microprobe mass analyzer," *Rev. Sci. Instr.* **45**, No. 6, 852–853 (1974).

2711. Tsukizoe, T., *et al.*, "Ion-beam plating using mass-analyzed ions," *J. Appl. Phys.* **48**, 4770–4776 (November 1977).

Ion Microprobe Analyzer— General and Miscellaneous

2712. Gavrilovic, J., "Identification of thin surface films on small particles," *Microscope* **25**, No. 1, 119–126 (1977).

2713. Liebl, H., "History of the development of ion microprobe analyzers and discussion of future prospects in this instrumentation," *Anal. Chem.* **46**, 22A–32A (1974).

2714. Muller, E. W., "Advances in atom-probe field ion field microscopy," *J. Microscopy* **100**, 121–132 (1974).

2715. Scilla, G. J., and G. H. Morrison, "Sampling error in ion microprobe analysis," *Anal. Chem.* **49**, No. 11, 1529–1536 (1977).

2716. Valkovic, V., *Trace Elements in Human Hair*, Garland STPM Press, New York, 1977.

Scanning Transmission Electron Microscope

2717. Bauer, B., and R. Speidel, "Herabstezung der kontaminationsrate im STEM bei einem druck von 10^{-5} torr," *Optik* **48**, No. 2, 237–246 (1977).

2718. Crewe, A. V., and T. Groves, "Thick specimens in the CEM and STEM. I. Contrast," *J. Appl. Phys.* **45**, No. 8, 3662–3672 (1974).

2719. Crewe, A. V., "Scanning transmission electron microscopy," *J. Microsc.* **100**, 247–259 (1974).

2720. Drummond, I. W., "Scanning transmission electron microscopy," *Am. Lab.* **8**, No. 4, 83 (1976).

2721. Koike, H., T. Matsuo, K. Ueno and M. Suzuki, "Applications of scanning transmission microscopy with high resolution scanning device," *JEOL News* **10**e, 6 (1972).

2722. Komoda, T., H. Todokoro and S. Nomura, "Single atom image observation by means of scanning transmission electron microscope," *Hitachi Rev.* **26**, No. 4, 151–156 (1977).

2723. Maher, D. M., and D. C. Joy, "Scanning transmission electron microscope; a micro-area analytical system," *J. Metals* **29**, 26–30 (February 1977).

2724. Thompson, M. N., P. Doig, J. W. Edington and P. E. J. Flewitt, "Influence of specimen thickness on x-ray count rates in STEM-microanalysis," *Philos. Mag.* **35**, No. 6, 1537–1542 (1977).

2725. Thomson, M. G. R., "Resolution and contrast in the conventional and the scanning high resolution transmission electron microscopes," *Optik* **39**, 15–38 (1973).

Diffraction—Electron and X-ray

2726. Abstracts, *X-ray diffraction abstracts*, quarterly, Volume I, P. R. M. Science and Technology Agency Ltd., London, 1973.

2727. American Crystallographic Association, *Transactions of the American Crystallographic Association—Proceedings of the Symposium Commemorating Fifty Years of Electron Diffraction*, Polycrystal Book Service, Pittsburgh, 1977.

2728. Armigliato, A., P. G. Merli and G. Ruffini, "Low angle electron diffraction with the Elmiskop 101 electron microscope," *J. Phys. E.* **6**, 35 (1973).

2729. Azaroff, L. V., *Elements of X-ray Crystallography*, McGraw-Hill Book Company, New York, 1968.

2730. Azaroff, L. V., and M. J. Buerger, *The Powder Method in X-Ray Crystallography*, McGraw-Hill Book Company, New York, 1958.

2731. Ball, C. J., *An Introduction to the Theory of Diffraction*, Pergamon Press, Oxford, 1971.

2732. Buerger, M. J., *Crystal-Structure Analysis*, John Wiley & Sons, Inc., New York, 1960.

2733. Buerger, M. J., *X-ray Crystallography*, John Wiley & Sons, Inc., New York, 1953.

2734. Crowley, John M., *Diffraction Physics*, North-Holland Publishing, Amsterdam, 1975.

2735. Cullity, B. D., *Elements of X-ray Diffraction*, Addison-Wesley Pub. Co., Inc., Reading, MA 1956, 1959.

2736. Donnay, J. D. H., *Crystal Data Determination Tables*, Polycrystal Book Service, Pittsburgh, 1963.

2737. Goodhew, P. J., *Electron Microscopy and Analysis*, Wykeham Publications, Ltd., London, 1975.

2738. Graham, D., *The Use of X-ray Techniques in Forensic Investigations*, Churchill Livingston, London, 1973.

2739. Grieger, G. R., and I. M. Stewart, "Electron diffraction: a time for rediscovery," *Am. Lab.* **9**, No. 4, 61 (1977).

2740. Hall, Cecil E., *Introduction to Electron Microscopy*, McGraw-Hill Book Company, Inc., New York, 1953.

2741. Head, A. K., *et al.*, *Computed Electron Micrographs and Defect Identification*, American Elsevier Publishing Company, New York, 1973.

2742. Heinrich, K. F. J., C. S. Barrett, J. B. Newkirk and C. O. Ruud, Eds., *Advances in X-Ray Analysis, Proceedings of the Twentieth Annual Conference on Applications of X-Ray Analysis* (August, 1971) Plenum Press, New York, 1972.

2743. Henry, N. F. M., H. Lipson and W. A. Wooster, *The Interpretation of X-ray Diffraction Photographs*, MacMillan and Co., Ltd, London, 1953.

2744. International Union of Crystallography, *International Tables for X–ray Crystallography*, Volumes 1–4, Kynoch Press, Birmingham, England, 1969.

2745. James, R. W., *The Optical Principles of the Diffraction of X-rays*, G. Bell and Sons, Ltd., London, 1958.

2746. Kelly, A., and G. W. Groves, *Crystallography and Crystal Defects*, Addison-Wesley Publ. Co. Inc., Reading, MA, 1970.

2747. Klug, H. P. and L. E. Alexander, *X–ray Diffraction Procedures*, John Wiley & Sons, Inc., New York, 1954.

2748. Knox, J. R., "Protein molecular weight by x-ray diffraction," *J. Chem. Educ.* **49**, 476–479 (1972).

2749. Lipson, H. S., *Crystals and X-rays*, Wykeham Publications, Ltd., London, 1970.

2750. Lipson, H., and W. Cochran, *The Determination of Crystal Structures*, G. Bell and Sons, Ltd., London, 1957.

2751. Loretto, M. H., and R. E. Smallman, *Defect Analysis in Electron Microscopy*, John Wiley & Sons, New York, 1975.

2752. Nuffield, E. W., *X-ray Diffraction Methods*, John Wiley and Sons, Inc., New York, 1966.

2753. Pfluger, C. E., "X-ray diffraction," Review, *Anal. Chem.* **46**, 469R–478R (1974).

2754. Pfluger, C. E., "X-ray diffraction," Review, *Anal. Chem.* **50**, No. 5, 161R–166R (April 1978).

2755. Rymer, T. B., *Electron Diffraction*, Chapman and Hall, London, 1975.

2756. Stout, George H., and Lyle H. Jensen, *X-ray Structure Determination*, Macmillan Company, New York, 1968.

2757. Tompsett, M. F., "Scanning high-energy electron diffraction (SHEED) in materials science," *J. Mater. Sci.* **7**, 1069 (1972).

2758. Warren, B. E., *X-ray Diffraction*, Addison–Wesley Publ. Co., Inc., Reading, MA, 1969.

2759. Woolfson, M. M., *An Introduction to X-ray Crystallography*, University Press, Cambridge, 1970.

2760. Zachariasen, William H., *Theory of X-ray Diffraction in Crystals*, Dover Publications, Inc., New York, 1945.

2761. Zuyagin, Boris B., *Electron-Diffraction Analysis of Clay Mineral Structures*, Plenum Press, New York, 1967.

Mass Spectroscopy

2762. Briggs, R., D. Dix, D. Glover and R. Kleinman, "A multi-instrument data acquisition system for use with mass spectrometry," *Am. Lab.* **4**, 57 (1972).

2763. Brown, R., M. L. Jacobs and H. E. Taylor, "A survey of the most recent applications of spark source mass spectrometry," *Am. Lab.* **4**, 29 (1972).

2764. Franzen, J., *Analysis by Mass Spectrometry*, Academic Press, New York, 1972.

2765. Horning, E. C., *et al.*, "New picogram detection system based on a mass spectrometer with an external ionization source at atmospheric pressure," *Anal. Chem.* **45**, 936 (1973).

2766. Maccoll, A., *Mass Spectrometry*, Volume 5 of MTP International Review of Science Physical Chemistry, Series One, University Park Press, Baltimore, 1972.

2767. Ogata, K., and T. Hayakawa, *Recent Developments in Mass Spectroscopy*, Proceedings of the International Conference on Mass Spectroscopy, Japan, University Park Press, Baltimore, 1970.

Electron Spectroscopy

2768. Baker, A. D., A. B. Brisk and D. C. Liotta, "Electron spectroscopy: ultraviolet and x-ray excitation," Review, *Anal. Chem.* **50**, No. 5, 328R–346R (April 1978).

2769. Baker, A. D., and D. Betteridge, *Photoelectron Spectroscopy: Chemical and Analytical Aspects*, Pergamon Press, Oxford, 1972.

2770. Briggs, D., Ed., *Handbook of X-ray and Ultraviolet Photoelectron Spectroscopy*, Heyden & Son Ltd., London, 1977.

2771. Carlson, T. A., Ed., *X-ray Photoelectron Spectroscopy: Benchmark Papers in Physical Chemistry and Chemical Physics*, Vol. 2, Dowden, Hutchinson and Ross, Inc., Stroudsburg, PA, 1978.

2772. Carson, T. A., *Photoelectron and Auger Spectroscopy*, Plenum Press, New York and London, 1975.

2773. Eland, J. H. D., *Photoelectron Spectroscopy*, Butterworth and Co. Ltd., London, 1974.

2774. Hercules, D. M., "Electron spectroscopy: X-ray and electron excitation," Review, *Anal. Chem.* **48**, No. 5, 294R–313R (April 1976).

2775. Jonathan, N., A. Morris, M. Okuda, D. J. Smith and K. J. Ross, *Electron Spectroscopy*, D. A. Shirley, Ed., North Holland, New York, 1972.

2776. Kemp, N. R., *The Potential of UV Photoelectron Spectroscopy as a Technique of Analytical Chemistry*, Ph.D. Thesis, University of Wales, 1971.

2777. Lever, A. B. P., *Inorganic Electronic Spectroscopy in Physical Inorganic Chemistry*, Monograph 1, M. F. Lappert, Ed., Elsevier Publishing Co., Amsterdam, 1968.

2778. MacDonald, G. L., "X-ray spectrometry," Review, *Anal. Chem.*, **50**, No. 5, 135R–142R (April 1978).

2779. Schrenk, W. G., *Analytical Atomic Spectroscopy*, Plenum Press, New York and London, 1975.

2780. Siegbahn, K., C. Nordling *et al.*, *ESCA: Atomic, Molecular and Solid State Structure Studied by Means of Electron Spectroscopy*, Almquist and Wiksells Boktryckeri AB, Uppsala, 1967.

2781. Swartz, W. E., and D. M. Hercules, "X-ray photoelectron spectroscopy of molybdenum compounds," *Anal. Chem.* **43**, 1774–1779 (1971).

2782. Wood, W. G., "X-ray spectroscopy reborn," *Ind. Res.* **14**, 38 (1972).

Image Analysis

2783. American Society for Testing and Materials, *Stereology and Quantitative Metallography,* American Society for Testing Materials, Easton, PA, 1972.
2784. Cruttwell, I. A., "Pattern recognition by automatic image analysis," *Microscope* **22**, 27 (1974).
2785. Eins, S., "Automatic image analysis in the medical and biological sciences," *Microscope* **22**, 59 (1974).
2786. Elias, H., Ed., *Stereology,* Springer-Verlag, New York, 1967.
2787. Hougardy, H. P., "Recent progress in automatic image analysis," *Microscope* **24**, 7 (1976).
2788. Hougardy, H. P., "Instrumentation in automatic image analysis," *Microscope* **22**, 5 (1974).
2789. Jesse, A., "Information sources in automatic image analysis," *Microscope* **22**, 81 (1974).
2790. Jesse, A., "A review of image analysis," *Microscope* **22**, 1 (1974).
2791. Jesse, A., "Bibliography on automatic image analysis (1973–1975)," *Microscope* **24**, 65 (1976).
2792. Laboratory Staff, "Computer-controlled image analyzer for JSM 50A scanning microscope," *JEOL News* **10**e, 26 (1972).
2793. Nazaré, S., and G. Ondracek, "Automatic image analysis in materials science," *Microscope,* **22**, 39 (1974).
2794. Parker, B. A., and P. L. Rossiter, "Simple image analysing, attachment for a scanning electron microscope," *J. Austral. Inst. Met.* **21**, No. 4, 191–194 (1976).
2795. Slater, J., and B. Ralph, "The status of automatic image analysis in materials science and technology," *Microscope* **24**, 25 (1976).
2796. Underwood, E. E., "Trends in stereology," *Microscope* **24**, 45 (1976).
2797. Underwood, E. E., "Stereology in automatic image analysis," *Microscope* **22**, 69 (1974).

Index

AAA yarn (viscose rayon), 962, 966
abaca, 965, 967, 1276, 1563, 1565
Abax ater, 1359
Abbe condensers, 15, 1034
Abbe theory of resolution, 19, 1034
aberrations, 1034
  chromatic, 1037
    light microscope, 8, 9, 11, 15
      TEM, 133
    electron lens, 133
    mirror, 4
  spherical, 1055
    light microscope, 4, 8, 11
      TEM, 133
Abies balsamea, 1278, 1564
abrasives, 310, 320, 407, 658, 824, 826,
    828, 832, 834, 1370
abundance of elements, 319
Acacia longifolia, 1191, 1480
Acacia pollen, 1191, 1480
Acacia trees, 1331, 1628
accessory minerals, 319
Acer saccharum, 335, 361, 593, 615, 1279,
    1565
acetate rayon, 310–311, 362, 367, 616,
    820, 841, 842, 848
acetolysis, 1355
achromatic-aplanatic condensers, 15
achromatic objectives, 9, 11, 14
acicular, 1034
acid igneous rocks, 1353
acoustic tile, 368, 622, 811, 813, 851
Acrilan®, 362, 616, 820, 841, 847, 961,
    966
acrylic fibers, 362, 616–617, 820, 841,
    847, 961, 966
actinium, 991
actinolite asbestos, 853, 1226, 1231, 1232,
    1238, 1374, 1500
acute bisectrix, 81, 1034
addition compounds, 119
adhesives, 1329–1333
advances, electron optical methods, 1461–
    1465
AEI-EMMA-4, 1462
aerosol centrifuge-elutriator, 212
aerosol spectrometer, 213
Aesculus hippocastanum, 334, 360, 592,
    614
Agaricus campestris, 344, 599
agate, 851

Agave sisalna, 355, 610, 848, 1281, 1568
age of soil, 1354
Ailanthus altissima, 1218, 1493
air bubbles, 312
air conditioner, 206, 551, 781, 858
air monitoring, 204–217, 1363
air quality maintenance, 1362
alabaster, 852
α-alanine, 1289, 1574
albite, 371, 625, 640, 815, 822, 839, 852,
    1034, 1227, 1238, 1502
alcohol, polyvinyl, 505, 743, 827, 842
alder (red) pollen, 1191–1192, 1480
aldrin, 1302, 1587
alfa, *see* aleurone, esparto, 1034
alfalfa, 437, 685, 811, 814, 817, 821, 831,
    848
algae, 315, 328–330, 448, 588–589, 814,
    819, 823, 825, 827–828, 848–849
alignment, microscope, 43
alizarin, 1312, 1321, 1408, 1601, 1614
alkyl sulfonate detergents, 425, 675
alloy (metal) spray, 467, 480, 708, 835,
    840
almandite, 382, 401, 636–637, 814, 839,
    854, 873, 880, 899, 935–938
Alnus rubra, 1191–1192, 1480
Alsibronz®, 510, 746, 823, 839
Alternaria, 315, 342, 597, 826–828, 847
alumina, 585
  activated, 510, 746, 812, 818, 853
  calcined, 465, 706, 818, 824
  catalyst, 414–418, 664–669
  iota-, 144
aluminum, 852, 978
  fluoride, 465, 707, 853
    manufacturing, 465, 707, 812, 818,
      824, 835, 837
  oxide (hydrated), 1257, 1543
  powder, 1264, 1552
  recovery, 1305, 1590
  "sawdust," 465, 707, 836–837, 839
  silicates, 414–418, 664–669, 1227,
    1248, 1533
  slag, 466, 707, 812, 824, 835
  stearate, 510, 746, 812, 839, 847, 1248,
    1533
  stubs, 1473
alunite, 371, 625, 820, 837–839, 852
Amaranthus hybridus, 337, 594
amber, 847

Amberlite®, 1337, 1635
amblygonite, 371, 626, 815, 839, 853, 873,
    882, 896–897, 919–920, 922–924
Ambrosia sp., 311, 339, 595
American beech pollen, 1194, 1481
American elm
  pollen, 332, 591, 825
  trichomes, 360, 614, 820
americium, EDXRA, 992
aminoacetic acid, 1293
amino-phenylamino-p-tolyl ditolazolium
    sulfate, 1322
2-aminopropanoic acid, 1574
ammonium
  alum, 849, 873, 884, 890, 908
  bromide, 851, 884, 898, 929–931
  chloride, 310, 429, 679, 811, 843, 848
  chromium sulfate dodecahydrate, 885,
    890, 909
  dichromate, 850
  dihydrogen arsenate, 851, 885, 893,
    895, 911–912, 917
  dihydrogen phosphate, 849, 885, 893,
    909, 913, 1003
  ferrocyanide-ammonium chloride
    double salt, 848, 885, 895–896,
    918–919, 921
  fluoroborate, 849
  iodine, 851, 885, 930
  iron selenate hexahydrate, 885, 893–
    894, 911–913
  iron sulfate hexahydrate, 885, 891, 909–
    910
  nitrate, 429, 679, 816, 845, 849, 873,
    885, 889, 897, 906, 923, 1265,
    1552
  perchlorate, 849, 885, 890–891, 909,
    1552
  phosphate, 430, 680, 816, 821, 845, 849,
    858, 885, 890, 909
  selenate, 850, 885, 895, 915–918
  silicofluoride (cryptohalite), 850, 874,
    885, 889, 903–904
  sulfate, 430, 680, 685, 816, 838, 845,
    849
amobarbital, 1397
amorphous, 1044
amorphous silica, 1341
amorphous sulfur, 535, 767, 815, 824–825,
    829, 833, 845, 850

Vol. I: pp. 1–296   Vol. II: pp. 297–570   Vol. III: pp. 571–794   Vol. IV: pp. 795–1138   Vol. V: pp. 1139–1454   Vol. VI: pp. 1455–1703

1675

amosite, 142, 373, 627, 820, 825, 830, 833, 844, 852, 873, 880, 898, 1237, 1516
  SAED pattern, 1646
amphiboles, 393, 645, 852, 1232, 1369, 1644–1645
Amphipleura pellucida, 329, 589
amyl acetate, 230
analcime, 850
analytical electron miscroscopy, 1464–1465
analytical tool, choice of, 280–283
analyzer, 16, 1034
anatase, 586, 854, 1152, 1153, 1226, 1229, 1313, 1501, 1505, 1602
andalusite, 853, 1227, 1238, 1501
Andersen sampler, 215
andesine, 1227, 1502
andradite, 383, 636, 814, 824, 843, 854
Andreason pipette, 212
anesthesine, 1258
angle of reflection, 3
anglesite, 855, 873, 886, 899, 946–950
Angora goat, 348, 603, 848
angular aperture, 12, 133, 1035
angularity, particle, 1347
anhedral, 1035
anhydrite, 372, 626, 815, 838, 843, 852, 873, 879, 895–896, 916–917, 920–921, 1229, 1407
anhydrous
  borax, 1249
  chromium oxide, 1317
  cobalt phosphate, 1316, 1607
animal
  feeds, 322, 691, 817, 821–822, 829, 831, 848, 1360
  fibers, 310, 317, 346–353, 601–606, 857, 1282–1288, 1358–1359, 1381–1384, 1569–1573
  glue, 1329, 1625
  hairs, 310, 317, 346–353, 601–606, 857, 1282–1288, 1358–1359, 1381–1384, 1569–1573
  tissue, 113
anisotropic materials, 77, 82
anisotropic unknowns, dispersion staining, 110
annular illumination, 1151
annular phase plate, 40–41
annular screening, *see* annular stop
annular stop, dispersion staining, 97, 1035
Anophthalmus beetle, 1359
anorthite, 386, 640, 852, 1227, 1502, 1506
anorthoclase, 851
Antabuse®, 1395–1396
antelope hair, 1282, 1569, 1571
anthophyllite, 373, 628, 820, 844, 852, 873, 882, 896–897, 1373–1374, 1528
anthracite coal, 544, 774, 836, 849
anthraquinone dyes, 1321
antigorite, serpentine, 372, 626, 815, 820, 822, 844, 851, 1239, 1373, 1520

antimony, 466, 708, 815, 828–829, 845, 855, 985, 1242
Antron®, 961, 966
apatite, 310, 372, 627, 633, 815, 822, 843, 853, 1341, 1374, 1508
aperture
  angular, 12
  numerical, 11–15, 44–46
  system, Hoffman modulation contrast microscopy, 1156
  SAED, 136–137
  TEM, 133
aplanatic condensers, 15
apochromatic objectives, 11, 14, 20, 1035
Apochromount®, 308
Apollo 12 moon dust, 557, 785
apophyllite, 851, 1227, 1502
Aquaresin®, 77, 308, 1035
aragonite, 310, 373, 627, 824–825, 840, 852, 873, 878, 893, 898, 912–913, 927–929, 1526, 1531
aramid, *see* Kevlar
arcanite, 873, 882, 891, 910
archaeology, 1402–1413
area vs. diameter, particles, 806
areal analysis, 268
areas and volumes, equations, 1019–1027
argentite, 855
argon, 979
Arizona road dust, 561, 788
armorganic tankage, 431, 681, 811, 817, 826, 829, 848, 1035
Arnel®, 367, 621, 820, 842, 848
Aroclor®, 43, 97, 224–225, 236–237, 305–306, 312, 968, 1035, 1166
  characteristics, 224–225, 305, 312, 968, 1166–1174
  dispersion, 97
  fluorescence, 43
  mounting particles, 305, 306
  recovery of particles from, 236–237
  refractive indices, 305, 968
arrowroot starch, 457–458, 702, 842
arsenic, 855, 982, 1323
  selenide, 307
  tri-iodide-sulfur complex, 877, 899, 946
  trioxide, 476, 840, 854
  trisulfide, 853, 1616
arsenolite, 873, 877, 898, 934–935, 1503
arsenopyrite, 855, 1228
art and archaeology, 1402–1413
Artemisia absinthium, 1220, 1494
asbestos, 97, 116, 142–144, 310, 373, 404, 582, 627–628, 669, 820, 825, 830, 833, 844, 851, 852, 1369–1378
  acid treatments, 1651
  actinolite, 853
  amphiboles, 1644
  ashing, 1648–1650
  brake lining, 374, 629, 820, 826, 834, 844, 848
  bulk sample preparation, 1370–1371, 1646
  computerized, 1646

asbestos—*cont'd*
  condensation washing technique, 1646–1647
  darkfield dispersion staining, 1159
  definition, 1644
  dispersion staining identification, 1371–1378
  fiber counting, 1371
  fluid samples, 1646
  identification, 1369–1378, 1644–1651
  in beverages and foodstuffs, 1650–1651
  Jaffé wicking method, 1647–1648
  low temperature ashing, 1648–1651
  MESA counting method, 1371
  mortar insulation, 419, 669, 811, 821, 844, 848
  optical crystallographic properties, 1376
  OSHA counting method, 1371
  oxygen plasma ashing, 1648–1651
  positive identification, 1646
  powder sample preparation, 1371
  processing, 375, 629, 815, 820
  SAED, 1644
  sample preparation, 1370–1371, 1646–1651
  SEM, 1644
  serpentines, 1644
  TEM, 1644
  tissue digestion, 1648–1650
  tissue samples, 1648–1650
  tissue sections, 1648–1649
  water sample preparation, 1371
  see also amosite, anthophyllite, chrysotile, crocidolite, tremolite
ash
  bone, 1314
  cigarette, 542, 772, 813–814, 819, 836, 847
  fireplace, 1632
  incinerator, 850
  leaf burning, 542, 772
  pollen, 1192, 1480, 1489
  volcanic, 563, 674, 790, 813, 821, 833, 836, 850
ashing
  asbestos, 1648–1650
  low-temperature, 221
  particle, 115
Aspergillus niger, 342, 597, 811, 819, 823, 826, 830–831, 848
asphalt, 307, 311, 511, 747, 756, 823, 835–836, 847, 1603
asphalt road pavement, 1338, 1635
aspirin, 511, 747, 821, 842, 848
associated particles, 1353
astatine, 990
astigmatism, 1035
  light microscope, 9
  TEM, 133
Astragalus gummifer L., 1333, 1630
atacamite, 1228, 1503
Atlas, use of, 582
atmospheric dust particles
  counting, 1366
  estimations, 1366

atmospheric dust particles—*cont'd*
  examination of, 1362–1368
  hi-vol glass filters, 1365
  litigation, 1362
  qualitative analyses, 1364
  quantitative analyses, 1366
    errors, 1366
  reporting, 1367
  sampling, 1363
attapulgite clay, 375, 382, 629, 635, 822, 839, 851, 1522, 1645
Auger microprobe scanning, 1466–1467
Auger spectroscopy, 180–181
augite, 375, 381, 630, 833, 843, 853, 873–874, 878, 898, 929–934, 1325
aureolin, 1313, 1602
authentication, art and archaeology, 1402–1413
auto brake lining, 1338, 1636
auto emission, 541, 771, 825, 833, 836, 858
autofluorescence, 42
automatic image analysis, 268–270, 1035
automatic specimen stage drive, EMA, 164
automation, 1652–1660
  advances at Walter C. McCrone Assoc., 1653
  EMA, 161, 1653–1657
  EMMA, 1653
  ESCA, 1654
  future, 1660
  GC/MS, 1659–1660
  IMA, 1657–1659
  MOLE, 1660
  particle analysis, 1655–1657
automobile exhaust, 144–145, 173, 586, 833
automotive tire wear products, 1348, 1361
auxiliary illuminator, 28
auxiliary telescope, 231
average particle diameters, 266
Avicel, 1289, 1575
avogadrite, 874, 881, 889, 901–902
Avril® (viscose rayon), 962, 966
azurite, 376, 630, 824, 832, 841, 854, 1409

back focal plane, objective, 16, 22–25, 1035
back lens, 1035
back-scattered electron image, EMA, 158, 166
baddeleyite, 492, 732, 855
badger, 964, 967
bagasse, 550, 780, 828, 836–837, 847, 1277, 1334, 1386, 1563, 1630
baggy cells, 318
Bahco microparticle classifier, 212
Bakelite, 500, 738, 812, 818, 821, 830, 835, 849, 1338
bald cypress pollen, 1200, 1484
ballistics, drugs, 1398
balloons, glass, 523, 758, 812, 814, 847
balloons, Japanese incendiary, 1351
balsam, copaiba, 1329, 1626

balsam poplar
  catkins, 358, 612, 820, 823, 826, 1224
  fir, 1278, 1564, 1567
  pollen, 338–339, 594
bamboo, 1386–1387
Ban rock D, 1288, 1574
barbecue pit, 542, 772, 819, 836
barite, 376–377, 512, 630–631, 815, 822, 838, 840, 874, 897, 922–925, 1229
barium, 986
  bromide dihydrate, 853, 877, 898, 930–934
  carbonate (witherite), 954
  chloride dihydrate, 853, 1597
  chromate, 1321, 1613
  dithionate dihydrate, 853, 878, 895, 917–921
  feldspar minerals, 1230
  glasses, 852
  nickel cyanide tetrahydrate, 851, 877, 895, 897, 916–919, 925
  nitrate (nitrobarite), 953
  oxide, 855, 877, 899, 956–957
  palladium cyanide tetrahydrate, 852, 877, 895, 897, 917–920, 924–925
  platinum cyanide tetrahydrate, 853, 877, 898–899, 926–927, 944–960
  silicate, 854, 878, 895–898, 918–922, 925–928
  sulfate, 512, 747, 818, 838, 840, 854, 975, 1328–1329, 1626 (*see* barite)
  yellow, 854, 1321
bark
  burner, 1631
  dust, 1497
  tree, 1223, 1334
barley grain, 437–438, 450, 686, 696, 813, 817, 821, 831, 847, 1387
Barnesite®, 85, 407, 659, 832, 843, 855
barrier filters, 42–43, 1036
basalt, 851
basic igneous rocks, 1353
basswood (linden) pollen, 1193, 1481
bast fibers, 310, 354, 355, 608–610, 1386
battery lead, 479, 720, 815, 845, 855
bauxite, 376, 631, 826, 829, 840, 851
bayberry pollen, 1193–1194, 1481
bayerite, 1515
beach sand, 398, 650, 832, 846, 854, 1351–1354
beam and stage controls, EMA, 184, 186–187
beam scanning
  electron, EMA, 157
  SEM, 146
  size, EMA, 155, 168
  system, IMA, 170
beam splitting prism, 47
bean, 438, 686, 817, 826, 829, 848
bear, black, 1283, 1569
Becke line, 40, 72, 74, 106, 1036, 1043
beech pollen, 1194, 1481
beeswax, 847
beet pulp, 438, 463, 686, 705, 811, 817, 826, 829, 848

bentonite, 377, 574, 631, 716, 815, 850, 1520
benzocaine, 1258, 1546
benzoic acid, 512, 748, 824, 842, 847
Berek compensator, 85, 1036
berkelium, EDXRA, 992
Bermuda grass pollen, 1195, 1482
Bertrand lens, 16, 23, 41, 46, 1036
beryl, 377, 631, 815, 839, 852, 874, 878, 895, 915–919
beryllium
  cleaning, 1476
  detection, 117, 155
  sample mounts for EMA, 162
  selenate tetrahydrate, 850, 878, 890–891, 908–910
  SEM, 1474
  sulfate tetrahydrate, 849, 878, 889, 907
beryllonite, 874, 883, 894–895, 914–916
Bessemer converter, 466, 708, 832, 835, 855, 1036
Betula lenta, 1195, 1482
beverages and foodstuffs
  asbestos in, 1650–1651
biaxial crystals, 81–82, 86–93, 109–110, 1036, 1164
bibliography, 1058–1117, 1414–1426, 1661–1674
binary code classification, 805
binocular microscope, stereo, 17, 239, 1044
biological microscope, 16
biologicals, 328–345, 588–600, 857, 1191–1226, 1354, 1497–1500
biotite, 390, 643, 822, 825, 831, 834, 839, 852, 1353
birch pollen, 1195, 1482
birefringence, 83–84, 312, 323, 1036
birefringent substances, 313
bisectrix, acute 81, 1034
  acute, 81, 1034
  figure, 86
  obtuse, 81, 1050
bismuth, 990
  cadmium alloy spray, 467, 480, 708, 835, 840
bitumen, 1313, 1603
bituminous coal, 544, 774, 827, 829, 836, 848
black bear hair, 1283, 1569
black gum pollen, 1203, 1486
black lamp, 1409
black pigments, analytical scheme, 1410
black powder explosive, 1399
black spruce, 1282, 1568
black sugar, 516, 752, 836
black walnut
  California, 1494
  cuticle, 1357
blast furnace, 467, 468, 479, 709, 720, 812, 818, 827, 832–833, 835, 858, 1311
blasting agents, 1398–1399
blood, spray-dried, 551, 781, 813, 827, 848

blue pigments, 1410
blue verditer, 493, 732, 833, 841, 854, 1409
blue-violet fluorescence, 41–42, 857–871
bobcat hair, 1283, 1569
bodytube, 16
boehmite, 853
Bolleana poplar trichomes, 1222, 1496
Bombax malabarica, 355, 609
bone ash, 1314
bone black, 493, 732, 828–829, 834, 837, 841, 851, 1319, 1409
bone, calcined, 1314, 1407
bone dust, 439, 687, 732, 817, 822, 829, 831, 843, 849
bone meal (steamed), 1289, 1575
bone white, 1314
borax, 424, 674, 816, 840, 849, 874, 883, 889–890, 907, 909, 1249, 1534
Borazon®, 1256, 1542
  nickel-coated, 1255
boric acid, 512, 748, 818, 823, 840, 848
bornite, 854, 1228, 1504
borosilicate crown glasses, 851
Botrychium virginianum, 342, 596
boussingaultite, 874, 885, 890, 909
Brace-Köhler compensator, 38
Bragg equation, 127, 138, 1036
brake lining, 374, 629, 826, 834, 844, 848, 1636
brass
  fume, 468, 710, 846
  identifying characteristics, 824, 855, 858
  melting furnace, 1305, 1591
  pouring dust, 1305, 1591
  red, 855
  slag, 1306, 1592
  yellow, 855
Brassica napus L., 1583
braunite, 1229, 1504
Brazilian tow, 1282, 1568
brewer's grain, 1290, 1575
brewer's grits, 310, 439, 687, 817, 848
Brewster angle, 3, 21, 1036
Brewster's law, 21
brick, 522, 781–782, 813, 819, 830, 833, 851, 858
brightfield illumination, 29
brightfield image, TEM, 134, 142
Brillo®, 1288, 1574
Bri-Nylon® (66), 962, 966
British standard sieve sizes, 807
bromine, EDXRA, 982
2-bromoethanol, 856
bromoform, 856, 1352
α-bromopropionic acid, 856
bronze
  powder, 468, 710, 837, 844, 855
  shot, 469, 710, 837, 844
brookite, 854, 1226, 1229, 1505
Broussonetia papyrifera, 1208, 1280, 1488, 1566
brown, Van Dyke, 498, 737, 827, 829, 837, 849, 1409

Brownian motion, 1036
brucite, 851
Brulé high efficiency incinerator, 550, 780
built-in illuminators, 25
bunsenite, 855
burned wood, 1334, 1336
burnt sienna, 497, 736, 829, 833, 844, 853, 1407
burnt umber, 853, 1326, 1407, 1621
bytownite, 1227

Cab-O-Sil®, 513, 748, 812, 846, 849
cadmium, 984
  orange, 1314, 1603
  red, 493, 733, 828, 838, 843, 854, 1407
  selenide photocell, 47
  sulfide photocell, 47
  sulfide pigment, 1314
  yellow, 854, 1314, 1408, 1604
caffeine, 322, 440, 824–825, 841, 847
calcined alumina, 465, 706, 818, 824
calcined bone, 1314, 1407, 1604
calcined clay, 470, 712, 812, 818, 850
calcite, 21, 79, 83, 310–311, 377, 380, 632, 634, 649, 652, 815, 840, 852, 858, 874, 878, 891, 897, 909, 924–926, 1233, 1235, 1327, 1338, 1375, 1538, 1622
calcium, 980
  alginate, 363, 617, 820, 841, 965, 967
  aluminate, 420, 670, 811, 815, 839, 850, 853
  aluminoferrite, 419, 670, 832, 839, 854
  aluminum silicate (glass), 852, 878, 896, 920–922
  barium silicate, 878, 898, 925–928
  carbide, 513, 749, 825, 840
  carbonate, 513, 528–529, 632, 749, 818, 840, 852, 858, 874, 878, 891, 897, 909, 1252, 1335, 1336, 1342, 1344, 1641
  citrate, 1249, 1534
  copper-silicate, 1323, 1616
  dithionate tetrahydrate, 850, 879, 894, 913–915
  ferrocyanide dodecahydrate, 849, 878, 895, 917, 919
  fluoride, 853, 874, 878, 889, 907
  magnesium carbonate, 852
  metaphosphate, 429, 679, 843
  molybdate, 854
  nickel cyanide pentahydrate, 849, 878, 894, 897, 923–925
  oxalate, 354–355, 514, 542, 749, 772, 818, 840, 850, 1223, 1224, 1291, 1343, 1350
  oxide, 853
  palladium cyanide pentahydrate, 850, 879, 894, 897, 913–915, 923
  pantothenate, 1290, 1576
  phosphate, 432, 451, 682, 696, 817, 821–822, 843, 850–851, 878, 891, 893, 896, 909–915, 918–920
  platinum cyanide pentahydrate, 852, 879, 896, 899, 921–922, 926–958

calcium—*cont'd*
  silicate, 419–423, 670, 824, 843, 853
  stearate, 514, 750, 829, 842, 847
  sulfate, 853
  tungstate (scheelite), 855
calibration
  density gradient column, 218–219
  electron diffraction camera, 138
  ocular micrometer scale, 261, 263
  x-ray diffraction camera, 126–127
California black walnut pollen, 1219, 1494
californium, EDXRA, 993
calmeta, 429, 679, 811, 814, 852
calomel, 855, 874, 880, 899–900, 957
camel hair, 848, 1284, 1570
camera, photomicrographic, 44–50
camera, XRD, 126–127
camphor, 514, 750, 818, 842, 847
Canada balsam, 94, 224, 305, 307–308
cane sugar, 462, 704, 818, 823
Cannabis sativa, 336, 354, 360, 593, 609, 615
Caprolan®, 961, 966, 1273, 1560
Capsicum minimum, 453, 698, 829, 848
Capsicum sp., 1296
carbon, 1535
  black, 469, 517, 711, 752–753, 840, 850, 1249, 1250, 1320
  build-up in probes, 1467
  channel black, 470, 711, 835, 840
  coating, 1473
  fibers, 363, 617, 820, 840, 848, 849
  soft black, 469, 711, 835, 840
  see also graphite
carbonaceous dusts, by fluorescence, 1366
carbonates, 1352
  see also calcite
carbon-coated TEM grids, 240
carbon film sample mounts for EMA, 162
carbonyl iron, 478, 719, 835, 844, 855
Carborundum®, 310, 407, 408, 411, 659, 824, 832, 843, 853, 1360
carboxymethyl cellulose, 500, 739, 821, 841, 848
cardioid darkfield condenser, 53
Carex sp., 1214, 1491
Cargille liquids, 77, 97, 100, 103–110, 112–114, 116, 307, 969–974, 1166–1174, 1363
caribou hair, 1284, 1570
carmine, 1315, 1324, 1605
carminic acid, 1315
carnallite, 849
carnauba wax, 847
caroa, 1386
Caryophyllus aromaticus, 1291
cascade impactors, 215
casein, 451, 697
casein fibers, 848
cashmere wool, 964, 967
cassiterite, 378, 632, 832, 846, 855, 874, 887, 899–900, 958–960
cast iron, 855

cast iron—*cont'd*
  grindings, 477–478, 718–719, 833, 835,
    844
  sawdust, 478, 719, 833, 844
  white, 855
Castanea dentata, 1199, 1484
castor bean pollen, 1196, 1482
castor pomace, 440–441, 688, 811, 817,
    823, 826, 847
cat hair, 311, 346, 601, 819, 830, 857,
    1283
Catahoula sandstone, 1354
Catalpa sp., 1221
Catalpa trichomes, 1221, 1495
catalyst, 320, 414–418, 505, 664–669, 811,
    816, 826, 834, 850, 1250, 1360,
    1536
  fresh, 414–418, 665–668
  high alumina, 414–415, 665, 811, 826,
    834
  low alumina, 415, 665–666, 811, 826,
    834
  natural, 416, 666, 811, 821
  oil refinery, 310, 312, 320
  semisynthetic, 416, 666–667, 811, 816,
    826, 834
  silica, 1250
  spent, 415–418, 665–669, 826, 834, 853
  synthetic, 417, 667, 811, 826, 834
  zeolitic, 417–418, 668–669, 811, 816,
    826, 834
cathodoluminescence, 152, 154, 161
cattail, 358, 613, 820, 1197, 1483
Caucasian hair, 350, 604, 819, 830, 1358,
    1359, 1572
cayenne pepper, 453, 698, 817, 822, 829,
    848
cedar pollen, 1197, 1198, 1483
Cecropia moth cocoon, 346, 601, 819, 823,
    831, 847
Cedrus deodora, 1197, 1483
Celanese®, 848
celestite, 874, 887, 896, 921–923, 1148,
    1229, 1505
cells
  baggy, 318
  cadmium selenide, 47
  cadmium sulfide, 47
  epithelial, 316, 328, 588, 814, 822, 828,
    831, 848
  photoconductive, 47
  photovoltaic, 46–47
  plant, 315, 317, 318
  silica gel, 119
cellulose, 304, 821, 842, 857, 1289, 1354
  acetate, 501, 739, 812–813, 818, 821,
    842, 847, 848
  alpha, 848
  carboxymethyl, 500, 739, 821, 841, 848
  dust, 500, 739
  ethyl, 502, 740, 818, 842, 847
  fiber filters, 207, 231
  nitrate, 501, 740, 821, 841, 849, 1266,
    1553
  triacetate, 848

celsian, 1230, 1506
Celtis occidentalis, 1204, 1486
cement, 320–321, 419–423, 669–674, 811,
    816, 822, 824, 850, 858, 1312, 1400
cement, rubber, 230
cenosphere, 324, 1037
centerable condenser mount, 15
centerable objective mounts, 13
central illumination method for refractive
    index, 74
central screening, *see* central stop
central stop, 97, 100, 114, 1037, 1159
centrifuge, 212–213
cereal grain trichomes, 432, 681
cerianite, 855
cerite, 854
cerium, 986
  molybdate, 854, 879, 900, 960
  oxide, 515, 750, 815, 843
cerulean blue, 494, 733, 824, 829, 843,
    1408
cerussite, 855
cesium
  bromide
    alpha, 854, 879, 895, 917–918
    beta, 854, 879, 898, 928–930
  chloride
    alpha, 853, 879, 893, 913
    beta, 854, 879, 897, 923–924
  dithionate, 880, 893–894, 911–912, 914
  EDXRA, 985
  fluoride, beta, 879, 890, 895, 909, 916–
    918
  iodide, 854, 879, 898–899, 925–926,
    938–939
  mercuric chloride, 879, 899, 938–939
  perchlorate, 853, 879, 890, 909
  selenate, 854, 880, 896, 919–920
  sulfate, 854, 880, 894–895, 915–916
  thallium chloride, 880, 899, 937–938
chain grate stoker, 546, 776, 827, 836
chalcedony, 378, 632, 815, 845, 851, 1231,
    1319, 1611
chalcocite, 1228, 1230, 1504, 1506
chalcopyrite, 854, 1228, 1230, 1240, 1507,
    1522
chalk, 1315, 1327, 1605, 1622
chamotte, 470, 712, 812, 827, 850
channel (carbon) black, 470, 711, 835,
    840
characteristics of particles, 803
characterization of particles, 152, 272,
    309, 578, 583, 803, 1379–1413
charcoal, 542, 772, 847, 1315, 1409
  black, 1606
chemical and industrial markers, 1360
chemical binding energy, 178, 180
chemical shift, ESCA, 180
chemical spot tests, 188, 1153
chemical wood pulp, 357, 611, 1636
Chenopodium album, 334, 592
chert, 1231, 1507
chestnut pollen, 1199, 1484
Chicago red rain, 561, 787, 819, 821

chicken
  eggshell, 441, 688, 817, 840, 852
  feathers, 347, 601, 819, 822, 830–831,
    847
china, 515, 751, 812, 818, 850, 1250,
    1254, 1536
chinchilla hair, 1284, 1570
Chinese white, 1625
chitin, 315, 1037, 1359
chlorapatite, 1231, 1508
chlordane, 1302, 1587
chlorinated trisodium phosphate, 424,
    427, 675, 678
chlorine, 979
chlorite, 1231, 1244, 1372, 1508
trans-1-chloro-2-bromoethylene, 856
chlorofiber (Saran®), 364, 618, 820, 841,
    849, 962, 966
1-chloro-1,2,2-tribromoethane, 856
choice of analytical tool, 280–283
choice of equipment
  computer, 190–191
  EDXRA, 197
  EMA, 197
  ESCA, 198
  illuminator, microscope, 1405
  IMA, 198
  laser Raman microprobe (MOLE),
    1147–1157
  polarizing microscope, 195, 1404
  SEM, 196
  stereomicroscope, 194, 1405
  TEM, 195–196
Christiansen effect, 75, 76, 1037
Christmas tree flock, 1338, 1636
chromatic aberration, 1037
  light microscope, 9, 11, 15
  TEM, 133
chromatic emulsions, 75, 76
chromatography, 221, 1398
chrome alloy slag, 487, 727
chrome green, 494, 733, 827, 833, 841,
    855, 1317, 1408
chrome orange, 1317, 1608
chrome steel slag, 828, 835
chrome yellow, 494, 734, 833–834, 843,
    855, 1317, 1408, 1608
chromite, 854, 1232, 1509
chromium, EDXRA, 980
chromium oxide, 1408
chromium oxide green, 1317, 1326, 1609,
    1622
chrysoberyl, 853, 874
Chrysophyae, 1315
chrysotile, 116, 142–144, 374, 419, 582,
    586, 628, 669, 820, 844, 851, 874,
    883, 894, 1155, 1239, 1338, 1343,
    1369–1378, 1513, 1517, 1520,
    1522, 1636, 1641
  identification by electron microscopy,
    1644–1651
  "look-alikes," 1644–1645
C.I.E. color system, 1158, 1160
cigarette ash, 542, 772, 812, 814, 818,
    836, 847

cinephotomicrography, useful equations, 1016
cinnabar, 494, 734, 833, 838, 845, 855
Cinnamomum zeglanicum, 1290
cinnamon, 1290, 1576
circularly polarized light, 95, 1185
citric acid, 441, 688, 817, 842, 848
citrus fruit, 442, 689, 811, 824, 826, 829, 835, 848
classification of particles
    Bahco microparticle classifier, 212
    electron microscopy, 279–280
    light microscopy, 277–279, 314, 805, 810–837, 1380–1390
claudetite, 854
clay
    attapulgite, 375, 382, 629, 635, 822, 851
    bentonite, 631
    calcined, 470, 712, 812, 818, 850
    fire, 521–522, 712, 756, 830
        dead-burned, 470, 712, 812
    fluorescence, 858
    microchemical tests, 1183
    staining reactions, 1183
clean bench, 223, 284–285, 304
    decontamination, 285–286
    design, 283–285
        need for, 223
clean box, 284
clean room, 223, 283–285
cleaners and detergents, 321, 424–429, 674–679, 814, 816, 821, 822, 850, 851, 858
cleaning beryllium plates, 1476
cleavage, crystal, 66
climate indicators, 1350
clinochlore, 852
cloves, 1291, 1576
CMC-S, 308
CMC-10, 308
coal, 311
    anthracite, 544, 774, 836, 849
    bituminous, 544, 774, 827, 829, 836, 848
    brown, 544, 774
    chain grate stoker, 546, 776, 836
    coke, 517, 753, 836, 847
    differentiation from graphite, 311
    flyash, 547–549, 775, 777–779, 813, 827–828, 836, 850, 854, 1345, 1633
    lignite, 544, 547, 774, 777, 813, 827, 836, 837, 847
    spreader stoker, 546, 775, 836
    underfeed stoker, 545, 775, 836
    and wood, 545, 775
coal flyash, indications, 1360
coated paper, 560, 787
coatings, metal, 577
cobalt, 981
    aluminate, 1316, 1606
    blue, 854, 1316, 1409, 1606
    $CoF_2 \cdot 5HF \cdot 6H_2O$, 850, 879, 889, 904–905
    green, 1316, 1607

cobalt—*cont'd*
    violet, 1316, 1607
    yellow, 1313, 1602
cobaltite, 855
cobaltous acid fluoride hexahydrate, 850, 879, 889, 904–905
cocaine hydrochloride (Mexico), 1259, 1546
coccolith fragments, 1315, 1327, 1605
Coccus cacti, 1315, 1605
cocoa chaff, 442, 689, 817, 821, 823, 829–831, 848
Cocos nucifera, 1277
coffee, 443, 689–690, 817, 821, 829, 1577
coffee chaff, 310, 443, 690, 821, 830–831, 848
coffee, instant, 1291
coir, 1277, 1386, 1563
coke, 516–519, 829, 836, 1037
    black sugar, 516, 752, 836
    breeze to stack, 518, 753, 812, 827, 836
    coal, 517, 753, 836, 847
    "crystals", 517, 753, 827, 829, 836
    gas black, 516, 752, 836
    gas producer, 518–519, 754, 827, 836
    oven, 518, 754, 829, 836
    petroleum, 516, 751, 754, 835, 847
cold needle, 117
cold stages, 108, 114, 151
collagen fibers, 1291, 1577
collection of particles, 204, 206
collodion, 225, 230, 308
    film, recovery of particles from, 237
collophane, 378–379, 633, 811, 815, 826, 841, 852
color, 1037
    balancing filters, 51-53
    contrast filters, 31, 51
    correcting filters, 53-54
    dispersion staining, 98, 106–107, 110
    film, 56
    filters, 46
    interference, 83
    particles, 54, 71
    photomicrography, 54, 1185
    polarization, 83
    polars, 16
    structural, 329, 376
    synthesis pictures, EMA, 166
    temperature, 46, 51–53, 1038
coma, 9, 1038
combustion products, 323, 541–550, 771–780, 858, 1359–1360, 1630–1634
    blast furnace, 467, 709, 812, 832
    elemental information, 1360
    identification, 1350
    see also ash, flyash
compensating oculars, 11, 14, 1038
compensators, 16, 80, 84, 87, 1038
    Berek, 85
    Brace-Köhler, 38
    Ehringhaus, 38
    first-order red, 312
    quartz wedge, 84, 1038
    Senarmont, 38–39, 1054

compound microscope, 9–10
compounds, addition, 119
Comptonia perigrina, 1193
computer
    beam and stage controls, EMA, 184, 186, 187
    choice of, 190–191
    EMA, data translation, 188–189
    EMA interface, 161, 183–184, 186
    operation, EMA, 163, 183
    operation, IMA, 183
    programming, CPS, 1653, 1655–1657
    programming, EMA, 191–193
    spectrometer drives, EMA, 187–188
    stage and beam controls, EMA, 184, 186–187
concave lenses, 7
concave mirrors, 3–4, 11, 16
conchoidal fracture, 66, 1038
concrete block, 553, 782, 813, 819, 833, 851
concrete pavement, 1339, 1636
condensation washing method, 1646–1647
condensers, 1038
    Abbe, 15
    achromatic-aplanatic, 15
    aplanatic, 15
    centerable mount, 15
    darkfield, 53
    DIC, 36
    lamp, 23
    numerical aperture, 11–15, 44–46, 1050
    stigmator, TEM, 133
    strain-free, 36
    substage, 14, 22
conidia, 342–343, 597–598, 813, 826–827, 847, 857, 1038
coniferous chemical wood, 317, 318, 357, 612, 820, 823, 848, 1038, 1275, 1561
coniferous mechanical wood, 317, 357, 611, 820, 823, 830–831, 848, 1038
coniferous opals, 1357
conifuge, 213
Conimeter, 207
conjugate points (focii), 1039
conoscopic observation, 85, 1038
conservation, art and archaeology, 1402–1413
constancy of interfacial angles, 66
constructive interference, 34
contact dust, electrical, 520, 755, 836, 837
contact metamorphic rocks, 1353
contaminated samples, 223
contamination layers, electron microscopes, 151
contrast
    filters, 31, 51
    light microscope, 22, 39–40
    phase, 33, 39–40, 74, 1051
    SEM, 150
    TEM, 134
convergent lenses, 7
convex lenses, 7

convex mirrors, 4, 11
copaiba balsam, 1329, 1626
Copaifera landsdorfi, 1329, 1626
copal, 847, 1330, 1626
copper
    aceto-arsenite, 1318, 1609
    -coated diamond, 1256
    crusher residue, 1306, 1593
    density, 855
    EDXRA, 981
    fumes, 471, 712, 835, 843, 855, 858
    lining powder, 471, 713, 837, 843
    oxide, 471, 712, 1257, 1544
    phthalocyanine, 1623
    silicofluoride hexahydrate, 880, 889, 905
    smelting, 1306, 1592
    sulfate, 515, 751, 829, 838, 844, 851
    sulfide, 854
Coprinus comatus, 344, 599
Corchorus olitorius, 354, 609
cordierite, 851
core sand, 484, 724, 846
Corhart abrasive, 408, 660, 815–816, 824,
    834, 853
cork dust, 519–520, 754–755, 814, 818,
    823, 828, 831, 847–848
corn, 1386–1387
    ground, 443–444, 690, 817, 829–831,
      848
    meal, 443, 444, 461, 690, 691, 817, 822,
      848
    pollen, 1199, 1484
    powder, 445, 691, 817, 822, 831, 848
    silk, 1224, 1498
    tassel, 1224, 1498
corncob chaff, 444, 690, 817, 822, 829,
    831, 848
Corning filters, 30, 42
cornstarch, 439, 444–445, 454, 457–458,
    461, 687, 691, 699, 701–703, 842,
    1333, 1360
correction collar, objective, 261
corrosion products, photomicrographs and
    descriptions, 1258–1259, 1543–
    1545
corundum, 113, 379, 408–411, 633, 660–
    662, 824, 832, 834, 839–840, 854,
    874, 877, 899
    artificial, 409, 660, 824, 832, 834, 840
    artificial (Lionite brand), 409, 661,
      824, 832, 834, 840
    dispersion staining, 934–937
    and rubber, 410, 661
Corylus americana, 1205, 1487
cost, polarizing microscope, 16, 304
cost, stereo microscope, 18
cotton, 310–311, 352, 607, 820, 823, 841,
    849, 1289, 1386, 1495
    Egyptian, 963, 967
    linters, 353, 608, 820, 830, 841, 963,
      967
    mercerized, 311, 353, 607, 820, 841,
      963, 967
    rags, 963, 967
    raw, 963, 967

cotton—*cont'd*
    Sea Island, 963, 967
cottonseed animal feed, 445, 691, 817,
    821–822, 829, 831, 848
cottonwood
    pollen, 332–333, 591, 811, 825
    tree seed hairs, 359, 613, 820, 1224
counting analysis, 112, 266–268, 1366
counting fibers, 1155
Courlene Py., 365, 619, 820, 841, 962,
    966
Courlene X3, 962, 966
covellite, 854
coverslip
    correction, 261
    mounts, SEM, 1476–1477
    quartz, 43
    small, 229
    thickness, 14
cow hair, 347, 602, 819, 830
CPS, 1653, 1655–1657
Cremnitz white, 1320, 1630
Creslan®, 961, 966
crime laboratory, 1379–1401
cristobalite, 329, 379–380, 589, 633, 811,
    815, 845, 851
critical angle, 7, 1039
critical illumination (Nelsonian), 22–24
critical point drying, 577
crocidolite, 142, 374, 628, 833, 844, 853,
    874, 883, 1375
Crocus sativus, 1324, 1618
crossed polars, 82
crossed quarterwave plates, 1185
crown glass, 851, 1039
    borosilicate, 851
Crown Zellerbach® SWP, 1276, 1562
crushing single particles, 247–248, 251–
    252
cryolite, 380, 471, 634, 713, 812, 815, 818,
    839, 853
cryptohalite, 874, 885, 889
crystal optics, useful equations, 1011–1012
crystal spectrometer, 158, 160, 1002
crystallography, laws of, 66
crystals
    axes, 65, 67–68
    biaxial, 81, 87, 109–110
    cleavage, 66
    distortions, 66
    faces, 65–71
    forms, 68–70
    habit, 66
    hemimorphic, 67
    hemisymmetric, 67
    holosymmetric, 67
    lattice, 65
    morphology, 64
    negative, 79, 81, 87
    positive, 79, 81, 87
    refractive index, 77–78, 255–257
    rolling, 94
    spectrometers, EMA, 158, 160
    symmetry, 66, 67
    systems, 65, 69, 70

crystals—*cont'd*
    uniaxial, 78–79, 87, 108–109, 1057
cube, 65
cubic system, 65, 68
cultivated silk, 351, 606, 820, 847–848,
    963, 967
cummingtonite, 1232, 1237, 1509
Cuprama®, 962, 966
cuprammonium rayon, 363, 618, 820, 841,
    848, 962, 966
cupric silicofluoride hexahydrate, 850
cuprite, 855
cuprous chloride (nantokite), 853
Curcuma longa, 1586
curium, EDXRA, 992
current density, SEM, 155
curvature of field, 1039
curved crystal monochromator, EMA, 158
cuticle, leaf, 1357
cutin, 857
Cyamopsis tetragonolobus, 1331, 1628
cyanochroite, 874, 881, 890–891, 909–910
cyclones, 207, 216, 1039
cyclotrimethylene trinitramine, 1265, 1267
Cynodon dactylon, 1195, 1482
cypress pollen, 1200, 1484

Dacron®, 310, 366, 621, 825, 842, 848,
    962, 966
damar, 308, 1330, 1627
dandelion
    pollen, 333, 592, 826
    seed hairs, 359, 613, 820
dandruff, 316, 328, 588, 822, 831, 848,
    1332
darkfield, 1040
    cardioid condenser, 53
    dispersion staining, 1159
    illumination, 29, 114
    image, TEM, 134, 142
    microscopy, 1155
data processing, laser Raman microprobe,
    1151–1153
Daucus carota, 1213, 1491
daylight filters, 30–31
DDT, 520, 755, 814, 818, 821, 823, 828,
    975, 1302, 1588
dead-burned fireclay, 470, 712, 812, 827
decayed wood, 1226, 1500
decimal code classification, 805
decomposition, particle, 115
dedicated computer systems, 1653–1654
deer, white-tailed, 1285, 1571
dehydration temperature, 306
delustered fibers, 317, 362, 366, 616, 620
delustering agent, 317, 1040, 1387
denitrogenation and desulfurization
    catalyst, 1250, 1536
densities of particles, 224, 847–855
density
    liquids, 856
    separation, 217–220, 856
    standards, 219–220
density-gradient column, 218–219

density ranges for particles, 224
Deodora cedar pollen, 1197, 1483
deodorant spray, 553, 782, 813, 823, 849
depth of field, 1040
    light microscope, 44, 154
    SEM, 146, 154
    TEM, 130, 154
depth of focus, TEM, 130, 154, 1040
depth profiling, IMA, 1659
desert sand, 1345, 1354, 1642
desolvation, 115
destructive interference, 34
detection limits
    dispersion staining, 114
    EMA, 155
    IMA, 169
    laser Raman microprobe, 1154
detergents and cleaners, 321, 424–429,
    674–679, 816, 858
determination of n_D, n_F, n_C, 1160
dextrose, 446, 454, 692, 699, 817, 822,
    842, 848
diacetylmorphine HCl, 1259
diameter, particle, 264–266
diammonium phosphate, 430, 680, 816,
    845, 849, 858, 1248, 1534
diamond, 410, 661, 815, 840, 853, 1236
    copper-coated, 1256, 1543
    nickel-coated, 1256, 1543
Diaphane, 308
diaphram, field, 22–23, 1043
diaspore, 853
Diatomite®, 1357
diatoms, 589, 755, 813–814, 822–823,
    828, 845, 850
    crystallinity of, 1357
    SEM identification, 1357
m-dibromobenzene, 856
o-dibromobenzene, 856
1,2-dibromoethane, 856
cis-dibromoethylene, 856
trans-dibromoethylene, 856
1,3-dibromopropane, 856
2,3-dibromopropanol-1, 856
DIC, 35–36, 40, 1050, 1155
dicalcium phosphate dihydrate (brushite),
    851
β-dicalcium silicate, 419, 669, 843
Dicel®, 1357
1,2-dichloro-1,1,2-tribromoethane, 856
1,3-dichloro-1,2-dibromoethylene, 856
p,p-dichloro-diphenyl-1,1,1-
    trichloroethane, 1302
dichroism, 1040
dickite, 1232, 1510
didymium filters, 33
didymium molybdate, 854, 884, 900, 960
dieldrin, 1303, 1588
diesel exhaust, 1334, 1631
diethylamine hydrochloride, 847
differential interference contrast (DIC),
    35–36, 40, 1155
differential thermal analysis (DTA), 1369
diffraction, 1040
    disc, 1040

diffraction—cont'd
    electron, 130, 131, 134, 136–138, 140,
        143–145
    light, 18, 40
    x-ray, 119–129, 246–249, 1057, 1147,
        1349, 1369
diffuse illumination, 22–25
diffuse reflection, 3
diffuser, orange peel, 25
diffusion coefficients, particle, 803
1,2-dihydroxyanthraquinone, 1601
cis-diiodoethylene, 856
diiodomethane, 856
1,3-diiodopropane, 856
diopside, 1231, 1233, 1510, 1518
dioptase, 853, 1233, 1511
1,4-dioxane, 308
dipotassium magnesium sulfate
    hexahydrate, 875, 881, 890, 908
disodium acid hypophosphate
    hexahydrate, 849, 884, 891, 909,
        910
disodium arsenate
    dodecahydrate, 849, 884, 889, 907–908
    heptahydrate, 849, 890, 908–909, 993
disodium metaphosphate hexahydrate,
    884, 891, 909
disodium phosphate dihydrate, 431, 681,
    817, 845, 850
disodium phosphate dodecahydrate, 884,
    889, 907
disodium phosphate heptahydrate, 849,
    884, 889, 908
disodium pyrophosphate hexahydrate,
    884, 890, 908
dispersion of refractive index, 5, 75–76,
    103, 872, 1040
    Aroclors®, 968
    Cargille liquids, 969–974
    Kofler glass powder standards, 968
    liquids, 97
    optical glass, 969
    solids, 5
dispersion staining, 97–114, 1040, 1158–
    1165
    accessories, 1158
    advantages, 1165
    anisotropic unknowns, 110
    annular stop, 1161
    asbestos, 1159, 1369–1378
    biaxial crystal, 1164
    biaxial unknowns, 110
    borofluorides, 1162
    central stop, 1159, 1161
    charts, 900–960, 966, 967
    Christiansen effect, 75, 76
    chromates, 1162
    colors, 98, 106–107, 110, 1159, 1164
    color temperature, source, 1160
    cyanides, 1162
    darkfield, 1159
    data tables
        by common name, 873–877
        by formula, 877–888
        by increasing n_D, 889–900

dispersion staining—cont'd
    data tables
        detection limits, 114
        determination of n_D, n_F, n_C, 1160
        estimating λ_0 values, 1160
        extensions in method, 1160
        fibers, 317, 961–967
        glass, 113, 1391
        graphs, 102, 104–105, 108, 900–960,
            966, 967
        IR and UV, 1164
        isotropic substances, 1161
        isotropic unknowns, 108
        liquids, 98, 100, 961, 965
        magnification, 872
        multi-stop turret objective, 1158
        nitrates, 1162
        objective, 101, 1159
        phosphates, 1162
        quartz, 313
        requirements for good staining, 1158
        sensitivity, 114
        silicofluorides, 1162
        stops, 98, 1158
        submicrometer particles, 114
        tables, 872–900, 961–965, 968–974
        tabulation of colors as function of λ_0,
            1160
        three-in-one objective, 1159
        trick for crystals of high birefringence,
            1161
        uniaxial substances, 1161
        UV and IR, 1164
        vanadates, 1162
        versus Becke line, 872
        λ_0 corresponding to annular and central
            stop colors using both A and C
            colors, 1161
distiller's dried grain, 1292, 1577
distortions, crystal, 66
distribution, size, 264
divergent lenses, 7
dodecahedron, rhombic, 65
dog food, 446, 464, 692, 705, 813, 817,
    821–822, 831, 847
dog hair, 347–348, 602, 819, 830
dolomite, 377, 380, 632, 634, 824, 841,
    874, 878, 891, 898, 910, 927–928,
    1234, 1244, 1375
domestic furnace, 545, 775, 827, 828, 836
domestic incinerator, 550, 780, 819, 827–
    828, 836
    bagasse, 550, 780, 836
dot count, 267
double diaphram method, 75
double-grating spectrometers, 1149
double monochromator, 1151
double refraction, 21, 33, 83, 1041
    sign of, 79
double variation method, 77, 107, 258,
    1041, 1164, 1391
Douglas fir, 1350, 1355
dried egg white, 1330
dried sheep manure, 432, 681, 811, 817,
    821, 826, 830, 848

drill-bit lubricating material, 1253
drugs, 1398, 1546–1551
  ballistics, 1398
  benzocaine, 1258, 1546
  chromatography, 1398
  cocaine HCl, 1259, 1546
  crystal morphology, 1395
  heroin base, purified, 1260, 1548
  heroin HCl, 1259, 1260, 1546–1547
  identification of, 1395–1398
  microcrystals tests, 117–118, 1396,
      1398–1399
  microthermal methods, 1397, 1398
  morphine base, crude, 1261, 1548
  morphine base, purified, 1261, 1549
  morphine HCl, 1261, 1548
  norephedrine HCl, 1262, 1549
  novocaine HCl, 1262, 1549
  optics, 1395
  photomicrographs and descriptions,
      1258–1264
  PLM, 1395, 1398
  quinine, 1262, 1550
  spectroscopy, 1398
  streptomycin A, 1263, 1550
  strychnine, 1263, 1550
  sulfaguanidine, 1263, 1551
  sulfanilamide, 1263, 1551
  xylocaine HCl, 1264, 1551
Dryopteris marginalis, 341, 596
dry samples, 230
DTA, 1369
dune sands, 1354
Duralon® filters, 231
dust, atmospheric
  estimations, 1365–1367
  examination of, 1350, 1362–1368
  geographical origin, 1347–1361
  hi-vol glass filters, 1365
  house, 1345
  identification, 1366
  lime flue, 1538
  litigation, 1362
  mounting technique, 1366
  qualitative analysis, 1364
  quantitative analyses, 1366
    errors, 1366
  reporting, 1367
  sampling, 1363
dust-fall jars, 206
dynamites, 1398
Dynazoom, 16, 45
Dynel®, 364, 619, 820, 841, 848, 961, 966
dysprosium, EDXRA, 987

Eastern hemlock pollen, 1205, 1206, 1487
ebonite, 847
Edgeworthia papyrifera, 1280, 1566
EDXRA, 140, 146, 576, 577, 977–1003,
    1042, 1461–1469
  choice of equipment, 197
  with EMA, 160
  with SEM, 147, 155
  with TEM, 140

EDXRA—*cont'd*
  spectra
    conditions for, 577
    elements, 977–993
    x-ray energy levels by element, 579–
        582, 999–1003
EELS, 1461, 1463–1464
egg white, 1330, 1627
egg yolk, 1330, 1331, 1627
eggshell, chicken, 441, 688, 817, 840, 852
eglestonite, 855
Egyptian blue, 1323, 1616
Ehringhaus compensator, 38
einsteinium, 993
electric furnace, 472, 713–714, 812, 813,
    818, 824, 827–828, 835, 850–851
electric razor, 349, 604, 819, 822, 830–831
electrical contact dust, 520, 755, 836–837
electron
  beam scanning, EMA, 157
  collector, SEM, 149
  diffraction, 130, 134, 140, 143
  gun, 131–132, 149, 168, 1469
  lenses, 132, 133
    aberrations, 133
  microbeam instruments, 1466–1467
  microprobe analysis, 1349, 1364
    see also EMA
  microscope-microprobe analyzer, 141,
      156, 1365
    see also EMMA
  microscopy
    darkfield, 134
    high voltage, 141
    stereo, 135
  optical method advances, 1461–1465
  scattering, 134
  spectroscopy for chemical analysis
      (FSCA), 178
  transmission microscopy, scanning
      (STEM), 152
electron image, back-scattered, EMA, 158,
    166
electrostatic lenses, IMA, 169
electrostatic precipitator, 217
elemental analysis
  IMA, 173–178
  microchemical tests, 117–119, 1175–
      1184
  SEM, 154
  TEM, 140
elemental composition (tabulation of
    Atlas particles), 838–846
elements, abundance of, 319
elements of symmetry, 67
elk hair, 1285, 1569, 1571
elm (American), 360, 614, 820
ELMISKOP ST 100F, 1464
elongation, sign of, 80, 317, 1054
elutriation, 213, 214
eluxenite, 854
EMA, 155–168, 1466–1467
  automation of, 161, 164–166, 183–194,
      1653–1655
  choice of equipment, 197

EMA—*cont'd*
  color synthesis pictures, 166
  EDXRA, 160
  mass scanning of particles, 163
  mounting procedures, 162, 164, 237–246
  new generation, 1468
  particle mapping, 245
  sample preparation, 162, 164, 237–246
  stage and beam controls, 184, 186–187
  subpicogram samples, 1467–1468
  WDXRA, 158–161
  x-ray distribution image, 158, 166
emerald green, 1318, 1408, 1609
emery, 408–409, 485, 660, 854
emission spectroscopy, 1042
EMMA, 141, 156, 1365, 1461–1463,
    1466–1468
Emmons' double variation method, 1164,
    1391
empty magnification, 14, 44, 1047
emulsions, chromatic, 76
enamel dust, 521, 756, 812, 850
enargite, 1233, 1511
endrin, 1303, 1588
energies of characteristic x-rays, 579–582,
    977–1002
energy-dispersive x-ray analysis
    (EDXRA), 140, 146, 160, 576,
    1042
English clay, 1234, 1512
English plantain pollen, 1211, 1490
engraving dust, 468, 710, 837
enstatite, 853, 1234, 1238, 1244, 1512
environmental dust, 551, 563, 564, 781,
    788–790, 1347–1368
eolian sands, 1354
EPI-illuminator, 29
epidote, 381, 634, 832, 839, 853, 874, 878,
    898–899, 932–937, 1353
epithelial cells, 316, 328, 588, 814, 822,
    828, 831, 848, 1332
epoxy resins, 847
epoxy and glass fibers, 527, 761, 812, 814
epsomite, 849, 874, 883, 889–890, 907–908
equant, 1042
equations, useful, 1009–1027
Equus caballus, 1286, 1572
eraser
  ink, 1339, 1637
  pencil, 1339, 1637
erbium, 988
ESCA, 119, 178–182
  automation, 1653
  choice of equipment, 198
  peak binding energies, 1005
esparto, 317, 353, 608, 820, 823, 848, 965,
    967, 1386, 1387
    see also alfa
etching, ion beam, 151, 175
ethyl cellulose, 502, 740, 818, 842, 847
ethyl tribromoacetate, 856
ethyl urea, 847
p-ethylamino benzoate, 1258
Eucalyptus globulus, 1201, 1485
eucalyptus pollen, 1201, 1485

euhedral, 1042
Euparal, 308
europium, EDXRA, 987
evaporated film supports, TEM, 135
excitation filters, 42, 1042
exfoliated mica, 526–527, 760, 818, 823, 831, 851
exhaust, auto, 541, 771, 825, 833, 836, 858
exhaust, diesel, 1334
exine, pollen, 1042, 1356
expanded shale, 534, 766, 819, 830
explosives, 114, 1264–1268, 1398–1399, 1552–1556
  aluminum powder, 1264
  ammonium nitrate, *see* same
  ammonium perchlorate, *see* same
  HMX, Form I, 1149, 1265
  identifying characteristics, 1398–1399
  military, 1398
  nitrocellulose, 501, 740, 821, 841, 849, 1266
  PETN, 1266
  photomicrographs and descriptions, 1264–1269
  picric acid, 1266
  potassium chlorate, 1267
  potassium nitrate, 850, 875, 881, 889, 892, 910, 1267
  RDX, 1265, 1267, 1268
  sodium chlorate, 851, 883, 892, 911, 1268
  sodium nitrate, 534, 766, 819, 845, 850, 876, 884, 889, 895, 902, 1268
  TNT, 1269
  water gels, 1398
  water soluble, 1399
exposure control
  photomicrography, 45–49, 59
  x-ray diffraction, 125
external shutter, 50
extinction, crossed polars
  angle, 83, 1042
  elimination, 1185
  positions, 83, 1185
  symmetrical, 82–83
  undulose, 1056
extraction replicas, 234–235, 1648–1649
eyepiece goniometer, 1042
eyepieces, 1042–1043

face powder, 554, 783, 819, 825, 827
faces, crystal, 65–71
facial tissue, 358, 612, 815, 820, 823, 848
Fagus americana, 1194, 1481
fayalite, 854
feathers, 1355, 1358
  chicken, 347, 601, 819, 822, 830–831, 847
  poultry, hydrolyzed, 554, 783, 813–814, 827
  tankage, 446, 692, 811, 813, 826, 847
feeds
  animal, 322, 691, 817, 821–822, 829, 831, 848
  mill, sorghum, 457, 701, 831, 847

feldspars, 319, 386, 639, 1043, 1227, 1253, 1306, 1352
Feret's diameter, 265
fermium, EDXRA, 993
fern spores, 341–342, 596, 811, 826, 857
ferric ferrocyanide pigments, 1323
ferric oxide, 585
ferric sulfate, 853, 880, 898–899, 909, 935–937, 940–942
ferrite, 474, 715, 832, 844, 855
ferroactinolite, 1500
ferrochrome, 474, 715, 812, 827–828, 837, 843, 849
ferromagnesian silicates, 319
ferromanganese, 474–475, 716, 832, 835
ferrosilicon, 475, 716, 812, 835, 850
ferrous ammonium selenate hexahydrate, 850
ferrous ammonium sulfate hexahydrate, 849
ferrous potassium sulfate hexahydrate, 850, 890, 891
ferrous silicofluoride hexahydrate, 880, 889, 903–904
ferrous sulfate heptahydrate, 849, 875, 880, 890–891, 909
fertilizers, 321–322, 429–436, 679–685, 811, 817, 858, 1269–1271, 1360, 1556–1558
fiber filters, 207, 1381
fiber glass, 311, 368, 527, 623
  reinforced plastic, 368, 622, 811, 813
fiber identification scheme, 116
fiber pipe dust, 521, 756, 823, 836
Fiberglas®, 962, 966
fibers, 116, 316–318, 346–370, 600–625, 1271–1288, 1380–1390, 1558–1574
  acetate, 310–311, 362, 616, 820, 841, 848
  acrylic, 362, 616–617, 820, 841, 847, 961, 966
  animal, 310, 317, 346–353, 601–606, 857, 1282–1288, 1358–1359, 1381–1384
  bast, 310, 354, 355, 608–610, 1386
  carbon, 363, 617, 820, 840, 848, 849
  casein, 848
  classification of, 1380–1390
  counting, 1155
  delustered, 317, 362, 366, 616, 620
  dispersion staining, 317, 961–967
  Dynel®, 364, 619, 820, 841, 848, 961, 966
  filter, 207, 1381
  fluorescence, 857–858
  fluorocarbon, 364, 618, 830, 841
  glass, 310, 851, 857, 1386–1389
  grass, 340, 353, 595, 608, 811, 826, 848, 1195, 1356, 1357, 1386
  identification scheme, 116, 1380–1390, 1413
  insulation, 1381, 1388–1390
  leaf, 310, 316, 361, 615, 616, 847, 1056, 1221–1223, 1335, 1386

fibers—*cont'd*
  man-made, *see* synthetic
  metal, 1288
  milkweed, 1224
  mineral, 116, 373–375, 627–629, 1369–1378, 1390
  miscellaneous, 1390
  modacrylic, 364, 619, 820, 841, 961, 966
  mohair, 348, 603, 819, 848, 964, 967
  mounting of, 316
  natural, 316, 346–361, 600–616, 963, 964, 967, 1380–1387
  nonwoven textile, 1380
  olefin, 365, 619, 820, 841, 962, 966
  organic, 1375
  paper, 352–354, 356–358, 607, 608, 611, 612, 1277, 1335, 1355, 1380, 1385
  plant, 317, 1385, 1386
  Pluton®, 363, 617, 820, 840
  polyester, 310, 366, 621, 825, 842, 962, 966
  refractive indices, 961–967, 1388, 1390–1392
  rope, 1381, 1386
  rubber, 1390
  rug, 1381
  seed hairs, 1386
  sources, 1380–1381
  synthetic, 316–317, 362–370, 616–624, 857, 961–962, 966, 1387
  Teklan®, 961, 966, 1274, 1388
  textile, 1380, 1385–1388
  triacetate, 367, 621, 820, 842, 1388
  vicuña, 964, 967, 1288
  wood, 310–311, 317–318, 1355, 1380, 1385
Fibrary, 1385
field curvature, 9, 11
field diaphram, 22–23, 1043
field emission electron gun, 1469
figures, interference, 85–97
filar micrometer ocular, 260–266, 1043, 1048
film
  collodion, 225, 230, 237, 308
  color, 56
  measurement, x-ray diffraction, 125–126
  packs, 49
  Polaroid®, 44–45, 49, 1051
  speed, 46, 48
  see also thin films
filters
  air conditioner samples, 206
  barrier, 42–43, 1036
  cellulose fiber, 207, 231
  color balancing, 51–53
  color contrast, 31, 51
  color correcting, 53–54
  colored, 46
  contrast and resolution, 31
  Corning, 30, 42
  daylight, 30-31
  didymium, 33
  Duralon®, 231

filters—cont'd
excitation, 42, 1042
factors, 46–48
fiber, 207, 1381
gelatin, 33
Gelman, 1371
glare reduction, 33
glass fiber, 232
interference, 32–33
wedge, 33, 106
light, 30
light-balancing, 1047
membrane, 208, 230, 231, 556, 785,
813–814, 848, 1048
neutral density, 28, 31, 46, 53, 1049
Nuclepore®, 208, 1371
nylon, 231
particle recovery from, 1363, 1364
photographic, 51
photometric, 31
Polaroid®, 57–58
samples, 231
sodium light, 32
split-polarizing, 57
Wratten, 30–32, 42, 1282, 1285
filtration, 207
fir, balsam, 1278, 1564
fire clay, 521–522, 712, 756, 818, 827, 830
dead-burned, 470, 712, 812, 827
firebrick, 1251, 1254, 1536
firebush pollen, 1201–1202, 1485
fireplace ash, 1335, 1632–1634
first-order red plate, 84, 87, 312, 1038
first surface mirrors, 16, 1043
fish eggs, freeze-dried, 1292, 1578
fish meal, 447, 693, 811, 817, 821–822,
826, 848
fixing techniques, SEM, 577
flatfield objectives, 11
flatfield oculars, 11, 14
flax, 354, 608, 820, 830, 848, 963, 967,
1282, 1386, 1568
flaxseed, 447, 693, 811, 817, 821, 826,
828, 830, 847
flint glass, 522, 757, 812, 852, 1043
flotation techniques, 1349
flour, silica, 1254
flour, wheat, 461, 704
Fluid-mount, 141, 308
fluorapatite, 432–433, 682, 874, 878–879,
922–924
fluorescence, 857–871, 1043
blue-violet, 41–42, 857–871
filters, 53
laser Raman microscopy, 1149
microscope, 42
microscopy, 41
photomicrography, 53
primary, 42
secondary, 42, 1054
ultraviolet, 857–871
fluorescent light phosphor, 1341
fluorine, EDXRA, 978
fluorite, 310–311, 381, 635, 811, 843, 853,
874, 878, 889, 907, 1235, 1353

fluorite—cont'd
objectives, 11, 14, 1043
Fluormount®, 43
fluorocarbon (Teflon®), 364, 509, 618,
745, 821, 823, 830, 841, 850, 858,
1388
fluorochromes, 42
flyash, 1043
chain grate stoker, 546, 776, 827, 836
coal, 547–549, 775, 777–779, 813, 827–
828, 836, 850, 854, 1345, 1360,
1633
domestic furnace, 545, 775, 827, 828,
836
fireplace, 1335
lignite, 544, 547, 774, 813, 827, 836–
837, 847
oil, 136, 1634
pulverized fuel, 547–549, 777–779, 827,
836
spreader stoker, 546–547, 776–777,
814, 836, 837
underfeed stoker, 545, 775, 813, 827,
836
focal length, 7, 12
focal screening, 101, 1044
focus, mirrors, 3
focusing oculars, 261
foliage, particle collection on, 206, 1348
folic acid, 1292, 1578
Fontainbleau sand, 381, 635, 815
food
dog, 437–464, 685–706, 813, 817, 821–
822, 831, 847, 858
photomicrographs and descriptions,
437–464, 685–706, 1289–1301,
1574–1587
processing, 322
Foraminifera, 309, 330, 590, 815, 819,
822, 829–831, 840, 852
forensic applications, 106, 113, 1347–
1368, 1379–1413
formaldehyde, urea, 509, 745, 812, 814,
818, 841, 848
forms, crystal, 68–70
Formvar®, 134, 230
forsterite, 853, 874, 883, 897–898, 924–
925, 927–929, 1234, 1374, 1513
Fortisan®, 848, 962, 966
Fortrel®, 962, 966, 1271, 1388, 1558
foundry, 144, 322, 475, 716, 818, 824,
832, 835, 1307, 1593
Fourier plane, 1156
see objective back focal plane
Fourier-transform system, 1147
fox hair, 1286, 1571
fractionation, particle, 210–222
fracture, conchoidal, 66, 1038
francium, EDXRA, 991
franklinite, 406, 658, 854, 1235, 1513
Fraunhofer lines, 856
Fraxinus toumeyi, 1192, 1480
freeze-dried fish eggs, 1292, 1578
freeze-drying, 151, 577
Fresnel lens, 1044

frit dust, 522, 757, 812, 818, 827, 850
frothy cement, 1400
fruit bat hairs, 346, 600
fuchsin, 847
Fuller's earth, 382, 584, 635, 815, 822,
829, 834, 849
Funaria sp., 345, 600
fungal conidia, 342, 343, 597, 598, 813,
826, 827, 847, 857, 1038
fungal spores, 315, 857
fungus, 315, 343–344, 598, 811, 813–814,
826, 847, 857, 1044
Furcraea gigantea, 1279, 1566
fur hairs, 847, 1357
furnace
blast, 467, 479, 709, 714, 720, 812,
815, 818, 827, 832–833, 835, 858,
1348
domestic, coal and wood, 545, 775
slag, 468, 709, 812, 832
flyash, 545–549, 775–779
fumes, 472, 713–714, 812
gas, 1335
industrial, 1348

gadolinite, 1235, 1514
gadolinium, EDXRA, 987
bromate nonahydrate, 852, 880, 894,
896, 914–915, 916–920
galena, 855, 1235, 1242, 1309, 1514
gallium, EDXRA, 981
galvanized kettle, 1307, 1594
gamboge, 1318, 1408, 1610
Garcinia hanburii, 1318, 1610
garden soil, 562, 788, 819, 1340, 1637
garlic salt, 1293, 1578
garnet, 382–383, 636–637, 814–815, 824,
828, 832, 839, 843, 853–854, 875,
878, 898, 933–935, 1353
Garrya elliptica, 1215, 1492
gas black, 517, 753
coke, 516, 752, 836
gas cleaning, 803
gas furnace, 1335, 1632
gaylussite, 849
GC/MS automation, 1659–1660
gel, silica, 119, 1341
gelatin, 308, 448, 694, 812, 826, 848
filters, 33
coated slides, 118–119
Gelman filter, 1371
general environmental dusts, 551, 563,
564, 781, 788–790, 1347–1368
general optics, useful equations, 1009
geographical origin of dust sample, 1347–
1361
geometrical relationships, 1019–1027
germanium, EDXRA, 982
dioxide (glass), 853, 880, 896, 920
gibbsite, 851, 1236, 1515
ginger, 448, 694, 817, 821, 829, 847,
1293, 1579
Gladstone-Dale formula, 975
glair, 1330, 1627
see also egg white

glare reduction filters, 33
glass
    analysis by EMA, 1467–1468
    balloons, 523, 758, 812, 814, 847
    barium, 852
    beads, 312, 524, 758, 812
    borosilicate crown, 851
    dispersion staining, 113, 1391
    dust, 523, 757, 812
    Emmons' double variation, 1391, 1392
    epoxy and, 527, 761, 812, 814
    fiber brush, 228
    fiber filter, 232
    fibers, 310, 851, 857, 962, 966, 1386–
        1389
        characteristics, 1389
        elemental composition, 1389
        for XRD mounts, 246–247
        optical properties, 1389
        organic binder, 1389
        refractive indices, 1390–1392
        solubility in HCl, 1389
        trace element method, 1389
    flakes, 229
    flint, 522, 757, 812, 852, 1043
    frit, 522, 757, 812, 818, 827, 850
    germanium dioxide, 853
    ground, 311, 387, 522–523
    headlight, 106, 113
    identification, 1388–1393
    lead, 852
    melting furnace dust, 473, 715
    optical properties, 1388–1393
    powder standards, Kofler, 97, 110, 968
    refractive index, 1388–1393
    trace elements, 1392
    uranium, 43
    volcanic, 394, 412, 646, 663
    Vycor®, 850
glass wool, 811, 813, 828, 847, 851
    binder, 847
glassy sphere, 323–324
glassy state, 1044
glauberite, 852
glauber salt, 848
glaucodote, 1503
glauconite, 384, 637, 822, 831, 844, 851,
    1325, 1619
Gleditsia sp., 1221
glossary, 1034–1057
glue, 847, 1625
glycerin, 43
    jelly, 30, 1355
glycerol, 308
glycine, 847, 1293, 1579
goat hair, Angora, 348, 603, 819, 848
goethite, 384, 388, 637, 641, 854, 1236,
    1258, 1515, 1624
Goetz aerosol spectrometer, 213
gold
    EDXRA, 989
    smelter fume, 476, 717, 815
goldenrod pollen, 1202, 1485, 1488
goslarite, 874, 888–890, 908–909

grain, 848
    barley, 437, 438, 450, 686, 696, 813,
        817, 821, 831, 847, 1387
    insecticide, diatoms, 845
    malt, 450, 696, 813, 817, 821, 829, 831,
        847
    wheat, 464, 706, 813, 821, 829, 847
grain insecticide, 330, 590, 813–814
grain size graticule, 261
granite, 384, 637, 815, 822, 852
granite pegmatites, 1353
graphite, 310–311, 476, 563, 711, 717,
    789, 832, 835, 837, 840, 850, 1236,
    1400, 1516
grass
    opal, 1357
    Spanish, 353, 608, 848
        see also esparto
    timothy, 340, 595, 811, 826, 1195, 1356
graticules, 260–261, 263
gravitational setting, 803
gray backgrounds, photomicrographs, 54–
    56, 326, 1185–1186
gray iron cupola, 1307, 1594
Greek alphabet, 1019
greenalite, 874, 880, 898, 926–927
Greenburg-Smith impinger, 207
"green disease," 54–56, 1044
green-earth, 1325, 1619
greenockite, 854
Greenough binocular microscope, 1044
    see also stereobinocular microscope
green pigments, analytical scheme, 1411
grinding dust, 411, 662, 824, 826, 832
grinding single particles, 247–248, 251
grog, 470, 712
grossularite, 383, 636, 814, 824, 839, 853,
    875, 878, 898, 933–935
ground corn, 443–444, 690, 817, 829–831,
    848
ground glass, 311, 387, 522–523
grunerite, 1232, 1237, 1375, 1516
guar gum, 1331, 1628
guard hairs, 1044
gum
    arabic, 308, 848, 1331–1332, 1628
    black, 1203
    guar, 1331
    pollen, 1486
    red, 1277
    rubber, 847
    sweet, 1203, 1277
    tragacanth, 1333, 1630
    white, 1277, 1564
gunshot residue, 1340, 1399–1400, 1638
gypsum, 113, 306, 311, 384, 419, 455,
    638, 669, 699, 815, 838, 843, 851,
    875, 879, 893, 911–913, 1400, 1407

habit, crystal, 66
hackberry pollen, 1204, 1486–1487
hafnium, EDXRA, 988
hair
    angora goat, 348, 603, 848

hair—*cont'd*
    animal, 130, 346–353, 601–606, 1282–
        1288, 1358–1359, 1381–1384,
        1569–1573
    bear, black, 1283, 1569
    bobcat, 1283, 1569
    camel, 848, 1284, 1570
    caribou, 1284, 1570
    cat, 311, 346, 601, 819, 830
    Caucasian, 349, 604, 819, 822, 830, 831,
        1286, 1358–1359, 1572
    chinchilla, 1284, 1570
    cow, 347, 602, 819, 830
    deer, white tailed, 1285, 1571
    dog, 347–348, 602, 819, 830
    elk, 1285, 1569, 1571
    fox, 1286, 1571
    fruit bat, 346, 600
    fur, 847, 1359
    goat, 348, 603, 819, 848
    hog, 1287, 1573
    horse, 349, 603, 819, 830, 964, 967,
        1286, 1572
    human, 349–350, 604–605, 819, 822,
        830–831, 848, 1286, 1358, 1381–
        1383, 1572
    ion microprobe analysis (IMA), 1382
    mink, 964, 967, 1287, 1572
    mohair, 348, 603, 819, 848, 964, 967
    Negroid, 1358
    neutron activation analysis (NAA),
        1381
    opossum, 1287, 1573
    Oriental, 350, 605, 819, 830, 1358
    photomicrographs and descriptions,
        349–350, 604–605, 1282–1288
    pig, 1287, 1573
    rabbit, 350, 605, 819, 830, 964, 967
    rat, 351, 605, 820, 830, 1284
    scale edge shapes, 1384
    scale patterns, 1383
    skunk, 352, 606, 820, 830
    vicuña, 964, 967, 1288, 1573
halite, 875, 883, 894, 914
halloysite, 143–144, 584, 850, 1232, 1237,
    1517
halogen lamps, 46
hand-picking particles, 222, 1349
hardness of particles, 272, 1044
hardness scale, Mohs', 1049
hardwood pulps, 1385
hardwood sawdust, 539, 769–770, 829–
    831, 848
Hartshorne rotation apparatus, 91–94,
    257–258
hausmannite, 854
hazelnut pollen, 1205, 1487
headlight glass, 106, 113
heat pump dust, 1335, 1633
heat-treating salt, 1309
heavy liquids, 856
heavy mineral
    associations and provenance, 1353
    separation, 1352
    stability, 1353

hectorite, 1237, 1517
Helianthus sp., 1217, 1493
hematite, 476–477, 563, 661, 717–718, 789, 832, 834–835, 844, 855, 1236, 1407
hemicellulose, 857
hemimorphic crystals, 67, 1044
hemimorphite, 853
hemisymmetric crystals, 67, 1044
hemlock (eastern) pollen, 1205–1206, 1487
hemp, 354, 609, 815, 820, 848, 963, 967, 1282, 1386, 1387, 1568
henequen, 1386
heptachlor, 1303, 1589
heptasodium fluoro arsenate, 883, 890, 908
herapathite, 21
heroin, 1259, 1260, 1546–1548
Heropus chiroptera, 346, 600
γ-hexachlorocyclohexane, 1589
hexagonal system, 65, 68
Hibiscus cannabinus, 1278, 1565
hickory (white) pollen, 1206, 1487
Hicoria alba, 1206, 1211, 1487
Hicoria pecan, 1211, 1490
high-alumina catalyst, 414–415, 665, 811, 826, 834
high dispersion
    liquids, 100, 969–974
    solids, 106
high efficiency incinerator, 550, 780, 813
high explosives, 1398, 1399
high-resolution SEM, 1469
high strength carbon fiber, 849
high temperature stages, 114–115
high-voltage electron microscopy, 131, 141
high volume (hi-vol) filter, 1363
histograms, 270
HMX, 1149, 1150, 1265, 1398, 1399, 1553
Hoffman modulation contrast (HMC), 1155–1157
hog hair, 1287, 1573
"holey polar" method, 97, 326, 1185
holmium, 987
holographic microscopy, 61–63
holography, 1045
holosymmetric crystals, 67, 1045
home furnaces, 545, 775
homocyclonite, (see HMX)
honey locust trichomes, 1221, 1495
Hormodendrum, 315
hornblende, 310, 381, 385, 394, 561, 638, 647, 788, 834, 843, 853, 875, 878, 897–898, 923–926, 1325, 1353, 1374
horse chestnut
    pollen, 334, 592, 826
    trichomes, 360, 614, 820, 823, 830–831
horse hair, 349, 603, 819, 830, 964, 967, 1286, 1572
hotstage, 106, 108, 114–116
household dust, 553–554, 783, 1345, 1642
Howard disc, 261

H.S.R., mountant, 308
huebnerite, 385, 638, 832, 834, 845, 855
huebnerite-ferberite series, 1247
human hair, 848, 1358, 1381–1383
    Black, 350, 604, 819, 830, 1358
    Caucasian, 349, 604, 819, 830, 1286, 1572
    electric razor, 349, 604, 819, 822, 830–831
    Oriental, 350, 605, 819, 830
Huyghenian ocular, 14, 1045
hydrated aluminum oxide, 1257
hydrated magnesium oxide, 1252
hydrated particles, 115
hydrated tetrasodium pyrophosphate, 428, 678
hydrated trisodium phosphate, 428, 678
hydrocerussite, 855
hydrous sodium carbonate, 1254
5-hydroxy-6-methyl-3, 4-pyridinedicarbinol hydrochloride, 1297
hygiene, industrial, 210
hypersthene, 1238, 1353, 1518, 1519
Hyrax, 307

ice, 847, 875, 880, 889
identification
    fibers, 116, 1380–1390
    particles, 272, 276, 303, 325, 582, 1349
    pigments, 1406–1413
    pollen, 315
    soil, 1394
    trace evidence, 1379–1413
    unknowns, 272, 276, 325, 582
identifying characteristics of particles, 272, 309, 810–837, 1379–1413
illite, 1238, 1518
illumination, 1045
    annular, 1151
    auxiliary illuminator, 28
    Brace-Köhler compensator, 38
    built-in, 25
    darkfield, 29, 114
    diffuse, 22-25
    EPI illuminator, 29
    illuminator specifications, 1405
    incident brightfield, 29, 59
    incident darkfield, 29, 59
    incident light, 25, 29, 312
    Köhler, 22-25
    Nelsonian, 22–24
    oblique, 56–57, 74–75
    ping-pong ball, 29
    point, 1151
    unilateral, 27–28
    vertical, 27–29, 312
ilmenite ore, 385, 639, 815, 822, 834, 837, 844, 854, 1353
IMA, 168–178, 198, 254, 1349, 1382, 1393, 1470–1471, 1654
    choice of equipment, 198
    depth profiling, 1659
    detection limits, 169
    isotope ratioing, 1658

IMA—*cont'd*
    mass scanning, 175
    mounting particles for, 173, 254
    quantitative analysis, 175, 177–178
image analysis, automatic, 268–270, 1035
image converter, 41
image
    formation, 3
    projected, 8
    real, 3, 4, 1045
    reflection, 3
    refraction, 7
    SEM, 146–148
    TEM, 133–134
    virtual, 4, 1045
image shearing ocular, 260
immersion objectives, 12, 308, 1045
impaction, 215–216, 1045
impingers, 207
implantation, ion, 171
incidence, angle of, 3
incident light, 25, 29, 59, 312
incinerator, 850, 858
    bagasse, 550, 780, 828, 836–837, 847, 1277, 1334, 1386
    Brulé high efficiency, 550, 780
    high efficiency, 550, 780, 813
    industrial, 549, 779, 813, 827–828, 831, 836, 858
    large domestic, 550, 780, 819, 827–828, 836
    municipal, 549, 779, 813, 827–828, 836
inclusions, 1045, 1347
    in metals, 151
index measurement, variation methods, 76, 1391, 1392
index of visibility, 307
Indian yellow, 1319, 1408, 1610
indicatrix, optical, 80, 81, 1045
indices
    Miller, 68–69, 1048
    rational, 66
indigo, 495, 734, 834, 837, 841, 848, 1409
indium, 855, 984
indoor particle, indications of, 1350
industrial chemicals, photomicrographs and descriptions, 207–540, 658–771, 1248–1256, 1533–1543
industrial furnaces, 1348
industrial hygiene, 210
industrial incinerator, 549, 779, 813, 827–828, 831, 836, 858
industrial markers, 1360
inertial separation, 212, 1046
infrared absorption, 1046, 1147, 1369
infrared spectroscopy, 119, 1148, 1471
Infrasizer, 214
infusorial earth, 330, 589, 811, 814–815, 819, 823, 825, 827–828, 847, 850
ingested particles, 210
ink eraser, 1339, 1637
ink, printing, 560, 787, 819, 821, 824, 836
inorganic microchemical tests, 118, 1178–1180

insecticides, 330, 590, 813–814
  aldrin, 1302
  chlordane, 1302
  DDT, purified, 520, 755, 814, 818, 821,
      823, 828, 975, 1302, 1303
  descriptions and photomicrographs,
      1302–1304, 1587–1590
  diatoms in, 330, 590, 845
  dieldrin, 1303
  endrin, 1303
  heptachlor, 1303
  lindane, 1304
  malathion, 1304
  methoxychlor, 1304
insect parts, 315, 331, 590, 814, 822, 825,
    827–828, 831, 834, 837, 847, 1359
in situ examination, 1363
insoluble particles, 1181–1182
instant coffee, 1291, 1577
instant tea, 1300, 1585
instrumentation, automation, 1652–1660
insulation fibers, 1381, 1388–1390
insulator, 524, 758, 815, 849
integrated circuits, 173, 249
integrating stages, 268
interface, computer-EMA, 161, 183–184,
    186
interfacial angles, constancy of, 66
interference, 33, 1046
  colors, 83
  constructive, 34
  contrast, differential, 35–36, 40
  destructive, 34
  figures, 85–97
  filters, 32–33
    Michelson microscope, 36
    thin film, 34, 250–251
    wedge filters, 33, 106
interference microscopes, 35–39
  Jamin-Lebedeff, 35–37, 1047
  Mach-Zehnder, 39
  Michelson, 36
interference microscopy, 33–39
  useful equations, 1014
interferometer, simple, 34
interpupillary distance, 1046
inverted microscope, 205
iodine, 985
iododimethyl ether, 856
iodoethane, 856
iodomethane, 856
3-iodopropanol-1, 856
ion beam
  etching, 151, 175
  machining, 175
  sputtering, 170
ion emission, IMA, 171–172
ion etching, 1470
ion exchange resins, 1337, 1635
ion implantation, 171
ion microprobe analysis (IMA), 168–178,
    198, 254, 1349, 1382, 1393, 1470–
    1471
ionization efficiency, 170–171
Ipscaphot, 49

IR
  asbestos, 1369
  dispersion staining in, 1164
iridium, EDXRA, 989
  alloy, 855
iron, 833, 835, 844, 854
  carbonyl, 478, 719, 835, 844, 855
  cast, 477–478, 718–719, 833, 835, 843,
      855
  EDXRA, 981
  ore, 402, 654
  oxide, 411, 477, 562, 662, 718, 788, 832,
      844, 1309, 1338, 1339, 1343, 1346,
      1541
  particles, 1311, 1338, 1342
  roasting dust, 478, 719, 818, 833–835
  sawdust, 478, 719, 833, 835
  scale, 1258, 1545
  sponge, 479, 720, 818, 833, 835, 844,
      855
  wrought, 855
irradiance levels, 1154
isogyres, 86, 1047
isokinetic sampling, 209
isolation of paint medium, 1393
isolation of paint pigments, 1393
isomorphism, 71, 1047
isotope ratioing, IMA, 1658
isotopic abundances, 1006–1008
isotropic substances, 77, 82, 312, 1047
  dispersion staining, 1161
isotropic unknowns, 108
ivory, 849
  black, 493, 732, 1319, 1611

jade, 393, 645
jadeite, 393, 645, 853, 1238, 1519
Jaffe wicking method, 1647–1648
Jamin-Lebedeff interference microscope,
    35–39, 1047
jasper green, 1319, 1611
Jello®, lime, 1294, 1579
jeweler's rouge, 411, 662, 832, 844, 854
Juglans californica, 1219, 1494
Juglans cinerea, 1219
Juglans nigra, 1219
Juniperus virginiana, 1198, 1483
jute, 354, 609, 820, 848, 930, 963, 967,
    1282, 1386, 1568

kainite, 850
kalicinite, 875, 881, 889, 895, 904, 916–
    917
kaliophilite, 851
kaolin, 386, 584, 639, 816, 839, 852,
    1254, 1512, 1540
kaolinite, 145, 1232, 1236, 1237, 1510
kapok, 355, 609, 820, 823, 847, 965, 967,
    1224, 1386
Karo® syrup, 94, 308
kelp, 448, 694, 831, 847
kemps, 1047
kenaf, 965, 967, 1278, 1386, 1565
keratin, 1355, 1358
Kermoccus vermilio, 1324, 1618

Kerria lacca, 1333, 1629
Kevlar® Aramid, 1272, 1559
kiln dust, 481–482, 722
  burned, 480, 721, 814, 835
  lime, 812, 827–828, 850
King's yellow, 1322
kitchen cleanser, 424, 675, 816, 821
Kleenex®, 358, 612
known particle, description, 325
"known-unknown" practice, 1351
Kochia scoparia, 1201, 1485
Kodel®, 847
Kofler
  glass powder standards, 97, 110, 968
  hot stage, 106, 108, 114–116
  sublimation block, 117
Köhler
  Brace-Köhler compensator, 38
  illumination, 22–25
kordofan, 1331
kozo, 1280
Kraft paper process, 531, 763
krypton, EDXRA, 982
Kuralon®, 848
kyanite, 386, 397, 639, 824–825, 840, 853,
    875, 877, 898, 929–933, 1227, 1353
Kynol®, 1272, 1559

laboratory design, 283–288
labradorite, 113, 386, 640, 816, 822, 839,
    852, 875, 884, 894–895, 915–916,
    1227
α-lactose, 449, 695, 817, 842, 848, 1295,
    1580
Lake Michigan suspended particles, 555,
    784, 814, 819, 823–824
Lakeside 70, 1370
lamb's quarters pollen, 334–335, 592, 826
lambda zero, 1047
lampblack, 849, 1409, 1612
lampblack C, 1320
lamp condensers, 23
lamps
  tungsten-halogen, 46
  ultraviolet, 42
lanarkite, 855
langbeinite, 387, 640, 811, 838, 845,
    852, 875, 881, 893, 912–913
lanthanum, EDXRA, 986
  hexaboride filament, 1469
lapping-wheel, 1370
laser Raman microprobe, 1147–1157,
    1365, 1394, 1471
latex, 555, 784, 813, 827, 830, 848
lattice, crystal, 65
lattice spacings, 127–129
lattice, reciprocal, 139
laundry detergent, 425, 675, 816, 858
lausenite, 853, 875, 880, 896–897, 920,
    925
lawn mowing, 555–556, 784, 813–814,
    819, 847
law of reflection, 3
laws of crystallography, 66, 1047
lazurite, 851, 1239, 1519, 1620

lead, 855, 990
  accumulator, 479, 720, 815, 845, 855
  blast furnace dust, 479, 720, 833, 835
  carbonate (basic), 145
  chlorofluoride, 855
  chromate, 1317, 1645
  dithionate tetrahydrate, 853, 886, 897, 923–925
  glasses, 852
  -indium shot, 480, 721, 835, 845, 855
  monoxide, 482, 723, 833
  nitrate, 854, 886, 899, 937–938
  orthophosphate, 885
  oxide, 1251, 1537
  oxide fume, 479, 720
  particles, computerized EMA search, 164
  pencil, 1400
  phosphate, 886, 899, 952–957
  red, 496, 735, 833–834, 845, 1407
  smelter, 1308–1309, 1595–1596
  stearate decanoate crystal, 1003
  sulfate, 855, 1309
  super oxide (minium), 1251
  tetroxide, 1251, 1537
  tin yellow, 1320, 1408, 1612
  white, 323, 495, 735, 825, 842, 855, 1320, 1407, 1613
leaf burning, 542, 772, 813–814, 819, 836, 847
leaf cuticle, 1357
leaf fibers, 310, 316, 361, 615, 616, 847, 1056, 1221–1223, 1335, 1386
leather, 524, 759, 813, 821, 827, 847
  buffing, 525, 813, 827
lemon powder, 449, 695, 812, 848
lemon yellow (deep), 1321, 1613
lens aberrations
  electron, 133
  light, 8–9, 11, 15
lenses
  Bertrand, 16, 23, 41, 46, 1036
  concave, 7
  convex, 7
  electron, 132–133, 1041
  electrostatic, IMA, 169
  focal length, 7, 12
  formula, 4
  magnetic
    EMA, 157
    SEM, 149
  negative, 8
  positive, 8
  zoom, 16, 261
lepidocrocite, 388, 854
lepidolite, 387, 641, 822, 839, 852
LePoole mini-lens, 1461
leucite, 387, 640, 811, 816, 839, 851
lewisite, 854
light balancing filters, 1047
light diffraction, 18, 40
light filters, 30
light microscope, 9, 11, 15
  contrast, 22
  depth of field, 44, 154, 1040

light microscope—cont'd
  EMA, 160–161
  magnification, 13–14
  resolution, 12, 15, 18–20, 22
  spherical aberration, 4, 8, 11
  working distance, 11–12
lighter "flint" sparks, 1342, 1639
lighting, top, 25–28, 59, 312
lignin, 315, 525, 759, 827–828, 842, 847, 857, 1354
lignite, 847
  coal, 544, 774, 813, 827, 836, 847
  spreader stoker, 546–547, 776–777, 837
Ligustrum lucidium, 1212, 1490
lime, 481, 722, 812, 818, 827, 828, 843, 850, 853, 875, 878, 899, 939–944
  cement, 1400
  flue dust, 1252, 1538
  kiln burned dust, 480, 721, 812, 814, 818, 827–828, 835, 850
  kiln cyclone, 482, 722, 812, 827, 835
limestone, 319, 388, 562, 564, 641, 788, 790, 816, 840, 852, 858, 1254, 1327, 1335, 1339, 1352–1353, 1541
limonite, 384, 388, 637, 641, 828, 832, 834, 844, 852, 1236
lindane, 1304, 1589
linden pollen, 1193, 1481
linen, see flax
linseed meal, 310, 447, 449–450, 693, 695, 812, 817, 821, 826, 828, 830, 847
linseed oil, 1332, 1628
linters, cotton, 353, 608, 820, 823, 830, 841, 963, 967
Linum usitatissimum, 1332, 1628
Lionite, artificial corundum, 409, 661, 824, 834, 840
Liquidambar styraciflua, 1203, 1277, 1486, 1564
litharge, 855, 1321, 1408, 1614
lithium
  detection, 117, 155
  dithionate dihydrate, 850, 882, 894–895, 914–915, 917–918
  fluoride, 852, 882, 889, 905, 1003
  potassium platinocyanide trihydrate, 882, 896, 921–922
  potassium sulfate, 851, 882, 890, 908–909
  rubidium platinocyanide trihydrate, 882, 896, 899, 921, 944–960
litigation, 1362
live oak pollen, 1209, 1489
lizardite, 1239, 1520, 1528
llama vicuña, 964, 967, 1288, 1573
locating particles in EMA, 162–163, 244–245
locomotive (steam), 1336, 1633
London red rain, 560, 787, 821
long working distance objectives, 12, 28
"look-alikes," 311
Lorentz-Lorenz equation, 974
low-alumina catalyst, 415, 665–666, 811, 826, 834

low-power stereomicroscope, 1349
low temperature ashing, 221, 1349
  asbestos, 1648–1651
Lucite®, 1332, 1629
ludwigite, 388, 642, 832, 834, 837, 840, 853
lumen, 1047
lung tissue, size of particles in, 303
lutetium, 988
Lycopodium spores, 345, 600, 826, 857
Lycra®, 962, 966, 1272–1273, 1559, 1562
Lynx rufus pallescens, 1283, 1569

Macbeth Prooflite 5000, 327
machining, ion beam, 175
Mach-Zehnder interference microscope, 39
Maclura pomifera, 1210
madder lake, 1321, 1408, 1614
magnesioferrite, 854
magnesite, 377, 389, 482, 632, 642, 722, 812, 815, 818, 824, 842, 853, 1375
magnesium, 978
  aluminate, see spinel
  carbonate, see magnesite
  cerium nitrate, 882, 892–893, 911, 912
  chlorostannate hexahydrate, 850
  chromate heptahydrate, 849, 882, 893–895, 911–912, 916
  lanthanum nitrate, 882, 892–893, 911–912
  neodymium nitrate, 883, 893, 911–912
  oxide, see periclase
    hydrated, 1252, 1538
  platinocyanide heptahydrate, 883, 894, 899, 915–916, 948–952
  praseodymium nitrate, 883, 892–893, 911–912
  silicate, 525, 760, 818, 821, 845, 853
  silicofluoride hexahydrate, 849, 883, 889, 902–903
  sulfate heptahydrate (epsomite), 849, 874, 883, 889–890, 907–908
  sulfate monohydrate, 851
  tin chloride hexahydrate, 883, 895–896, 917–921
magnetic lenses
  EMA, 157
  SEM, 149
magnetic separation, 220, 1349
magnetic tape coating, Mylar® tape, 503, 741, 833, 844, 858
magnetite, 310, 312, 389, 561, 642, 788–789, 834, 844, 854, 1322, 1353, 1615
  spheres, 324, 547, 854
magnification
  changers, 16, 261
  EMA, 158
  empty, 14, 44, 1047
  light microscope, 13–14
  maximum useful, 14, 1048
  objective, 13
  ocular, 13–14, 19
  photomicrography, 44–45
  SEM, 146, 150, 152

magnification—*cont'd*
 simple magnifier, 8
 TEM, 133
magnifier, simple, 7
mail-handling dust, post office, 560, 786
maize, starch, 458, 702
major x-ray energies for the elements,
 999–1003
malachite, 376, 389, 643, 832, 834, 841,
 854, 1228, 1408
malathion, 1304, 1589
malt grain dust, 450, 696, 813, 817, 821,
 829, 831, 847
malt sugar, 451, 696
d-maltose, 451, 696, 812, 817, 842, 848
manganese, 980
 oxide, 144, 145
 silicofluoride hexahydrate, 849, 883,
  889, 903–904
manganite, 854
manganosite, 855
manila, 1279, 1386, 1565
man-made fibers, *see* synthetic fibers
manufacturers and suppliers, 1028–1033
manure, sheep, 432, 681, 811, 817, 821,
 830, 826, 848
maple (sugar) fibers, 1279, 1565
maple (sugar) pollen, 335, 593, 826
mapping particles for EMA, 245
maps, particle origin determination, 1351
Maranta arundinacea, 458, 702
marble, 852, 1231
marcasite, 854
marigold pollen, 1207, 1488
marihuana
 pollen, 336, 593, 826
 trichomes, 360, 615, 820, 830
marjoram, 1294, 1580
markers (sample origin), 1360
mars black, 1322, 1615
Martin's diameter, 265
mascagnite, 875, 885, 893, 911–913
Masonite® sawdust, 526, 760, 812, 821,
 823, 827, 831, 848
massicot, 482, 723, 833, 845, 855, 1251,
 1321, 1537, 1614
mass scanning of particles, 1655–1657
 EMA, 163
 IMA, 175
 SEM, 155
mass separation, 211
mass spectrometry, 119, 169
mass spectroscopy, 1147
mastic, 308
matchbox striker dust, 411, 662, 816, 826,
 846
matlockite, 855, 875, 886, 900, 959, 960
mauritius, 965, 967, 1279, 1566
mauritius hemp, 1386, 1387
mauve, 1322, 1615
maximum horizontal intercept, 265
maximum useful magnification (MUM),
 1048
 EMA, 158
 light microscope, 14

meal
 bone, steamed, 1289
 corn, 443–444, 461, 690–691, 817, 822,
  848
 fish, 447, 693, 811, 817, 821–822, 848
 linseed, 310, 447, 449–450, 693, 695,
  812, 817, 821, 826, 828, 830, 847
 peanut, 1297
 poultry, by-product, 453, 698, 817, 822,
  829, 831, 847
 wood, 540, 770, 819, 823, 848
mechanical wood pulp, 317, 356–357, 611,
 820, 822–823, 830–831, 848, 1038
meerschaum, 1522
melamine formaldehyde, 502, 740, 812,
 814, 841, 848, 858
melanterite, 875, 880, 890–891, 909
melatopes, 91, 1048
melting furnace, brass, 1591
melting point, 115, 1347
membrane filters, 208, 230, 231, 1048
 dust, 556, 785, 813–814, 848
 samples, SEM, 1476
mental attitude, of microscopist, 1348
mercerized cotton, 311, 353, 607, 819,
 841, 963, 967, 1048
mercuric cyanide, 854, 880, 891, 897,
 910, 923–924
mercurous chloride (calomel), 855, 874,
 880, 899–900, 957
mercury, 855, 990
mercury vapor lamp, 1149
mesquite pollen, 1207, 1208, 1488
metal, 465–492, 707–732, 858
 alloy spray, 467, 480, 708, 835, 840
 coatings, 577, 1473–1474
 fibers, 1288, 1574
 finish belt, 1309, 1597
 heat-treating salt, 1309, 1597
 inclusions, 151
 monel, 855
 processing, 322
 processing, photomicrographs and
  descriptions, 1305–1312, 1590–
  1601
 refining, 322
 shadowing, 135, 1054
 wood's, 855
metallographic, 1048
meteorology, particle origin
 determination, 1351
methods for size analysis, 803
methoxychlor, 1304, 1590
methyl methacrylate, 503, 741, 812, 818,
 842, 847, 1629
methylene iodide, 307, 1352
metric units, international system of units,
 1018
Mettler hotstage, 114
mica
 exfoliated, 526–527, 760, 818, 823, 831,
  851
 identifying characteristics, 310
 mineral occurrence, 1352
 paint extenders, 510

mica—*cont'd*
 phlogopite, 852
 vermiculite, 852
 see also biotite, lepidolite, muscovite
Michel-Lévy chart, xi-xiii, 38, 84, 1048
Michelson interference microscope, 36
microbeam, electron instruments, 1466–
 1467
microchemical analysis, dust, 1349
microchemical reactions, 1175–1184
 complex substances, 1182–1184
 inorganic compounds, 1178–1180
 insoluble substances, 1181–1182
 organic compounds, 1180–1181
 reagents, 1177
microchemical tests, 117–119, 1175–1184
 drugs, 117–118, 1398–1399
 inorganic, 118
 microminiaturization, 119
 organic, 118
 pigments, 1406, 1411–1413
microcline, 310, 391, 644, 816, 822, 839,
 851, 875, 881, 892, 894, 911–913
microcomputers, 1652
microcrystal tests, 1175
microdrops, 228–229
microforge, 246
microlite, 855
micromesh sieves, 211
micrometeorites, 173
micrometer
 ocular, 260–266, 1043, 1048
 stage, 260, 1048
micrometers
 net, 262
 precision, 263
micrometry, useful equations, 1017
microminiaturization of microchemical
 tests, 119
"micron" disc, 263
microphotograph, 1048
microprobe
 analyzer, *see* EMA, EMMA, IMA and
  MOLE
 proton, 182–183
microprocessors, 1652
microscope objectives, 11–14, 16, 20, 22–
 25, 29, 1404
microscope optics, useful equations, 1009
 1011
microscope stands, 16
microscopical examination of airborne
 dust samples, reasons for, 1362
microscopist's attitude, 1348
microstereology, 268
microtaggants, 1340, 1638
microvacuum cleaner, 231
mildew-mold, 857
military explosives, 114, 1264–1268, 1398,
 1399
milk
 powder, 451, 697, 812, 817, 842, 848,
  1294, 1580
 smear graticule, 261
 substitute, 1295, 1580

milk–*cont'd*
  sugar, 449, 695
milkweed fibers, 1224, 1498
mill scale, 310, 483, 490, 723, 730, 835,
    837, 854
Miller indices, 68–69, 1048
Millipore® filter, 1371
milorganite, 432, 682, 817, 823, 829, 847,
    858, 1049
mineral oil, 308
mineral wool, 318, 369–370, 624, 813,
    815, 826–827, 852, 857, 1288, 1389
minerals, 97, 113, 318, 371–406, 625–658,
    858, 1226–1247, 1500–1532
  accessory, 319
  coating substances, 1353
  fibers, 116, 373–375, 627–629, 1369–
    1378, 1390
  grain weathering, 1353
  heavy, association and
    provenance, 1353
      stability, 1353
  identity, 1351–1354
  shape and surface texture, 1353
minicamera, XRD, 121
mini-lens, LePoole, 1461–1462
miniprobe, 156, 162
minium (red lead), 855
mink hair, 964, 967, 1287, 1572
mirrors
  aberrations, 4
  concave, 3–4, 11, 16
  convex, 4, 11
  first surface, 16
  focus, 3
  plane, 3
  substage, 15
miscellaneous fibers (carbon, metallic,
    feather etc.), 1390
miscellaneous particles, 510–540, 746–
    771, 858, 1635–1643
mispickel, 1503
mitscherlichite, 851, 875, 881, 896–897,
    920–921, 924
mitsumata, 1280, 1386, 1566
mixed refractive index liquids, 76
MM165, 307
modacrylic fibers, 364, 619, 820, 841, 961,
    966
mohair, 348, 603, 819, 848, 964, 967
Moh's hardness scale, 1049
mold, 315, 342–344, 597–598, 811, 813–
    814, 826, 847, 857
molding sand, 310–311, 322, 483–486,
    723–726, 818, 829, 833, 835, 837,
    846–847, 858
  synthetic, 483, 723–724, 818
  synthetic, cured, unused, 485, 725, 818
  synthetic, used, 484–485, 726, 818, 835,
    837
  unused, 484, 725, 818
  used, 485, 725, 818
  zircon, 486, 726, 824, 833, 846
MOLE, 1147–1157, 1365, 1660
molecular refraction, 974–975

molybdenite, 854
molybdenum, 983
molybdenum roaster, 1310, 1597
monastral blue, 1327
monazite, 392, 644, 832, 843, 854, 875,
    879, 899, 936–938, 941–943, 1353
monel metal, 855
monoammonium phosphate, 430, 680, 816,
    821, 845, 849, 858, 885, 890, 909
monocalcium phosphate, 451, 696, 699,
    817, 821–822, 851, 878, 894, 896,
    913–915, 918–920
  monohydrate, 843, 850, 878, 891, 893,
    909–913
monochromator, curved crystal, EMA, 158
monochromator optics, 1049, 1151
monoclinic system, 65, 68
monopotassium phosphate, 881, 890, 892,
    908, 910
monosodium arsenate monohydrate, 883,
    894–895, 913
monosodium glutamate, 1299, 1585
monosodium phosphate dihydrate, 884,
    889, 907, 909
monosodium phosphate monohydrate,
    884, 889, 891, 908–909
montmorillonite, 584, 1239, 1517, 1520
montroydite, 855
moon dust, 557, 785, 813, 819, 825, 836
morphine, 1261, 1397, 1548–1549
morphological analysis, 152, 272–276,
    1049
morphology, crystal, 64
morphology of particles
  electron microscope, 152, 275–276
  light microscope, 272–275
mortar, 419, 669, 811, 821, 844, 858
  cement, 321
  mix, 423, 674, 815–816, 822, 824, 832,
    850
moss
  leaf, 1348
  Spanish, 310, 341, 596, 822, 831, 848
  spores, 345, 600, 826, 857
moth
  Cecropia cocoon, 346, 601, 819, 823,
    831, 847
  scales, 309, 331, 591, 814, 828, 848
Mount, 308
mounts
  beryllium sample, EMA, 162
  carbon film, 162
  glass fiber, XRD, 122–123, 246–249
  objective, 13
mountain ash trichomes, 361, 615, 820,
    823
mounting media, 223–225, 305–308
  phase contrast, 308
  recovery of particles from, 236–237, 245
  viscous, 224–225
mounting particles
  EMA, 237–246
  fibers, 316
  IMA, 254
  MOLE, 1154

mounting particles–*cont'd*
  pollens, 308, 315
  refractive index, 254–258
  SEM, 252–253, 1472–1478
  TEM, 134, 240, 249–252, 583
  XRD, 122–123, 246–249
mulberry, 1386
  fibers, 1280, 1566
  pollen, 1208, 1488
mullite, 853
MUM, 14, 158, 1048
municipal incinerator, 549, 779, 813, 827–
    828, 836
Musa textilis, 1276, 1279, 1563, 1565
muscovite, 391, 643, 822, 839, 852, 1227,
    1236, 1244, 1352–1353
mushroom spores, 315, 344, 599, 826, 857
mustard, 452, 697, 812, 817, 822, 826, 848
mustard seed, 1295, 1581
Mustela vision, 1287, 1572
mycelium, 1049
Mylar® tape magnetic coating, 503, 741,
    833, 844, 858
Myrica cerifera, 1193–1194, 1481

NA, 11–15, 44–46, 1050
Nacconol® beads, 425, 675, 811, 822, 848
nacrite, 1510
nantokite, 875, 880, 899, 956–957
Naphrax, 307
Naples yellow, 496, 735, 829, 845, 855,
    1408
narcotics, 113, 117, 1258–1260, 1395–
    1398
natrolite, 392, 644, 816, 820, 839, 850
natural aquamarine, 1325
natural emery, 408–409, 660
natural fibers, 316, 346–361, 600–616,
    963, 964, 967, 1380–1387
NBS laser Raman microprobe, 1149–1151
needles
  cold, 117
  polyethylene, 227
  tungsten, 225–227
needle in the haystack analysis, 1049
negative crystals, 79, 81, 87, 1049
negative lenses, 8
negative ocular, 14
Negroid hair, 350, 604, 819, 830, 1358
Nelsonian illumination, 22–24
neodymium
  EDXRA, 986
  molybdate, 854, 884, 900, 959–960
  praseodymium molybdate, 854, 885,
    900, 960
  sulfate octahydrate, 852, 884, 894–895,
    913–916
neon, EDXRA, 978
neoprene, 847
nepheline, 851, 875, 881–882, 893–894,
    913–914
nephelite, 392, 645, 816, 839
nephrite, 393, 645, 824–825, 843, 853,
    1226

neptunium, EDXRA, 992
net micrometer, 262
nettle pollen, 1209, 1489
neutral density filters, 23, 31, 46, 53, 1049
neutron activation analysis (NAA), hair, 1381
Newton's color series, xi–xiii, 38, 84, 1049
niacin, 1295, 1581
niacinamide, 1296, 1581
nichrome, 885
nickel, 885, 981
  fluoride-hydrogen fluoride hexahydrate, 885–886, 889, 905
  nitrate, 1252, 1539
  processing, 1310, 1598
  selenate hexahydrate, 851, 886, 892, 913
  silicofluoride hexahydrate, 850, 886, 889, 905
  sulfate hexahydrate (retgersite), 850, 876, 886, 891–892, 909–911
nickel-coated
  Borazon®, 1255
  diamond, 1256
Nicol prism, 21, 1049
nicotinamide, 1296
nicotinic acid, 1295
Nies scales, 126
niobium, EDXRA, 983
niter, 875, 881, 889, 892, 910
nitrobarite, 875, 877, 895, 916–917
nitrocellulose, 501, 740, 821, 841, 849, 1266, 1553
nodes, 1050
Nomarski differential interference contract (DIC), 35–36, 40, 1050, 1155
Nomex®, 365, 619, 825, 841, 848, 961, 966
  HT-1, 961, 966
nonbrightfield photomicrography, 48–49
nonconiferous chemical wood, 357, 611, 820, 823, 848, 1226
nonconiferous mechanical wood, 356–357, 611, 820, 822–823, 830–831, 848, 1500
nonconiferous wood fibers, 318, 1050
noncrystalline materials, 64
nonplastic blasting explosives, 1399
nonwoven textiles, 1380
nordstrandite, 1515
norephedrine hydrochloride, 1262, 1549
northupite, 851, 875, 884, 892, 911
nosepiece
  "quick-change," 13
  rotating, 13, 1053
novocaine hydrochloride, 1262, 1549
NPK ratio, 436, 1050
Nuclepore® filters, 208, 1371
number of atoms, particle size and weight, 804
numerical aperture, 11–15, 44–46, 1050
nutritional yeast, 1301, 1587
nylon, 311, 365–366, 620, 820, 841, 847
  Caprolan®, 961, 966, 1273, 1560
  fibers, 961, 966

nylon—cont'd
  filters, 231
  type SC-16, 962, 966
  type 66, 962, 966
  type 716, 961, 966
  Tynek®, 1274
  undrawn, 1273, 1274, 1560
Nyssa sylvatica, 1486

oak
  (live) pollen, 1209, 1210, 1489
  white, 1280, 1567
oats, 1387
objectives
  achromatic, 9, 11, 14
  apochromatic, 11, 14, 20, 1035
  back focal plane, 16, 22–25, 1035
  correction collar, 261
  dispersion staining, 101
  flatfield, 11
  fluorite, 11, 14, 1043
  half-screening, 57
  immersion, 12, 308, 1045
  long working distance, 12, 28
  microscope, 11–14, 16, 20, 22–25, 29, 1404
  mounts, centerable, 13
  oil immersion, 12, 308
  phase contrast, 41
  plan-achromatic, 11
  plan-apochromatic, 11
  plano, 9, 11
  quartz, 12, 41
  reflection, 11–12, 41, 1151
  reflection-refraction, 12
  semiapochromatic, 11
  strain-free, 11
  Ultropak, 29
  vertical illuminator, 27–29, 312
  water immersion, 12
oblique extinction, 82–83
oblique illumination, 56–57, 74–75
obsidian, 394, 646, 811, 839, 850
obtuse bisectrix, 81, 1050
occlusion, 1050
ochre, red, 496–497, 736, 833, 844, 854, 1407
ochre, yellow, 1328, 1407, 1624
octahedron, 65, 1050
oculars, 9, 11, 14, 260–261
  compensating, 11, 14, 1038
  filar, 260–266, 1043, 1048
  flatfield, 11, 14
  focusing, 261
  graticules, 260–261, 263
  Huyghenian, 14, 1045
  image-splitting, 260
  micrometer scale, 260–266, 1043, 1048
  negative, 14
  positive, 14
  Ramsden, 14, 1052
  reticles, 260
  scale calibration, 261, 263
  shearing, 260
Odocoileus virginianus, 1285, 1571

office dust, 558, 785–786, 858
oil immersion objectives, 12, 308
oil
  drilling mud, 1253, 1539
  flyash, 1336, 1634
  mineral, 308
  shale, 528, 761, 818
  silicone, 1355
  soot, 312, 516, 543, 771, 773, 828, 836, 847, 1334, 1348, 1582
okenite, 851
olefin, 365, 619, 820, 841, 962, 966
oligoclase, 852, 1227
olivine, 310, 393, 645, 825, 844, 853, 1239, 1244
opal, 393, 646, 811, 845, 849, 1341, 1357, 1358
"opaque" chromium oxide green, 1326
opaque particles, 25–26, 1050
open hearth, steel, 585, 858
  burned-out furnace, 489, 729, 818, 833
  charging period, 488, 728, 833
  combustion product, 489, 729, 833
  hot metal to lime-up, 488, 728, 833
  tap to charge, 488, 728, 833
opossum hair, 1287, 1573
optical crystallographic properties, 71–119, 1156–1165, 1369, 1388, 1397–1398, 1407–1409
  effect of solid solution on, 1372
optical glasses, 969
optical indicatrix, 80, 81, 1045
optical sectioning, 36
optic axial angle, 81, 86, 88–91, 1050
optic axial plane, 81, 88, 1050
optic sign, 79, 87–89, 1050
Optovar, 16, 45, 261
orange peel diffuser, 25
orange shellac, 1333
ores, 322, 402, 654
  ilmenite, 385, 639, 815, 822, 834, 837, 843, 844, 854, 1353
  taconite, 402, 654, 816, 832, 834, 844
  uranium, 404, 655, 816, 832
  zinc, roasted, 491, 731, 833, 846
organic fibers, 1375
organic microchemical tests, 118, 1180–1181
organic nitrogen
  20% fertilizer, 1271, 1558
  40% fertilizer, 1271, 1558
organic particles, 1471
  MOLE, 1147, 1151, 1471
organization of the Atlas, 1187
"organized" particles, 314
Oriental's hair, 1358
origin of sample, 1360
Orlon®, 311, 362, 617, 820, 841, 847, 961, 966
orpiment, 1322, 1408, 1616
orthoclase, 394, 646, 816, 822, 839, 851, 875, 881, 893–894, 911–912, 914–915
orthorhombic sulfur, 850
orthorhombic system, 65, 68

orthoscopic observation, 85, 1050
Oryza sativa, 459, 703
osage orange pollen, 1210, 1489
OSHA counting method (asbestos), 1371
osmium, 989
Osmunda cinnamonea, 341, 596
Ottawa sand, 1253, 1539
oven deposits, 1296, 1582
oxalate, calcium, 354–355, 514, 542, 749, 772
oxalic acid, 528, 761, 818, 821, 842, 849
oxide
    chromium, 1408
    zinc, 323, 492, 585, 731, 824, 843, 1328, 1407
oxygen, 978
oxygen plasma ashing
    asbestos, 1648–1651
oyster shell, 852, 1327
    milled, 529, 762, 818, 840
    pearl button, 529, 762, 818, 825, 840
    powder, 528, 762, 818, 825, 840

paint
    chips, 529–530, 559, 763, 786, 813–814, 819, 824–825, 833, 848
    extender, 510, 525, 589, 746, 760, 814, 818, 821, 823, 845, 1329, 1626
    isolation of medium, 1393
    isolation of pigment, 1393
    macroscopical measurement on crossection, 1393
    microscopy table of common pigments, 1407–1409
    physical fit, 1393
    pigment analysis, 1393–1394, 1402–1413
    pigment isolation, 1393
    spray dust, 530, 763, 812, 827, 848, 1360
paint pigments table, 1407–1409
palladium, EDXRA, 984
palma, 965, 967
paper
    coated, 560, 787
    fibers, 352–354, 356–358, 607, 608, 611, 612, 1277, 1335, 1355, 1380, 1385
    mill, 531, 763, 812, 819, 823, 827, 836, 848
    mulberry pollen, 1488
    processing, Kraft, 531, 763
    punch-card system, 1385
papermaking, indication of, 1355
paprika, 1296, 1582
paracelsian, 875, 878, 895, 916
paraffin, 847
parallel extinction, 82
parallel polars, 84, 95
parenchyma, 317, 318
parfocal, 1051
pargasite, 394, 647, 816, 823, 829, 839, 853
Paris green, 1318
particle
    analysis (automatic), 1655–1657

particle—*cont'd*
    ashing, 115
    association, 1353
    characterization, 152, 272, 309, 578, 583, 803, 1379–1413
    classification
        light microscopy, 277–279, 314, 805, 810–837, 1380–1390
        electron microscopy, 279–280
    coatings, 1347
    collection, 204, 206
        for SEM, 1477
    color, 54, 71
    correlation, 1347
    counting, 112, 266–268, 1155, 1366
    crushing, 247–248, 251–252
    decomposition, 115
    density ranges, 224
    description, 325
    diameters, statistical, 264–265
    examination, 1347
    fractionation methods, 210–222
    fracturing for SEM, 1477
    handling, 205, 222, 1349
    hardness, 272, 1044
    identification, 272, 276, 303, 325, 582
        ingested, 210
        microchemical reactions, 1175
    in situ examination, 1363
    insoluble, 1181–1182
    morphology, 1049
        electron microscopy, 152, 275–276
        light microscopy, 272–275
    mounting
        EMA, 237–246
        IMA, 254
        MOLE, 1154
        refractive index, 254–258
        SEM, 252, 253, 1472–1478
        TEM, 134, 240, 249–252, 583
        XRD, 246–249
    opaque, 25–26
    "organized," 314
    origin, 1351
    picking, 205, 222–223, 1349
    provenance, 1353
    refractive index, 254–258
    recovery, 234–237, 245, 1477
    removal from filter
        needle, 1363
        scalpel, 1363
        ultrasoneration, 1364
    removal from substrate, 1349
    replication, 1477–1478
    sampling, 204, 209, 233–234
    shape, 274, 582
    size, 803, 1354
        analysis, automated, 268
        averages, calculation, 266
        distribution, 264, 1347, 1354
        in lung, 303
        measurement, 258–260
        stability, 1353
        versus weight, 804

particle—*cont'd*
    study in art, archaeology, conservation and authentication, 1402–1413
    submicrometer, 114
    surface texture, 582
    suspended, Lake Michigan, 819, 823–824
    zoological, 1354
Particle Atlas, organization, 1187
particle diffusion coefficient, 803
particle size of typical particles, 803
particle size, useful equation, 1017
particle size, weight and number of atoms, 804
"pasteurization," 222, 1349
path difference, 38–39
Patterson globe and circle graticule, 263
PCB, 1166
peach
    fuzz, 1225, 1499
    trichomes, 1221, 1495
peanut
    hulls, 452, 697, 817, 821–822, 823, 831, 848
    meal, 1297, 1582
    skins, 452, 698, 831, 848
pearl button, 529, 762, 818, 825, 840
pecan pollen, 1211, 1490
pectin, 857
pectolite, 395, 647, 820, 830, 843, 852, 875, 880, 896–897, 918–920, 922–924
pedion, 68
pegmatites, granite, 1353
pencil eraser, 1339, 1637
pencil lead, 1400
pencil sharpener dust, 559, 786, 813, 819, 824, 831, 848
Penicillium notatum, 343, 597, 811, 819, 823, 826, 848
pentaerythritol tetranitrate (PETN), 1266, 1553
pepper, cayenne, 453, 698, 817, 822, 829, 949
periclase, 395, 401, 405, 647, 815, 845, 853, 875, 883, 898, 932–934
periodic table, inside back cover, Vol. IV
perlite, 311–312, 531, 764, 814, 839, 850
Perlon®, 962, 966
Permount®, 308
perovskite, 854
PESIS, 178–179
PESOS, 178–179
PETN, 1266, 1553
petrography, 1051
petroleum coke, 516, 518, 751, 754, 835, 847
pharmaceuticals, 114
phase contrast, 33, 39–41, 74, 1051
    asbestos, 1371
    microscope, 39–40
    mounting media set, 308
    objectives, 41
phase difference, 38–39
phase plate, 40–41

phase telescope, 41
phenacite, 853
phenazine dyes, 1322
phenolformaldehyde, 848, 1272
phenolic resin 504, 741, 812, 842, 848
Pheleum pratense, 340, 595
p-phenylene terephthalamide, 1272
phenylpropanolamine hydrochloride, 1262
phloem, 1051
phlogopite mica, 852
phormium, 1386, 1567
Phormium tenax, 1281, 1567
phosphate rock, 321, 432–433, 532, 627,
    682, 764, 812, 817, 827, 829, 853,
    1269
  calcined, 532, 764, 812, 827, 843, 853
  fluorapatite, 432–433, 682, 843, 874,
    878–879, 922–924
phosphor, fluorescent light, 1341, 1638
phosphorus, 979
photocells, 47
photoelectron spectroscopy, 178–182
  inner shells (PESIS), 178–179
  outer shells, (PESOS), 178–179
photographic filters, 51
photomacrography, useful equations,
    1016, 1051
photometers, 46–47
photomicrographic records, 50–51
photomicrographs, 326
photomicrography, 44–61, 95, 1051
  brightfield, 47
  color, 54, 1185
  filters for, 51
  fluorescence, 53
  high resolution, 54
  "holey polar" method, 1185
  nonbrightfield, 48–49
  particle color, 54
  reciprocity failure, 54, 1052
  stereo, 56–61
  useful equations, 1009–1027
photomultiplier tube, 47, 1151
photophoresis, 1051
phthalic acid, 531–532, 764, 825, 842, 849
phtalic anhydride, 1253, 1540
phytoliths, opal, 1357–1358
Picea marina, 1282, 1568
Picea sp., 1197
picking particles, 205, 222–223
picogram particles, 1147
picric acid, 1266, 1554
picromerite, 850, 875, 881, 890, 908–909
picture points, 269
pig (hog) hair, 1287, 1573
pig iron graphite, 476, 717, 835, 840
pigments, 323, 493–499, 732–738, 858
  analytical schemes, 1393–1394, 1402–
    1413
    black, 1410
    blue, 1410
    green, 1411
    red, 1412
    white, 1406
    yellow, 1411

pigments—*cont'd*
  identification, 1406–1413
  microchemical tests, 1406, 1411–1413
  microscopy table of common paint,
    1407–1409
  pigment reference slides, 1403
pigments and media, photomicrographs
    and descriptions, 1312–1333,
    1601–1630
pigweed pollen, 337, 594, 826
pinacoid, 68
pine pollen, 310–311, 338, 594, 826
pine, scotch, 1281, 1567
ping-pong ball illumination, 29
Pinus silvestris, 1281, 1567
Pinus sp., 310–311, 338, 597, 1197
pipettes
  Andreason, 212
  polyethylene, 228–229
pirssonite, 851, 875, 883, 892, 895, 916–
    917
pitch, 847
pits
  coniferous, 317–318
  nonconiferous, 318
plagioclases, 319, 1227
plan-achromatic objectives, 11
plan-apochromatic objectives, 11
plan mirror, 3
plano (flatfield) objectives, 9, 11
plant
  cells, 315
  fibers, 317, 1385, 1386
plant, opal, 1357, 1358
Plantago lanceolata, 1211, 1490
plantain (English) pollen, 1211, 1490
plaster, 559, 786
plaster of Paris, 384, 533, 765, 821, 838,
    843, 852
plastic explosives, 1399
plastics, 113
  ethyl cellulose, 502, 740, 818, 842, 847
  impregnated wood pulp, 540, 771, 828,
    831–832, 1355
  fiber glass reinforced, 368, 622, 811,
    813
Platanus occidentalis, 1217, 1222, 1493
Platanus sp., 359, 614
platinum, 989
platinum-iridium alloy, 855
pleochroism, 21, 72, 1051
pleurax, 307
PLM, drugs, 1398
plumbicon tube, 269
plum trichomes, 1222, 1496
Pluton® fibers, 363, 617, 820, 840
plutonium, 992
PMA (proton microprobe analyzer), 182–
    183
Pocatello fertilizer plant, 1269, 1556–1557
point-counting graticule, 261
point illumination, 1151
polar, "holey," 97
polarization, 3, 16, 20–21, 33–34, 44–45,
    49, 57–58, 83

polarization—*cont'd*
  colors, 83
polarized light, 20, 77, 1051
  circularly, 95, 1185
  reflected, 3, 21
polarizing microscope, 16, 575
  choice of equipment, 195
  cost, 304
polarizing microscopy, 33–34
  crime laboratory, 1379
  dust, 1349
  instrument
    desirable additional features for,
      1404
    minimum specifications for, 1404
    specifications for a tungsten filament
      illuminator, 1405
  minerals, 1352
  pigment identification, 1406
Polaroid®
  film, 44–45, 49, 1051
  filter, 57–58
polars, 1051
  color of, 16
  crossed, 82
  parallel, 84, 95
  slightly uncrossed, 54, 95
polishes, 320
polishing compounds, 407, 659
polishing, samples, 1370
pollen, 847–857, 1191–1220, 1480–1494
  acacia, 1191, 1480
  alder (red), 1191–1192, 1480
  alfalfa, 437, 685
  American elm, 332, 591, 825
  ash, 1192, 1480
  balsam poplar, 338–339, 594, 826
  basswood (linden), 1193, 1481
  bayberry, 1193–1194, 1481
  beech, 1194, 1481
  Bermuda, 1195, 1482
  birch (sweet), 1195–1196, 1482
  castor (bean), 1196, 1482
  cattail, 1197, 1483
  cedar (deodora), 1197–1198, 1483
  cedar (red), 1198, 1483
  chestnut, 1199, 1484
  corn, 1199–1200, 1484
  cottonwood, 332–333, 591, 811, 825
  cypress, 1200, 1484
  dandelion, 333, 592, 826
  dating sediments, 1356
  elm, 332, 591, 825
  eucalyptus, 1201, 1485
  firebush, 1201–1202, 1485
  geographical origin, 1356
  goldenrod, 1202, 1485
  gum (black), 1203, 1486
  gum (sweet), 1203–1204, 1486
  hackberry, 1204, 1486
  hazelnut, 1205, 1487
  hemlock (eastern), 1205–1206, 1487
  hickory, 1206, 1487
  horse chestnut, 334, 592, 826
  identification of, 315, 1355–1357

pollen—*cont'd*
  lamb's quarters, 334–335, 592, 826
  linden, 1193
  marigold, 1207, 1488
  marihuana, 336, 593, 826
  mesquite, 1207–1208, 1488
  mounting, 308, 315
  mulberry, 1208, 1488
  nettle, 1209, 1489
  oak (live), 1209–1210, 1489
  origin of dust storms, 1356
  osage orange, 1210, 1489
  pecan, 1211, 1490
  pigweed, 337, 594, 826
  pine, 310–311, 338, 594, 826
  plantain, 1211–1212, 1490
  privet, 1212, 1490
  pussy willow, 1212, 1491
  Queen Anne's lace, 1213, 1491
  ragweed, 311, 339, 595, 826
  red oak, 336–337, 593, 826
  rhododendron, 1215–1216, 1492
  Russian thistle, 1216, 1492
  sedge, 1214, 1491
  silk tassel bush, 1215, 1492
  sugar maple, 335, 593, 826
  sunflower, 1217, 1493
  sycamore, 1217–1218, 1493
  timothy grass, 340, 595, 811, 826
  tree of heaven, 1218, 1493
  Veronica, 555, 784
  walnut, 1219, 1494
  willow (red), 1219–1220, 1494
  wormwood, 1220, 1494
polonium, 990
polyacrylostyrene, 847
polyamide
  fibers, 619–620
  Nomex®, 365, 619, 825, 841, 848
  nylon, 365–366, 620, 820
polycarbonate, 504, 742, 818, 842, 847
polychlorobiphenyls, 1166
polyester fibers, 310, 366, 621, 825, 842, 962, 966
polyethylene, 847
  needles, 227
  pipettes, 228–229
  scraper, 234
polymer, 323, 500–509, 738–745, 858
  wood fiber reinforced, 504, 742, 821, 823
polymerization, 1052
polymorphic transformations, 115
polymorphism, 71, 114–115, 119, 1052
polypropylene, 365, 619, 847
polystyrene, 505, 742, 812, 818, 841, 847
polystyrene particle spectra, 1154
polyurethane, Vyrene®, 1275
polyvinyl
  acetate, 505, 743, 812, 842, 847, 1332, 1629
  alcohol, 505, 743, 812, 827, 842, 847
  resins, 312, 847
Pompeian blue, 1323, 1616

poplar catkin seed hairs, spring "showers," 1357
poplar, Bolleana trichomes, 1222, 1496–1497
  (yellow) trichomes, 1223
Populus balsamifera, 338, 594
Populus deltoides, 332, 591
porcelain, 408, 659, 811, 816, 850, 1254, 1536, 1540
  insulator, 849
portland cement, 310, 320–321, 419–422, 524, 669, 673, 1052, 1641
  basic types, 321
Porton graticule, 263
positive crystals, 79, 81, 87
positive lenses, 8
positive ocular, 14
post office mail handling, 560, 786
postulation of a hypothetical environment, dust, 1350
potassium, 979
  alum, 849, 875, 880, 889, 908
  bicarbonate (kalicinate), 850, 875, 881, 889, 904
  bromide, 852, 881, 894, 915
  cadmium chloride, 881, 895, 918–919
  chlorate, 1267, 1554
  chloride, 434, 436, 682, 685, 811, 843, 849, 858, 881, 891, 909
  chlorostannate, 852
  chromium cyanide, 849, 881, 893–894, 912–913
  cobaltinitrite, 1313, 1602
  copper chloride dihydrate (mitscherlichite), 851, 875, 881, 896–897, 920–921, 924
  copper cyanide, 881, 893, 911–912
  cyanide, 848, 849, 881, 894, 915
  dihydrogen phosphate, 434, 683, 817, 821, 844, 851
  dithionate, 851, 882, 889, 892, 896, 908, 911, 919–920
  ferricyanide, 849, 881, 895, 916, 918
  ferrous selenate hexahydrate, 851, 881, 892–893, 910, 913
  iodide, 853, 881, 898, 926
  iron sulfate hexahydrate, 881, 890–891, 909–910
  mercuric cyanide, 851, 881, 890, 908
  nickel cyanide trihydrate, 882, 890, 895, 908–909, 919
  nitrate (niter), 850, 875, 881, 889, 892, 910, 1267, 1554
  perchlorate, 851, 881, 890, 909
  periodate, 853, 881, 896–897, 921, 924
  permanganate, 852
  phosphate, 881, 890, 892, 908, 910
  platinocyanide, 882, 899, 940–946, 948–950
  platinonitrite, 853, 882, 895, 898, 917–921, 924–933
  platinothiocyanate, 851, 882, 899, 940–946, 948–950
  selenate, 853, 882, 893–894, 913–914

potassium—*cont'd*
  sulfate, 434, 436, 683, 685, 817, 838, 845, 852, 873, 875, 881, 890–891, 908, 910
  tin chloride, 882, 897, 925–926
  trithionate, 851, 882, 891, 910
  uranyl sulfate dihydrate, 853, 882, 892–895, 911, 917
  zinc cyanide, 849, 882, 889, 906
potato starch, 459, 702, 842
poultry
  by-product meal, 453, 698, 817, 822, 829, 831, 847
  feathers, 347, 554, 601, 783, 813–814, 819, 822, 827, 830–831, 847, 1390
pouring dust, brass, 1591
powder
  bronze, 468, 710, 837, 844, 855
  carbonyl iron, 478, 719, 835, 844, 855
  cleansing, 425–426, 676
  copper lining, 471, 713, 837, 843
  corn, 445, 691, 817, 822, 831, 848
  deodorant spray, 553, 782, 813, 823, 849
  explosives, 114, 1264–1268, 1398–1399
  face, 554, 783, 819, 825, 827
  lemon, 449, 695, 812, 848
  milk, 451, 697, 812, 817, 842, 848, 1294
  oyster shell, 528, 762, 818, 825, 840
  scouring, 321, 424–429, 674–679, 814, 816, 821, 822, 850, 851, 858
  Tripoli, 413, 664, 816
powdered soap, 426, 676, 816, 848
powellite, 875, 878, 899, 955–958
power plant oil flyash, 1336
praseodymium, 986
  molybdate, 854, 886, 900, 958–960
  sulfate octahydrate, 852, 886, 894–895, 914–916
precipitators, 217
precision micrometers, 263
prehnite, 396, 648, 816, 822, 839, 852, 876, 878, 896, 898, 924–927
primary fluorescence, 42
printing ink, 560, 787, 819, 821, 824, 836
prisms, 7, 48, 68
  beam-splitting, 47
  Nicol, 21, 1049
  Wollaston, 36, 1155
privet pollen, 1212, 1490
procaine hydrochloride, 1259, 1262
processed soil, 562, 789, 819, 833
processing, metal, 322, 1310
profile angles, 66, 1052
programming, EMA, 191–193
projected area diameter, 265–266
projection distance, 44–45
promethium, 986
Prosopis juliflora, 1207, 1488
protactinium, 991
proton microprobe, 182–183
protractor graticule, 261
proustite, 855
provenance of particles, 1353

Prussian blue, 849, 1323, 1327, 1408, 1617
pseudomorphs, 115
pseudoscopic stereo, 59–60
psilomelane, 854
pubic hair, human male Caucasian, 1286, 1572
pudding mix, 454, 699, 812, 817, 822, 848
puffball, 345, 599, 826, 830–831
pulps
  hardwood, 1385
  softwood, 1385
pulpwood
  origin of, 1355
  species, 1355, 1385
pulverized coal-fired boiler, 547–549, 777–779, 827, 836
punch-card system for paper, 1385
pumice, 310–311, 393, 412, 507, 663, 674, 811, 839, 850, 1341
purified heroin base, 1260
purified morphine base, 1261
purpurin, 1321, 1614
pussy willow
  fiber, 1499
  pollen, 1213, 1219, 1225, 1491
PVC
  loss of Cl in EMA, 1468
pyramid, 68
pyrargyrite, 855
Pyrex® glass, 850
3-pyridinecarboxamide, 1296
3-pyridinecarboxylic acid, 1295
pyridine-2,4-dicarboxylic acid, 847
pyridoxine hydrochloride, 1297, 1583
pyrite, 854, 1228, 1240, 1521–1522
pyrochlore, 854
pyrolusite, 854, 1240, 1521
pyromorphite, 855, 876, 886, 900, 960
pyrope garnet, 853
pyrophyllite, 396, 648, 822, 831, 839, 852, 1244
pyrotechnics, 1398–1399
pyrrohotite, 1230, 1240, 1522

quality control by morphological analysis, 274
quantitative analysis
  dust samples, 1364
  EMA, 165–166
  IMA, 175, 177–178
quantitative electron microscopy, 1464–1465
quantitative interference microscopy, 37–39
quarter-wave plate, 84, 87, 95, 1038, 1185
quartz, 310–311, 319, 377–378, 396, 398–399, 424–425, 475, 483, 533, 536, 562, 564, 582, 648, 650–651, 658, 674–676, 716, 723, 765, 788, 790, 845, 852, 872, 876, 887, 894, 913–915, 1231, 1233, 1235, 1238, 1251, 1253, 1254, 1335, 1338, 1342, 1345, 1346, 1348, 1352, 1372, 1375, 1407, 1507, 1541

quartz—cont'd
  coverslips, 43
  detection, 97, 113
  dispersion, 112
  -iodine lamp, 42
  minerals, 319
  objectives, 12, 41
  refractives indices, 112
  slides, 43
  SEM morphology, 1354
  wedge, 84, 1038
Queen Anne's lace pollen, 1213, 1491
Quercus alba, 1280, 1567
Quercus rubra, 336, 593
Quercus virginiana, 1209, 1489
"quick-change" nosepiece, 13
quinine, 1262, 1550

rabbit hair, 350, 605, 819, 830, 964, 967
radiolaria, 310, 340, 595, 811, 814–815, 822, 838, 845, 850, 854
radium, 991
radon, 991
ragweed pollen, 311, 339, 595, 826, 1350, 1488
railroad right-of-way, 1345, 1643
rain
  red, Chicago, 561, 787, 819, 821
  red, London, 560, 787, 821
raisin cleaning dust, 1297, 1583
Raman
  effect, 1148
  microprobes, 1147–1154
  shifts, 1148
  spectroscopy, 1147–1154
ramie, 355, 610, 820, 823, 848, 963, 967, 1386
Ramsden disc, 1052
Ramsden ocular, 14, 1052
rape seed, 1298, 1583
rat hair, 351, 605, 820, 830, 1284
rational indices, 66
rattlesnake fern spores, 342, 596
raw cotton, 963, 967
raw natural catalyst, 416, 666, 811, 821
raw sienna, 497, 736, 829, 833–834, 844, 854, 1407
raw silk, 848, 963, 967
raw umber, 1326, 1407, 1621
Rayflex® (viscose rayon), 962, 966
Rayleigh scattering, 329, 330, 1148
rayon
  acetate, 310–311
  cuprammonium, 363, 618, 820, 841, 848, 962, 966
  saponified, 962, 966
  viscose, 310–311, 367, 621–622, 820, 830, 848, 857
razor, electric, 349, 604, 819, 822
RDX, 1265, 1267, 1268, 1555
reagents, microchemical tests, 1177
realgar, 307, 853, 1322, 1323, 1617
real image, 3–4, 1045
reciprocal lattice, 139, 1052
reciprocity failure, 54, 1052

recovery of particles, 234–237, 245, 1349, 1363, 1477
red alder pollen, 1191–1192
red cadmium, 1407
red cedar pollen, 1198, 1483
red gum fiber, 1277
red lead, 496, 735, 833–834, 845, 855, 1407
red oak pollen, 336–337, 593, 826, 1209
red ochre, 496–497, 736, 833, 844, 854, 1407
red pigments, analytical scheme, 1412
red plate, first-order, 84, 87, 312
red rain
  Chicago, 561, 787, 819, 821
  London, 560, 787, 821
red willow pollen, 1219, 1494
reference collection, 1347, 1361, 1403
  making aesthetic slides, 1371
refining, metal, 322
reflected polarized light, 3, 21
reflection, 1053
  angle of, 3
  diffuse, 3
  image, 3
  law of, 3
  objectives, 11–12, 41, 1151
  polarization by, 21
  prisms, 7
  Snell's law, 7, 1055
  specular, 3
refraction, 4, 6, 1053
  constants, inorganic compounds, 976
  double, 21, 33, 83, 1041
  image, 7
  objectives, 12
  sign of, 79
  Snell's law, 7
refractive index, 5–6, 39, 72–83, 110, 112–113, 254–258
  Aroclor®, 305
  Cargille liquids, 964–974
  crystals, 77–78
  determination, 6, 39, 72–77, 110, 112, 254–258
  dispersion, 5, 75–76, 103
  high dispersion liquids, 969, 974
  Kofler glass powder standards, 968
  liquids, 72, 76–77, 1166
  oblique illumination, 74–75
  optical glasses, 969
  refractive indices, 961–967, 1388, 1390–1392
  single particles, 255–257
  temperature coefficient, 5, 76–77, 108, 113, 116
  variation methods, 76
refractive index and dispersion, useful equations, 1013
refractivities of inorganic oxides, 976
regional metamorphic rocks, 1353
replicas, extraction, 234–235
replication, 135–136, 1053
report format, 1367
reporting, 1367

resin
  particles, 1338
  phenolic, 504, 741, 812, 842, 848
  polyvinyl, 312, 847
  spray-dried, 312, 507–508, 744, 812,
    814
  synthetic, 1332
  varnish, 1330
  wood, 847
resolution
  Abbe's theory of, 19, 1034
  EMA, 168
  IMA, 169
  light microscope, 12, 15, 18–20, 22
  MOLE, 1154
  photomicrography, 54
  SEM, 146, 154
  spatial, 169
  TEM, 130, 141
resolving power, useful equations, 1012,
  1053
retardation, xi–xiii, 34, 250–251, 1053
  by thin films, 34, 250–251
retgersite, 850, 876, 886, 891–892, 909–
  911
reticles, 260
reworked sediments, 1353
rhenium, 989
rhodium, 984
rhodochrosite, 377, 397, 632, 649, 824,
  842, 853, 876, 883, 896, 899, 918–
  920, 940–942
Rhododendron pollen, 1215, 1492
Rhododendron sp., 1215, 1492
rhodonite, 397, 649, 832, 834, 843, 853
rhombic dodecahedron, 65
rhombohedra, 66
rice, 1387
rice bran, 1298, 1584
rice hull dust, 454–455, 699, 817, 821–
  822, 848
  starch, 454, 459–460, 703, 842
Ricinus communis, 440–441, 688, 1196,
  1482
riebeckite, 853
rinneite, 876, 884, 895, 918–919
rippled, hair scale edge shape, 1384
road dust, 561, 788, 1346, 1643
road pavement wear, 1348, 1635
roasted iron ore, 478, 719, 818, 833–835
roasted zinc ore, 491, 731, 833, 846
rocks, 318
  phosphate, 321, 432–433, 532, 627, 682,
    764, 812, 827, 853, 1269
rock wool, 318, 369–370, 533, 624–625,
  765, 811–813, 826–827, 852
rolling crystals, 94
rope fibers, 1381, 1386
rosin dust, 533, 765, 813, 848
rotating nosepiece, 13, 1053
rotation apparatus, 91–94, 257–258
roto-blast steel shot dust, 412, 663, 834
rottenstone, 413, 663, 816, 822, 826, 832
rounding, degree of, 1347
rubber, 310, 847, 1339, 1342

rubber—cont'd
  black, 1348
  cement, 230
  and corundum, 410, 661
  dust, 506, 743–744, 812, 835
    from tire buffing, 506, 743, 812, 835
  fibers, 1390
  gum, 847
  particles, 1339, 1342
  septum dust, 562, 788, 813, 819, 833,
    848
  silicone, 507, 744, 812, 842, 848
Rubia tinctorum L., 1321, 1614
rubidium, 982
  acid phosphate crystal, 1003
  bromide, 853, 886, 894, 915
  chloride, 852, 886, 891, 910
  dithionate, 887, 889, 892, 908, 910
  ferrous selenate hexahydrate, 852, 886,
    890–891, 909–910
  fluoride, 854, 886, 889, 905
  iodide, 853, 896, 897, 924
  perchlorate, 853, 886, 908–909
  selenate, 854, 887, 894, 914–915
  sulfate, 853, 887, 892, 910–911
rug fibers, 1381
Russian thistle pollen, 1216, 1492
rust, stem, 315
ruthenium, 984
rutile, 378, 397–398, 403, 649–650, 832,
  846, 1226, 1229, 1501, 1505, 1602
  beach sand, 398, 650, 832, 846, 854
rye, 1387

Saccharum officinarum, 1277
SAED, 131, 136–138, 144–145, 576, 583,
  1369, 1644
safe insulation, 1400
saffron, 1324, 1618
salammoniac, 876, 885, 897, 923–924
Salix laevigata, 1219, 1494
Salix sp., 1213, 1491
Salsola pestifier, 1216, 1492
salt, 455, 699, 812, 838, 843, 848, 850,
  1293
salt-water beach sand test, 1353
SAM analyzer, 1470
samarium, 987
  bromate nonahydrate, 852, 887, 894,
    896, 914–915, 919
  sulfate octahydrate, 852, 887, 894–895,
    913–915
sample collection methods, 204, 209, 1363
sample contamination, 223
sample mounting
  carbon film, 162
  EDXRA, 577
  EMA, 162–164, 238–246
  glass fiber, XRD, 122–123, 246–249
  IMA, 173, 254
  MOLE, 1154
  refractive index, 254–258
  rotation apparatus, 257–258
  SEM, 150–151, 252–254, 577, 1472–
    1478

sample mounting—cont'd
  TEM, 134, 249–252, 583
  XRD, 122–123, 246–249
sample preparation
  EMA, 162, 164, 237–246
  laser Raman microprobe, 1154
  SEM, 150–151, 252–253
  TEM, 134, 240, 249–252, 583
samples, 206
  air conditioner filter, 206, 551, 781, 858
  contaminated, 223
  dry, 230
  origin, 1360
  tape, 205, 232
sampling
  art and archaeology, 1403–1405
  particles, 204, 209, 233–234
sand, 560, 788, 846, 852
  beach, 398, 650, 832, 846, 854, 1351–
    1354
  core, 484, 724, 846
  desert, 1345, 1354
  Fontainebleau, 381, 635, 815
  molding, 310–311, 322, 483–486, 723–
    726, 818, 829, 833, 835, 837, 846–
    847, 858
  rutile, 854
  salt-water beach sand test, 1353
  sandblasting, 413, 664, 816, 846
  sandstone, 398, 650, 816, 846, 1354
  shape and surface texture, 1353
  water-worn, 398, 650, 816, 846
  wind-worn, 399, 651, 816, 846
  zircon, 486, 726, 833, 854, 1353
sandarac, 308
sandblasting, 413, 664, 816, 846
sandstone, 398, 650, 816, 846, 1354
sapphire substrate, 1154
Saran®, 364, 618, 820, 841, 849, 962, 966
sartorius filter, 1371
savory, 1299, 1584
sawdust, 1355
  hardwood, 539, 769–770, 823, 848
  iron, 478, 719, 833, 835
  Masonite®, 526, 760, 812, 821, 823,
    827, 831, 848
  softwood, 538, 769, 823
  wood, 538–539, 769–770, 819, 823, 827,
    829–831, 848
sawmill, indications of, 1355
Saylor's double-diaphram method, 75
scale
  calibration, oculars, 261, 263
  iron, 1258
  mill, 310, 482, 723, 830
  Nies, 126
  patterns, hair, 1383
  steel, 490, 730, 833, 835, 855
  tea kettle, 1342
scale edge shapes, hair, 1383
scales, moth, 309, 331, 591, 814, 828, 848
scandium, EDXRA, 980
scanning Auger microprobe, 1466–1467,
  1470
scanning electron microscope, see SEM

scanning transmission electron microscopy (STEM), 152
scarlet lake, 1324, 1618
scheelite, 399, 651, 824, 834, 843, 855, 876, 879, 899, 949–954
Schleroderma aurantium, 345, 599
Schweinfurt green, 1318
scintillator-photomultiplier system, SEM, 150
Scotch pine, 1281, 1567
scouring powder, 425, 676, 816, 851, 858
scraper, polyethylene, 234
seaweed, 448, 694
secondary electron image, EMA, 158, 166
secondary fluorescence, 1054
sectioning, optical, 36
sedge pollen, 1214, 1491
sedimentation, 212, 1349
seed-cleaning dust, 455, 700, 817, 821, 829, 847
seed hairs, 1386
    cotton, 310, 311, 352, 607, 820, 823, 841, 849, 963, 967
    cottonwood, 359, 613, 820, 1214
    dandelion, 359, 613, 820
    sycamore, 359, 614, 820
selected area electron diffraction (SAED), 131, 136–138, 144–148, 576, 583, 1054
selection of analytical tool, 280–283
selection of equipment
    computer, 190–191
    EDXRA, 197
    EMA, 197
    ESCA, 198
    IMA, 198
    polarizing microscope, 195, 1404
    SEM, 196
    stereomicroscope, 194, 1405
    TEM, 195–196
selenium, 982
    -arsenic selenide melts, 307
    -sulfur melts, 307
    -tellurium melts, 307
SEM, 146–155
    advantages, 575
    asbestos, 1644
    beryllium plates, 1474
    carbon-coated specimens, 1473–1474
    choice of equipment, 196
    computerization, 1660
    coverslip mounts, 1476–1477
    elemental analysis, 154, 155
    metal-coated, 1473–1474
    membrane filter samples, 1476
    particle collection, 1472
    particle fracture, 1477
    particle handling, 1472–1478
    particle mounting, 1472–1478
    particle recovery, 1477
    particle replication, 1478
    resolution, 146, 154
    sample preparation, 150–152, 252–253
    single particle examination, 1475
    single particle mounts, 1475–1476

SEM—*cont'd*
    spray-mounted particles, 1477
    volatile particles, 1477–1478
semen examination, HMC, 1157
semiapochromatic objectives, 11
semisynthetic catalyst, 416, 666–667, 811, 816, 826, 834
Sénarmont compensator, 38–39, 1054
senarmontite, 855, 876, 887, 900, 960
sensitivity
    dispersion staining, 114
    EMA, 155, 1004
    IMA, 169, 174
separation
    of components, 1349
    inertial, 212, 1246
    magnetic, 220, 1349
    mass, 211
    size, 211
    solubility, 220, 1347
sepiolite, 850, 1241, 1522
serpentine, 372, 626, 820, 822, 844, 851, 1644
settling velocities, particles, 803
sewage sludge, 434, 683, 811, 817, 821, 826, 848
shadowing, metal, 135, 1054
shaggy ink cap, 344, 599, 826
shale, 399–400, 651, 766, 816, 834
    expanded, 534, 766, 819, 830
    oil, 528, 761, 818
shape factors, 267, 274
Sharples supercentrifuge, 213
shearing ocular, 260
sheep
    manure, 432, 681, 811, 817, 821, 826, 830, 848
    wool, 311, 348, 603, 848
shellac, 1333, 1629
Shorea wiesneri, 1330, 1627
shot
    bronze, 469, 710, 837, 844
    lead indium, 480, 721, 835, 845, 855
    rock wool, 370, 625, 813
    steel, 412, 490, 663, 730
shutter, 49
    external, 50
    testing, 50
    vibration, 50
SI units, 1019
siderite, 310–311, 377, 397, 400, 632, 649, 652, 824–825, 834, 841, 854, 876, 880, 896, 921–922, 943–946
sienna
    burnt, 497, 736, 829, 833, 844, 853, 1407
    raw, 497, 736, 829, 833–834, 844, 854, 1407
sieve sizes, 807–809
sieving, 211
sign of elongation, 80, 317, 1054
sign of refraction, 79
signal-to-noise ratio, MOLE, 1151
silica, 304, 513, 748, 850
    amorphous, 1341

silica—*cont'd*
    catalyst, 1250
    flour, 1254, 1541
    fumes, 1255, 1360, 1541
    gel, 1341, 1639
    sponge spicules, 341, 596, 813, 840, 845, 850, 852, 1358
    vitreous, 850
silica gel "cells," 119
silicon, 979
silicon carbide, 407–408, 658, 843, 853
silicone, 115, 225, 232
    oil, 1355
    rubber, 507, 744, 812, 842, 848
silk, 310, 351, 1387
    cultivated, 351, 606, 820, 847–848, 963, 967
    raw, 848, 963, 967
    wild, 351, 606, 823, 831, 847, 963, 967
sik tassel bush pollen, 1215, 1492
sillimanite, 853, 1227, 1353, 1533
silver, 855, 984
    bromate, 854, 877, 899, 942–945, 950–952
    chloride, 855
    dithionate dihydrate, 853, 877, 897–898, 923, 925–926
    maple trichomes, 361, 615, 820
    processing, 1310, 1598
    sulfate, 855, 877, 899, 934–936, 938
simple magnifier, 7
single particles
    identifiable size, 303
    SEM, 1474–1475
single superphosphate, 435, 684–685, 817, 853
sinter plant, 487, 727, 812, 818, 833
sintering dust (steel mill), 486, 726
sisal, 355, 610, 815, 820, 830, 848, 964, 967, 1281, 1386, 1568
six-digit code, 277–279, 805
size analysis, 803
size distribution, 264
size of particle identifiable by microscopy, 303
size separation, 211
skin scales, 328, 588, 822
skunk hair, 352, 606, 820, 830
slag, 815, 850
    aluminum, 466, 707, 812, 824, 835
    blast furnace, 468, 709, 827, 832, 835
    brass, 1306, 1592
    chrome alloy, 487, 727
    chrome steel, 828, 835
slate, 400, 682, 816, 834, 852
slides, permanent collection, 1371
slightly uncrossed polars, 54, 95
slow ray, 1055
smalt, 1324, 1408, 1619
smelter
    lead, 1308–1309
    stack, 1311, 1599
smithsonite, 854, 876, 888, 896, 899, 921–922, 943, 946, 1162–1163, 1241, 1523

smokeless powder explosive, 1399
smooth, hair scale edge shape, 1384
Snell's law, 7, 1055
snow, particle collection on, 206
snuff, 537, 768
soap, 321, 426, 676, 816, 848, 858
soapstone, 1241, 1523
sodalite, 401, 652, 811, 839, 851, 876, 883, 891, 909, 1519
sodium, 978
  acid hypophosphate hexahydrate, di-, 849, 884, 891, 909–910
  acid hypophosphate nonahydrate, tri-, 849
  alum, 849, 876, 883, 889, 907
  aluminosilicate glass, 851
  aluminum silicate, 1325, 1620
  arsenate dodecahydrate, 849
  arsenate dodecahydrate, di-, 849, 884, 889, 907–908
  arsenate dodecahydrate, tri-, 883, 890, 908
  arsenate monohydrate, mono-, 883, 894–895, 913
  beryllium phosphate (beryllonite), 852
  bicarbonate, 456, 700, 817, 821–822, 841, 850, 875, 884, 889, 895, 904, 917–919
  bromate, 853, 883, 896, 921
  bromide, 853, 883, 897, 923–924
  calcium carbonate dihydrate (pirssonite), 851, 875, 883, 892, 895, 916–917
  carbonate dehydrate, 1254
  carbonate monohydrate, 456, 701, 817, 842, 851
  chlorate, 851, 883, 892, 911, 1268, 1555
  chloride, 434, 455, 699, 883, 894, 914
  chromate tetrahydrate, 883, 895, 889, 901–903, 915–918
  citrate, 1299, 1584
  dichromate, 1258, 1545
  dihydrogen phosphate monohydrate, 850
  dithionate dihydrate, 850, 884, 890–892, 909, 911
  fluoride, 852, 883, 876, 899, 901
  fluorophosphate, hydrated, 850, 884, 889, 908
  fluorovanadate, 884, 893, 912
  glutamate, 1299
  hypophosphate nonahydrate, 884, 890, 908
  light filters, 32
  magnesium chlorocarbonate, 851, 875, 884, 892, 911
  metaborate dihydrate, 849
  metaphosphate, nonahydrate, tri-, 884, 890, 909
  (mono-) l-glutamate, monohydrate, 1299
  nitrate, 534, 766, 819, 845, 850, 876, 884, 889, 895, 902, 1268, 1555
  nitrite, 226

sodium—cont'd
  oxalate, 1341, 1639
  perborate, 425, 675, 822
  phosphate, 424, 427, 431, 675, 681, 884, 889, 891, 907–909
    dihydrate, di-, 431, 681, 817, 845, 850
    dihydrate, mono-, 884, 889, 907, 909
    dodecahydrate, 848
    dodecahydrate, di-, 884, 889, 907
    heptahydrate, di-, 849, 884, 889, 908
    monohydrate, mono-, 884, 889, 891, 908–909
    tri-, 425, 676, 845, 849
      chlorinated, 424, 427, 675, 678, 816, 821, 843, 849
      hydrated, 428, 678, 816, 821
  phosphomolybdate, 884, 895, 897, 919, 924–925
  platinocyanide trihydrate, 852, 884, 894, 896, 913–915
  pyrophosphate, 426, 677, 816, 845, 851
    decahydrate, 849, 884, 890, 908
    decahydrate, tetra-, 428, 678, 849, 884, 908
    hexahydrate, 884, 890, 908
    tetra-, 426, 678, 816, 845, 889
  silico aluminate (glass), 884, 891, 909
  silicofluoride, 535, 766, 819, 844, 852
  sulfate, 535, 767, 819, 838, 845, 852
  tetraborate, 424, 674, 816, 840
  thiosulfate pentahydrate, 849, 884, 891, 909, 913
  tripolyphosphate, 427, 677, 816, 845, 851
  vanadate
    decahydrate, 884, 893–894, 912–914
    dodecahydrate, 884, 892–894, 910–912, 914
soft black, carbon, 469, 711, 835, 840
softwood pulps, 1385
softwood sawdust, 538, 769, 848
soil
  age, 1354
  density gradient, 218–219, 1394
  determination of geographical origin, 1347–1361
  garden, 562, 788, 819, 1340, 1637
  identification of, 1394
  laser Raman microprobe (MOLE), 1147–1157, 1365, 1394
  PLM, 1394
  pretreatment, 1394
  processed, 562, 789, 819, 833
  screening information, 1394
  stereobinocular examination, 1394
solder, 855
Solidago sp., 1202, 1485
solubility separation, 220, 1347
solvent extraction, 1349
solvents for particle handling, 230
soot, 543, 773, 1340
  blowing operations, 324
  oil, 312, 516, 543, 771, 773, 828, 836, 847, 1334, 1348

sorghum mill feed, 457, 701, 817, 822, 829, 831, 847
sources of supplies and accessories, 1028–1033
soybean, 457, 462, 701, 704, 814, 817–818, 821, 848
Spandex®, 962, 966
Spanish grass, 353, 608, 848
Spanish moss, 310, 341, 596, 822, 831, 848
sparks from lighter "flint," 1342, 1639
spatial resolution, 169
  MOLE, 1151
specific surface, 266
  area of particles, 806
specifications (minimum)
  microscopic illuminator, 1405
  polarizing microscope, 1404
  stereobinocular microscope, 1405
spectral lines, 856
spectrometer
  aerosol, 213
  crystal, 158, 160, 1002
  double-grating, 1149
  drives, EMA, 187–188
  scanning speed, EMA, 160
spectrometry, mass, 119, 169
spectroscopy
  Auger, 180–181
  chemical analysis, ESCA, 119, 178–182
  drugs, 1398
  emission, 1042
  infrared, 199, 1148
  mass, 1147
  x-ray, 156
specular reflection, 3
spent catalyst, 415–418, 665–669
spermaceti, 847
spessarite, 383, 637, 815, 824, 828, 832, 839, 854
sphalerite, 397, 401, 403, 653, 828, 838, 845
sphene, 403, 655, 832, 843, 853, 1353
sphenoid, 68
spherical aberration, 1055
  light microscope, 4, 8, 11
  TEM, 133
spherulites, 1055, 1318, 1609
spicules, sponge, 341, 596, 813, 819, 840, 845, 850, 852
spider web, 352, 607, 820, 848, 1387
spinel, 393, 645, 853, 876, 882, 898, 930–932, 1242, 1513, 1524
split polarizing filters, 57
spodumene, 401, 653, 825, 839, 876, 882, 898, 924–928, 1238
sponge
  iron, 479, 720, 818, 833, 835, 844, 855
  spicules, 341, 596, 813, 819, 840, 845, 850, 852
spores, 315, 597, 847, 857
  fern, 341–342, 596, 811, 826
  fungal, 315
  lycopodium, 345, 600, 826
  mold, 315

spores—*cont'd*
   moss, 345, 600, 826, 857
   mushroom, 315, 344, 599, 826, 857
   puffball, 345, 599
   rattlesnake fern, 342, 596
   wheat smut, 343, 598, 826
spot tests, 188, 1153
spray
   deodorant, 553, 782, 813, 823, 849
   mounted particles, SEM, 1477
   paint, 530, 763, 812, 827, 848, 1360
   varnish, 847
spray-dried blood, 551, 781, 813, 827, 848
spray-dried resin, 312, 507–508, 744, 814
spreader stoker, 546–547, 776–777, 836
spring "showers," poplar catkin seed
   hairs, 1357
spruce, black, 1282, 1568
spun silk, 351, 606
sputtering, ion beam, 170
stability of particles, 1353
stack sampling, 209
stage and beam controls, EMA, 184, 186–
   187
stage micrometer, 260, 1048
stages
   cold, 108–114, 151
   high temperature, 114–115
   hot, 106, 108, 114–116
   integrating, 268
   tilting, 57–59
   vacuum, 114
staining tests, clays, 1183
stainless steel, 855
standard sieves, 809
standards, density, 219–220
starch, 322, 817–818, 848
   arrowroot, 457–458, 702, 842
   barley, 437–438, 450, 686, 696
   bean, 438, 686
   cocoa, 422, 689
   corn, 439, 444–445, 454, 457–458, 461,
     687, 691, 699, 701–703, 817, 842
   flaxseed, 447, 693
   ginger, 448, 694
   grains, 310
   maize, 458, 702
   paste, 1333, 1630
   peanut, 452, 697
   potato, 459, 702, 842
   rice, 454–455, 459–460, 699, 703, 842
   sorghum, 457, 701
   soybean, 457, 701
   tapioca, 460, 703, 842
   tortilla, 461, 703, 842
   wheat, 461–462, 704, 842
statistical particle diameters, 264–265
staurolite, 854, 1242, 1524
steamed bone meal, 1289
steatite, 402, 654, 816, 820, 822, 844, 852,
   1241, 1523
steel, 854–855
   basic oxygen process, 1311, 1599
   blast furnace, 1311, 1600

steel—*cont'd*
   combustion product, 487, 727, 812, 818,
     827, 835
   manufacturing dust (basic oxygen),
     487, 727, 833, 835, 1311, 1599
   manufacturing, open hearth, 488–489,
     728–729
   mill environment, 563, 789, 813, 819
   open hearth, 488–489, 585, 728–729
     burned-out furnace, 489, 729, 818
     charging period, 488, 728, 833, 835
     combustion product, 489, 729, 833
     hot metal to lime-up, 488, 728, 833,
      835
     tap to charge, 488, 728, 833, 835
   plate manufacturing process, 489, 729,
     812, 827, 835, 837
   scale, 490, 730, 833, 835, 855
   shot, 412, 490, 663, 730, 834
   sintering, 486, 726, 835
   sinter plant, 487, 737, 812, 833
   slag, 828, 835, 1360
   stainless, 855
   steatite, 402, 654, 816, 820, 822, 852
stellate hairs, 310, 361, 616, 820
STEM, 152, 1464, 1466–1467
stem grindings, tobacco, 1343
stem rust, 315
stereo
   binocular microscope, 17, 239, 1044,
     1349, 1405
   choice of equipment, 194
   electron microscopy, 135
   half-screened objective, 57
   pairs, 56–61
   photomicrography, 56–61
   pseudoscopic, 59–60
   SEM, 152
   viewer, 60–61
stereology, 268
stibnite, 854, 1235, 1525
sticky tape, 308
stigmator condensers, TEM, 133
stilbite, 850
stilpnomelane, 852, 1242, 1243, 1525
stoker
   chain grate flyash, 456, 776, 827, 836
   lignite, 547, 777
   spreader, 546–547, 776–777, 837
   underfeed, 545, 775, 813, 827, 836
Stoke's law, 1055
strain-free condensers, 36
strain-free objectives, 11
straw, 310–311, 356, 610, 820, 822–823,
   830–831, 848, 1386
street dust, 563, 789, 858, 1342, 1640
Streptomyces griseus, 1263
Streptomycin A, 1263, 1550
strontianite, 854, 876, 887, 892, 898, 911–
   912, 925–927, 1243, 1526, 1531
strontium, EDXRA, 983
   carbonate (strontianite), 854, 876, 887,
     892, 898, 911–912, 925–927
   chlorate, 853, 887, 895–896, 915–916,
     921, 922

strontium—*cont'd*
   chromate, 1321, 1613
   dithionate tetrahydrate, 851, 887, 893,
     912
   molybdate, 854, 887, 899, 950–953
   nickel cyanide pentahydrate, 850, 887,
     891, 896, 909–910, 921–922
   orthosilicate, 854
   oxide, 887, 899, 945–947
   platinocyanide pentahydrate, 852, 887,
     894, 897, 912–916, 923
   silicate, 887, 896–898, 919–920, 922–
     924, 931–936
   sulfate, 340, 595, 854
   trisilicate, 853
   yellow, 1321
structural colors, 329, 376
structure factor, 140
struvite, 849
strychnine, 1263, 1550
styrax, 307
Styrofoam®, 508, 745, 823, 841, 847
sublimation, 115, 117, 221
   block, 117
submicrometer particles
   dispersion staining for, 114
   identification of, 1466–1471
   mounting for EMA, 240
   special methods of sample preparation,
     1466–1471
substage condenser, 14, 22
substage diaphram, 13, 22–23
   de-centered, 56
   half-shaded, 56
substage mirror, 15
substitutional solid solution, 1372
sucrose, 454, 462, 699, 704, 818, 823, 842,
   849
sugar
   -beet, 438, 463, 686, 705, 811, 817,
     821–823, 826, 829, 831, 848
   black, (coke), 516, 752
   cane, 462, 704, 1387, 1630
     tassel, 1225, 1499
     α-lactose, 449, 695, 817, 842, 848
   malt, 451, 696
   maple fiber, 1279, 1565
   maple pollen, 335, 593, 826, 1356,
     1480, 1489
   milk, 449, 695
sulfaguanidine, 1263, 1551
sulfanilamide, 1264, 1551
sulfur, 490, 730, 838, 845, 887, 899–900,
   955–956, 979
   amorphous, 535, 767, 815, 824–825,
     829, 833, 845, 850
   MOLE image, 1153
   orthorhombic, 850
   Raman spectrum, 1152
sulfur-selenium melts, 307
sunflower pollen, 1217, 1493
sunn, 1386
supercentrifuge, 213
superphosphate, 321, 857, 1055

superphosphate—*cont'd*
    single, 435, 684–685, 817, 853
    triple, 321, 435, 684–685, 817, 853
super-SAM, 1470
suppliers and manufacturers, 1028–1033
surface coatings, particle, 1347
surface
    analysis, 181, 234–236, 582
    area *vs.* diameter, 806
    particles, 252, 582
    specific, 266
surfactant, 424–427, 674–677, 848, 858, 1055
suspended particles, Lake Michigan, 555, 784, 814, 819, 823–824
sweet birch pollen, 1195, 1482
sweet fern, 1193
sweet gum
    paper fiber, 1277
    pollen, 1203, 1486
SWP fibers, 1276
sycamore
    hairs, 359, 614, 820
    pollen, 1217, 1493
    trichomes, 1222, 1496
sylvite, 876, 881, 891
symmetrical extinction, 82–83
symmetry elements, 66, 67
synthetic catalyst, 417, 667, 811, 826, 834
synthetic fibers, 316, 317, 362–370, 616–624, 857, 961–962, 966, 1387
    delustering pigment, 317, 1040, 1387
        see also TiO$_2$
    density, 1387
    dye, 1387
    gas chromatography, 1387
    hotstage method, 1387
    infrared absorption, 1387
    morphology, 1387
    optical properties, 1387
    solubility data, 1387
synthetic molding sand, 483–485, 723–726, 818, 835, 837
synthetic resins, 1332
systems, crystal, 65, 69, 70
szaibelyite, 1243, 1526

table of sines and tangents, 1019
tabulation of particles (elemental composition), 838–846
taconite ore, 402, 654, 816, 832, 834, 844
Tagetes sp., 1207, 1488
taggants, micro, 1340, 1638
talc, 396, 402, 525, 554, 582, 653–654, 760, 783, 816, 820, 822, 844, 876, 883, 894–895, 913, 917–919, 1224–1245, 1523, 1527–1529, 1645
    steatite, 402, 654, 816, 820, 822, 852
tallow, 847
tankage
    armorganic, 431, 681, 811, 817, 826, 829, 848, 1035
    feather, 446, 692, 813–814, 826, 847
tantalite, 855

tantalum, 988
tape samples, 205, 232, 1472–1474
tape, sticky, 308
tapioca starch, 460, 703, 842
tar, 847
Taraxacum officinale, 333, 592
Taxodium distichum, 1200, 1484
tea, 463, 705, 818, 821, 828, 830, 848
    instant, 1300, 1585
teakettle scale, 1342, 1640
technetium, 983
techniques, determination of geographical origin of dust sample, 1347–1361
Teflon®, 364, 509, 618, 745, 821, 823, 830, 841, 850, 858, 1388
Teklan, 961, 966, 1274, 1388, 1560
telescope
    auxiliary, 23
    phase, 41
tellurium, 307, 985
TEM, 129–140, 576, 583, 1349, 1364, 1463–1465
    asbestos, 1644–1651
    choice of equipment, 195–196
    depth of field, 130, 154
    elemental analysis, 140
    examination of surfaces, 583
    high voltage, 131
    micrographs, conditions for, 583
    mounting particles for, 134, 240, 249–252, 583
    resolution, 130, 141
tempera medium, 1329–1333
temperature
    climate indicators, 1348
    coefficient of refractive index, 5, 76–77, 108, 113, 1056
    color, 46, 51–53, 1038
    dehydration, 306
    variation of refractive index, 116
tephroite, 1245, 1529
terbium, 987
terminal gravitational settling, 803
terre verte, 1325, 1408, 1619
Terylene®, 962, 966
tetartosymmetric crystals, 67
1,1,1,2-tetrabromoethane, 856
1,1,2,2-tetrabromoethane, 856
tetracalcium aluminoferrite, 419, 670, 832, 839, 854
tetragonal system, 65, 68
tetrahedrite, 854, 1246, 1530
tetrasodium pyrophosphate, 426, 677, 816, 845, 889
    decahydrate, 428, 678, 849, 884, 908
textile fibers, 1380
textiles, 1380
thalium, EDXRA, 990
thallous
    ferrous selenate hexahydrate, 854, 888, 898, 925–926
    ferrous sulfate hexahydrate, 854, 888, 895–897, 918–919, 921, 923
    formate, 856
    formate-malonate, 856

thallous—*cont'd*
    perchlorate, 854, 887, 897, 923–925
    selenate, 855, 888, 899, 954–956
    sulfate, 855, 888, 899, 945–949
thaumasite, 403, 654, 816, 821, 838, 841, 849
theory of resolution, 19, 1034
thermal precipitators, 217, 1056
thermoelectric stages, 114
thiamine HCl, 1300, 1585
thin films
    interference, 34, 250–251
    thickness, 34, 250–251
thin sections, 141
thorianite, 491, 730, 855
thorium, 991
thorium oxide, 491, 730, 815, 828, 846
three-in-one dispersion staining objective, 1159
thulium, 988
thyme, 1300, 1586
tile, 536, 767, 850
    acoustic, 368, 622, 811, 813, 819, 830, 851
Tilia sp., 1193, 1481
tilt angle, SEM, 152, 154
tilting stage, 57–59
    exposure control, 59
time-sharing computer systems, 1653–1654
timothy grass pollen, 340, 595, 811, 826, 1195, 1356, 1482
tin, 491, 731, 835, 846, 855, 985
tire buffing dust, 506, 743, 812, 835
tire cord, 1275, 1561
tire wear, 1348, 1361
tissue
    digestion for asbestos, 1648–1650
    facial, 358, 612, 815, 820, 823, 848
    thin-section for asbestos, 1648–1649
titanite, 403, 655, 832, 843, 853
titanium, 980
    dioxide, 317, 323, 586, 737, 1313
    white, 323, 498, 737, 824, 846, 854, 1313, 1328, 1407
TNT, 1269, 1556
tobacco, 311, 536–537, 768, 814, 819, 821, 823, 828–829, 831, 848
tobacco stem grindings, 1343, 1640
tomato pomace, 464, 705, 831
top lighting, 25–28, 59, 312
topaz, 403, 655, 816, 839, 853, 876–877, 896–897, 921, 923–924, 1353
torbernite, 853
tortilla
    flour, 461, 703
    starch, 461, 703, 842
tourmaline, 403, 655, 816, 822, 839, 853, 876, 883, 896–897, 920–925, 1353
tow, Brazilian, 1282, 1568
trace element method, glass, 1392
trace evidence, 1379–1413
tracheids, 317–318, 1043
transformations, polymorphic, 115
Transite® dust, 1343, 1641

transmission electron microscopy, *see* TEM

transmission interference microscopy, 39

"transparent" chromium oxide green, 1326

trap rock, 1246, 1530

tree of heaven
  pollen, 1218, 1493
  trichomes, 1223, 1497

trees, commercially important, 1355

tremolite, 39, 404, 645, 656, 816, 821–822, 843, 852, 876, 878, 896, 919, 921–923, 1226, 1244, 1373, 1500, 1528, 1645

tremolite-actinolite series, 1232, 1238

triacetate, bright, 367, 621, 820, 842

tricalcium
  aluminate, 420, 670, 811, 815, 839, 850, 853
  silicate, 419–423, 670, 824, 843, 853

trichomes, 310, 316, 847, 1056, 1221–1223, 1335, 1495–1497
  alfalfa, 437, 685
  American elm, 360, 614, 820
  barley, 437–438, 450, 686, 696
  catalpa, 1221, 1495
  cereal grain, 432, 681
  flaxseed, 447, 693
  honey locust, 1221, 1495
  horse-chestnut, 360, 614, 820, 823, 830–831
  marihuana, 360, 615, 820, 830
  mountain ash, 361, 615, 820, 823
  peach, 1221, 1495
  plum, 1222, 1496
  poplar, 1222, 1496
  rice, 454, 699
  sample provenance, 1357
  silver maple, 361, 615, 820, 1496
  sycamore, 1222
  tea, 463, 705
  tree of heaven, 1223, 1497
  wheat, 464, 706
  yellow poplar, 1223, 1497

triclinic system, 65, 68

triclinic plagioclase feldspar series, 317, 1227

tridymite, 851

trigonal system, 68

trigonometric tables, 1019

triple superphosphate, 321, 435, 684–685, 817, 853

tripoli powder, 413, 664, 816

2,4,6-trinitrotoluene (TNT), 1269, 1556

trisodium
  acid hypophosphate nonahydrate, 849, 884, 891, 909–910
  arsenate dodecahydrate, 883, 890, 908
  hypophosphate nonahydrate, 884, 890, 908
  metaphosphate nonahydrate, 884, 890, 909
  phosphate, 425, 676, 845, 849
    chlorinated, 424, 427, 675, 678, 816, 821, 843, 849
    hydrated, 428, 678, 816, 821

tristearin, 847

Tsuga canadensis, 1205, 1487

tube, body, 16

tube factor, 13, 1056

tubelength (mechanical), 13, 16, 29, 1056

tung nut, 538, 769, 819, 821, 827–828, 847

tungsten, 855, 989
  needles, 225–227

tungsten-halogen lamps, 46

turmeric, 1301, 1586

turpentine, Venice, 308

turquoise, 852

Tussah silk, 351, 606, 823, 847

TV camera, MOLE, 1151

twinning, 70, 1034, 1056

Tyler standard sieve sizes, 808

types of gas cleaning equipment, 803

Typha latifolia, 1197, 1483

Tynek®, 1274, 1561

types of gas cleaning equipment, 803

Ulmus americana, 332, 360, 591, 614

ultramarine, 498–499, 737, 827, 838–839, 851, 1409, 1620
  artificial, 1325, 1620
  natural, 1239, 1325, 1620

ultrascope, 41

ultrasoneration, 135, 232, 1056, 1352

ultrasonic probe, 232

ultraviolet
  fluorescence, 857–871
  lamps, 42
  microscopy, 41

Ultropak objective, 29

umber
  burnt, 853, 1326, 1407, 1621
  raw, 1326, 1407, 1621

uncovered specimens, 29

uncrossed polars, 54, 95

underfeed stoker, 545, 775, 813, 827, 836

undrawn nylon, 1273–1274, 1560

undulose extinction, 1056

uniaxial crystals, 78–79, 87, 108–109, 1057

uniaxial indicatrix, 80

uniaxial interference figures, 85

uniaxial substances, dispersion staining, 1161

unilateral illumination, 27–28

universal stage, 1057

unknown particle, identification, 325, 582

uraninite, 855, 1246, 1531

uranium, 992
  glass, 43
  ore, 404, 655, 816, 832

urban region indications, 1348, 1350

urea, 436, 684, 817, 841
  ethyl, 847
  formaldehyde, 509, 745, 812, 814, 818, 841, 848

Ursus americanus cinnamomum, 1283, 1569

Urtica gracilis, 1209, 1489

useful equation, 1009–1027

useful spectral lines, 856

use of the Atlas, 582

U.S. sieve sizes, 807–808

UV, dispersion staining in, 1164

vacuum cleaner, micro, 231

vacuum stages, 114
  system, clean, 1467

valentinite, 855

vanadium, 980

vanadium processing, 1312, 1600

Van Dyke brown, 498, 737, 827, 829, 837, 849, 1409

variation methods
  double, 77, 107, 1391, 1392
  index measurement, 76

Variotube, 16, 45

varnish spray, 847

varnish resins, 1330

velocity, 803

Venice turpentine, 308

verdigris, 499, 738, 829, 831, 842, 849, 1408

verditer, blue, 493, 732, 833, 841, 854, 1409

Verel®, 848

vermiculite, 405, 526, 656, 760, 816, 822, 831, 844, 1400

vermilion, 495, 1407

Veronica, 555, 784

vertical illuminator, 27–29, 312

vesuvianite, 405, 657, 824, 839, 853, 876, 878, 898, 929–930, 1247, 1353

vicara, 847

vicuña, 964, 967, 1288, 1573

vidicon tube, 269

viewing ocular, 1151

viewing stereopairs, 60–61

villiaumite (sodium fluoride), 852, 876, 883, 889

Vincel® 28 (viscose rayon), 962, 966

Vinyon®, 848

viridian, 1317, 1326, 1408, 1609, 1622

virtual image, 4

viscose rayon, 310–311, 820, 842, 848, 857
  bright, 367, 621
  dyed, 367, 622, 830, 842
  fibers, 962, 966
  tire cord, 1275, 1561

viscous mounting media, 224–225

visibility index, 307

visual angle, 8

vitamin
  A, 1301, 1586
  B$_6$, 1297

vitreous silica, 850, 1057

vivianite, 852

volatile mounting media, 224–225

volcanic ash, 563, 674, 790, 813, 819, 821, 825, 833, 836, 850

volcanic glass, 394, 412, 646, 663

vulcanized fiber, 1275, 1561

Vycor® glass, 850

Vyrene®, 1275, 1562

walnut (California black) pollen, 1219, 1494

walnut shell, 464, 706, 812, 818, 826, 829, 848
washing soda, 1254
water gel exposives, 1398
water immersion objectives, 12
water-soluble explosives, 1399
water spot deposits, 1344, 1641
water-worn sand, 398, 650, 816, 846
wavelength, x-ray, 156
wavelength dispersive detectors, 244, 977, 1369
wavelengths of useful spectral lines, 856
wavellite, 405, 657, 816, 821, 823, 839, 851
wax, 847
WDXRA (wavelength dispersive x-ray analyzer), 244, 977, 1369, 1461–1469
wedge, interference, 33, 106
wedge, quartz, 84, 1038
weight of small particles, 258–259
weight, particle size and number of atoms, 804
welding spheres, 1344, 1360, 1641
Western balsam fir, 1278, 1564
wheat, 1387
    flour, 461, 704
    grain dust, 464, 706, 813, 821, 829, 847
    smut, 343, 598, 826
    starch, 461–462, 704, 842, 848
    straw, 356, 610, 820, 822–823, 830–831
Whipple disc, 261
white
    gum fiber, 1277, 1564
    hickory pollen, 1206, 1487
    lead, 323, 495, 735, 843, 1320, 1328, 1407, 1613
    oak fiber, 1280, 1567
    -tailed deer, 1285, 1571
    titanium, 1407
white pigments, analytical scheme, 1406
whiting, 1327, 1407, 1622
wild silk, 351, 606, 823, 831, 847, 963, 967
willemite, 43, 406, 657, 824, 846, 854, 876, 888, 898, 928–929, 931–932
willow (red) pollen, 1219, 1494
wind-generated dust, 564, 790, 819
wind-worn sand, 399, 651, 816, 846
wine bottle sediment, 1344, 1642
Winsor blue, 1327, 1623
Winsor lemon, 1328, 1624
Winsor violet, 1327, 1623
witherite, 1247, 1531
wolframite, 855, 1247, 1532
Wollaston prism, 36, 1155
wollastonite, 852, 1233, 1247, 1532

wood
    burned, 1336, 1634
    -burning fireplace, 1337, 1634
    charcoal, 1315
    coniferous chemical, 317, 357, 612, 820, 823, 848, 1038, 1275
    coniferous mechanical, 317, 357, 611, 820, 823, 830–831, 848, 1038
    decayed, 1226, 1500
    fiber reinforced polymer, 504, 742
    fiber species identification, 318, 1385
    fibers, 310–311, 317–318, 1280, 1355, 1380, 1385, 1386
    meal, 540, 770, 819, 823, 848
    nonconiferous chemical, 357, 611, 620, 823, 848
    nonconiferous mechanical, 356, 611, 820, 822–823, 830–831, 848
    polymer, 504, 742
    pulp, plastic impregnated, 540, 771, 823–824, 828, 831–832
    resin, 847
    sawdust, 538–539, 769–770, 819, 823, 827, 829–831, 848
    shavings, 540, 770, 823, 831, 848
wood's metal, 855
wool
    angora, 964, 967
    Australian Merino, 964, 967
    cashmere, 964, 967
    fiber, 964, 967
    glass, 811, 813, 828, 847, 851
    kemp, 964, 967
    mineral, 318, 369–370, 624, 811, 815, 826–827, 852, 857
    rock, 318, 369, 533, 624–625, 765, 811–813, 826–827, 852
    sheep, 311, 348, 603, 848
working distance
    light microscope, 11–12, 1057
    SEM, 154
wormwood pollen, 1220, 1494
woven textiles, 1380
Wratten filters, 30–32, 42, 1282, 1285
wrought iron, 855
wulfenite, 855

xenon, 985
xenotime, 854
Xerox toner, 564, 790, 813, 836, 848
x-ray distribution image, EMA, 158, 166
x-ray energies for the elements, 977–1002
x-ray fluorescence, 1057
x-ray microscope, 182
x-ray powder diffraction, 119–129, 246–249, 1057

x-ray spectroscopy, 156
x-ray wavelength, characteristic, 156
x-rays
    dispersive analysis, EDXRA, 140
    energies of characteristic, 579–582
XRD, 119–131, 246–249, 1057, 1147, 1349
xylocaine hydrochloride, 1264, 1551

yellow
    cadmium, 1408
    chrome, 1408
    Indian, 1408
    lead monoxide, 1321, 1614
    lead tin, 1408
    Naples, 1408
    ochre, 1328, 1407, 1624
    poplar trichomes, 1223, 1497
    zinc, 1408
yellow pigments, analytical scheme, 1411
ytterbium, 988
yttrium, 983
    molybdate, 854, 888, 900, 960

ZAF correction procedure, 1466
Zea mays, 458, 702, 1199, 1484
Zefran®, 961, 966, 1276, 1562
Zefkrome®, 961, 966
zeolite, 416, 644, 816, 1502
    catalyst, 417–418, 668–669, 811, 816, 826, 834, 1057
Zernike, 40
    phase contrast, 1155
zinc, 855, 858, 981
    carbonate, 854
    concentrate, 1312, 1601
    ore, 491, 731, 833, 846
    oxide, 323, 492, 585, 731, 824, 843, 1328, 1407
    selenate hexahydrate, 851, 888, 892, 910
    silicofluoride hexahydrate, 850, 888–889, 904–905
    sulfate heptahydrate, 849, 874, 888–890
    sulfide, 854
    yellow, 499, 738, 933, 943, 953, 1408
    white, 1328, 1625
zincite, 406, 491, 658, 731, 832, 846, 854, 877, 888, 900, 960, 1235, 1305, 1312, 1591
Zingiber sp., 1293
zircon, 406, 658, 824, 846, 854, 1353
    sand, 486, 726, 824, 833, 1353
zirconium, 983
    oxide, 492, 732, 824, 846
zirconyl chloride, 1255, 1542
zone symbol, 69
zoom lenses, 16, 261